Teacher's Resources

GLOBE FEARON

American History

GLOBE FEARON
Pearson Learning Group

The following people have contributed to the development of this product:

Art & Design: Kathleen Ellison, Jenifer Hixson, Jim O'Shea, Eileen Peters, Angel Weyant
Editorial: Elaine Fay, Alisa Loftus, Colleen Maguire, Jane Petlinski
Manufacturing: Nathan Kinney
Marketing: Katie Erezuma
Production: Travis Bailey, Irene Belinsky, Louis Campos, Karen Edmonds, Phyllis Rosinsky, Cindy Talocci
Publishing Operations: Kate Matracia, Karen McCollum
Technology: Ellen Strain

Text Acknowledgments

"Letter from Jose Fernando Ramirez" reprinted from *Mexico During the War With the United States* by Jose Fernando Ramirez. Edited by Walter Scholes and translated by Ellito Scherr. Copyright © 1970 by the Curators of the University of Missouri.

"The Sky Tree Legend" from *Keepers of Life: Discovering Plants Through Native American Stories and Earth* by Michael J. Caduto and Joseph Bruchac. Used by permission of Fulcrum Publishing.

"Account" from *Hunger of Memory* by Richard Rodriguez. Copyright © 1982 by Richard Rodriguez. Reprinted by permission of David R. Godine, Publisher, Inc.

"Mother to Son" from *The Collected Poems of Langston Hughes* by Langston Hughes. Copyright © 1994 by The Estate of Langston Hughes. Used by permission of Alfred A. Knopf, a division of Random House, Inc.

"Battle of Tippecanoe" Gayle Thornbrough and Dorothy Riker, comp. Readings in Indiana History. Indianapolis: Indiana Historical Bureau 1956 reprinted 1991. Reprinted by permission of the Indiana Historical Bureau.

Letters of Benjamin Rush. reprinted by permission of the American Philosophical Society.

NOTE: Every effort has been made to locate the copyright owner of material reprinted in this book. Omissions brought to our attention will be corrected in subsequent printings.

Photo Credits

90: The Granger Collection. 103: FPG International LLC/Getty Images. 105: Smithsonian Institution/National Museum of American History. 109: l. Library of Congress; r. Courtesy, Jenifer Hixson. 186: American Antiquarian Society. 194: © Bettman/Corbis. 248: American Antiquarian Society. 254: © Bettman/Corbis. 262: The Granger Collection.

ISBN 0-130-23811-2

Printed in the United States of America
2 3 4 5 6 7 8 9 10 06 05 04 03

1-800-321-3106
www.pearsonlearning.com

Contents

Terms to Know

Review History

Build Your Skills

Assessment

Concept Builders

They Made History

Document-Based Questions

Reading, Writing, and Test Taking

Graphic Organizers / Outline Maps

Rubrics and Answer Key

Transparency Maps

Teacher's Resources Overview

The *Globe Fearon American History* program is designed to provide social studies content at a manageable reading level to ensure students' understanding. The complete program provides students with the information they need to successfully complete the requirements of rigorous district, state, and national frameworks, guidelines, and standards.

The Teacher's Resources provide support for reinforcing, reteaching, and testing all the content and skills in the *Globe Fearon American History* program. Reproducible worksheets and tests, plus complete answer keys and scoring rubrics, are included in one convenient book. The reproducible worksheets can be copied, reordered, and customized to meet the needs of a diverse classroom. The book is organized into the following tabs:

- **Terms to Know** worksheets offer a review and assessment of the vocabulary presented in each chapter.
- **Review History** worksheets assess student understanding of key concepts.
- **Build Your Skills** worksheets provide practice using the skills presented in the Student Edition.
- **Assessment** worksheets include a two-page test for each chapter of the Student Edition, a Midterm Exam, and a Final Exam.
- **Concept Builder** worksheets provide the support needed to develop critical thinking, reading, and writing skills. Students will also have the opportunity to develop skills for organizing and interpreting information.
- **They Made History** worksheets highlight important people in American history.
- **Document-Based Questions** worksheets test understanding of a variety of primary sources.
- **Reading, Writing, and Test-Taking** worksheets provide the tools students need to develop and strengthen their writing skills, especially in responding to essay questions found on standardized tests.
- **Graphic Organizers** help students organize, understand, and interpret information. Graphic Organizers can be used with any chapter of the Student Edition.
- **Outline Maps** reinforce geography skills. They can be used in conjunction with various chapters in the Student Edition.
- **Answer Key** provides answers to the Teacher's Resources and the Student Workbook.
- **Transparency Maps** provide a geographical context for students' understanding of historical events. They can be used in conjunction with various chapters in the Student Edition.

NCSS Correlation

CONTENTS	NCSS THEMES
Geography Handbook and Atlas	People, Places, and Environments
UNIT 1 EARLY AMERICA	
Chapter 1 The First Americans (Prehistory–1570)	
Section I Early Peoples	Culture
Build Your Skills: Read a Timeline	Time, Continuity, and Change
Section II Civilizations in the Americas	People, Places, and Environments
Section III Native Americans	People, Places, and Environments
Connect History & Art: Native American Art	Culture
Chapter 1 Review	
Chapter 2 Early Exploration (1000–1535)	
Section I West African Trading Kingdoms	Production, Distribution, and Consumption
Build Your Skills: Read a Historical Map	Time, Continuity, and Change
Section II Early European Expeditions	Production, Distribution, and Consumption
Section III Major Voyages to the Americas	Production, Distribution, and Consumption
Past to Present: Navigation	Science, Technology, and Society
Chapter 2 Review	
Chapter 3 New Settlements in the Americas (1512–1682)	
Section I Spanish Conquest and Colonies	Power, Authority, and Governance
Build Your Skills: Identify the Main Idea	People, Places, and Environments
Section II Other European Settlements	Individuals, Groups, and Institutions
Section III Slavery in the Americas	Production, Distribution, and Consumption
Points of View: The Slave Trade	People, Places, and Environments
Chapter 3 Review	
Unit 1 Portfolio Project Mapmaking Contest	People, Places, and Environments

CONTENTS	NCSS THEMES
UNIT 2 THE AMERICAN COLONIES	
Chapter 4 Founding Colonial America (1607–1733)	
Section I New England Colonies	People, Places, and Environments
Build Your Skills: Interpret a Bar Graph	Time, Continuity, and Change
Section II Middle Colonies	People, Places, and Environments
Section III Southern Colonies	People, Places, and Environments
Points of View: Religious Tolerance	Civic Ideals and Practices
Chapter 4 Review	
Chapter 5 The Thirteen Colonies (1650–1775)	
Section I The Colonial Economy	Production, Distribution, and Consumption
Build Your Skills: Take Notes and Outline	Time, Continuity, and Change
Section II Life in the Colonies	People, Places, and Environments
Section III Slavery in the Colonies	Individuals, Groups, and Institutions
Past to Present: Education	Time, Continuity, and Change
Chapter 5 Review	
Chapter 6 Roots of Rebellion (1689–1763)	
Section I England's Colonial Rule	Power, Authority, and Governance
Build Your Skills: Understand Cause and Effect	Time, Continuity, and Change
Section II Conflict With the French	Civic Ideals and Practices
Section III The French and Indian War	Power, Authority, and Governance
Connect History & Literature: The French and Indian War in Fiction	People, Places, and Environments
Chapter 6 Review	
Unit 2 Portfolio Project History Quiz Show	Time, Continuity, and Change
UNIT 3 FOUNDING A NATION	
Chapter 7 Road to Independence (1763–1776)	
Section I Resistance to British Taxes	Civic Ideals and Practices
Build Your Skills: Read Tables and Charts	Time, Continuity, and Change

CONTENTS	NCSS THEMES
Section II Growing Tensions	People, Places, and Environments
Section III A Declaration of Independence	Civic Ideals and Practices
Past to Present: Medicine	Science, Technology, and Society
Chapter 7 Review	
Declaration of Independence Handbook	Civic Ideals and Practices
Chapter 8 The Revolutionary War (1776–1783)	
Section I The Early Years of War	Power, Authority, and Governance
Build Your Skills: Read a Military Map	Time, Continuity, and Change
Section II The War Expands	Global Connections
Points of View: Independence From Great Britain	Civic Ideals and Practices
Section III An Independent Nation	Power, Authority, and Governance
Chapter 8 Review	
Chapter 9 Forming a Government (1777–1791)	
Section I The First Government	Power, Authority, and Governance
Build Your Skills: Make a Flowchart	Production, Distribution, and Consumption
Section II Problems in the New Nation	People, Places, and Environments
Connect History & Government: Creating the Post Office	Individuals, Groups, and Institutions
Section III The U.S. Constitution and the Bill of Rights	Civic Ideals and Practices
Chapter 9 Review	
Constitution Handbook	Civic Ideals and Practices
Unit 3 Portfolio Project School Constitution	Civic Ideals and Practices
UNIT 4 BUILDING THE REPUBLIC	
Chapter 10 A Government for a New Nation (1789–1800)	
Section I George Washington as President	Power, Authority, and Governance
Build Your Skills: Use Primary and Secondary Sources	Individuals, Groups, and Institutions

CONTENTS	NCSS THEMES
Section II Early Challenges	People, Places, and Environments
Section III The Presidency of John Adams	Power, Authority, and Governance
Past to Present: Presidential Elections	Civic Ideals and Practices
Chapter 10 Review	
Chapter 11 An Era of Expansion (1800–1815)	
Section I Jefferson as President	Power, Authority, and Governance
Build Your Skills: Interpret Political Cartoons	Civic Ideals and Practices
Section II The Louisiana Purchase	Time, Continuity, and Change
Section III The War of 1812	Power, Authority, and Governance
Connect History & Music: "The Star-Spangled Banner"	Individual Development and Identity
Chapter 11 Review	
Chapter 12 The Nation Grows (1810–1842)	
Section I The Rise of Nationalism	Civic Ideals and Practices
Build Your Skills: Draw Conclusions	Individual Development and Identity
Section II Jacksonian Democracy	Power, Authority, and Governance
Section III U.S. Policies Toward Native Americans	People, Places, and Environments
Points of View: Relocation of Native Americans	Time, Continuity, and Change
Chapter 12 Review	
Unit 4 Portfolio Project History Talk Show	Civic Ideals and Practices
UNIT 5 THE NATION EXPANDS	
Chapter 13 Life in the North and the South (1789–1860)	
Section I The Industrial Revolution	Science, Technology, and Society
Build Your Skills: Use a Circle Graph	Production, Distribution, and Consumption
Section II Cotton Is King	Science, Technology, and Society
Connect History & Economics: The Cotton Gin: Supply and Demand	Production, Distribution, and Consumption

NCSS Correlation

CONTENTS	NCSS THEMES
Section III The Slave System	Culture
Chapter 13 Review	
Chapter 14 The Spirit of Change (1800–1850)	
Section I Cities and a Growing Population	Time, Continuity, and Change
Build Your Skills: Make Inferences	Individual Development and Identity
Section II New Ideas Take Shape	Culture
Section III Reforming Society	Civic Ideals and Practices
Points of View: The Fight for Women's Rights in the 1800s	Civic Ideals and Practices
Chapter 14 Review	
Chapter 15 Westward Expansion (1821–1853)	
Section I Texas Wins Independence	Power, Authority, and Governance
Build Your Skills: Distinguish Fact From Opinion	Individual Development and Identity
Section II War With Mexico and the Movement West	People, Places, and Environments
Section III Settlement in California	People, Places, and Environments
Past to Present: Transportation	Science, Technology, and Society
Chapter 15 Review	
Unit 5 Portfolio Project A Stage Play	People, Places, and Environments
UNIT 6 A HOUSE DIVIDED	
Chapter 16 The Road to War (1820–1861)	
Section I The Question of Slavery in the West	People, Places, and Environments
Build Your Skills: Classify Information	Individuals, Groups, and Institutions
Section II Deepening Divisions Over Slavery	Civic Ideals and Practices
Points of View: Harriet Beecher Stowe and Uncle Tom's Cabin	People, Places, and Environments
Section III Challenges to Slavery	Power, Authority, and Governance
Section IV Breaking Away From the Union	Civic Ideals and Practices

CONTENTS	NCSS THEMES
Chapter 16 Review	
Chapter 17 The Civil War (1861–1865)	
Section I The Early Days of the War	Power, Authority, and Governance
Build Your Skills: Predict Consequences	Time, Continuity, and Change
Section II War and American Life	Individuals, Groups, and Institutions
Past to Present: Submarines	Science, Technology, and Society
Section III Victory for the North	Power, Authority, and Governance
Connect History & Technology: The Civil War in Photographs	Time, Continuity, and Change
Chapter 17 Review	
Chapter 18 Reunion and Reconstruction (1865–1877)	
Section I Reuniting a Nation	Power, Authority, and Governance
Build Your Skills: Compare and Contrast	Time, Continuity, and Change
Section II Conflicts Over Reconstruction	Production, Distribution, and Consumption
Section III The New South	People, Places, and Environments
Chapter 18 Review	
Unit 6 Portfolio Project Civil War Newspaper	Individuals, Groups, and Institutions
UNIT 7 GROWTH AT HOME AND ABROAD	
Chapter 19 Life in the West (1858–1896)	
Section I Railroads, Ranchers, and Miners	Individuals, Groups, and Institutions
Build Your Skills: Read a Special-Purpose Map	Time, Continuity, and Change
Section II Farming on the Great Plains	People, Places, and Environments
Connect History & Literature: Willa Cather, O' Pioneers!	People, Places, and Environments
Section III Native American Struggles	Culture
Chapter 19 Review	

NCSS Correlation

CONTENTS	NCSS THEMES
Chapter 20 The Rise of Industry (1869–1908)	
Section I Technology, Transportation, and Communication	Science, Technology, and Society
Build Your Skills: Choose a Research Topic	Individual Development and Identity
Section II Big Business and Labor Unions	Individuals, Groups, and Institutions
Section III Immigration	Global Connections
Past to Present: Working Conditions for Women and Children	Time, Continuity, and Change
Chapter 20 Review	
Chapter 21 The Progressive Era (1880–1933)	
Section I A Troubled Society	People, Places, and Environments
Build Your Skills: Make Generalizations	Individual Development and Identity
Section II The Progressive Movement	Civic Ideals and Practices
Section III Political Reforms	Power, Authority, and Governance
Chapter 21 Review	
Chapter 22 Expansion Overseas (1853–1919)	
Section I American Expansion in the Pacific	Global Connections
Build Your Skills: Use a Library	Individuals, Groups, and Institutions
Section II The Spanish-American War	Power, Authority, and Governance
Section III A New Role in Latin America	Production, Distribution, and Consumption
Points of View: United States and Imperialism	People, Places, and Environments
Chapter 22 Review	
Unit 7 Portfolio Project Voices of Immigration Audiocassette	People, Places, and Environments
UNIT 8 A TROUBLED NATION	
Chapter 23 World War I (1914–1918)	

CONTENTS	NCSS THEMES
Section I War in Europe	Power, Authority, and Governance
Build Your Skills: Conduct Research on the Internet	Science, Technology, and Society
Section II The United States Enters the War	Global Connections
Connect History & Media: Radio in War and Peace	Science, Technology, and Society
Section III Fighting the War	Power, Authority, and Governance
Chapter 23 Review	
Chapter 24 Life in the 1920s (1920–1929)	
Section I Business Booms	Production, Distributuon, and Consumption
Build Your Skills: Analyze Visuals	Time, Continuity, and Change
Section II The Roaring Twenties	Production, Distribution, and Consumption
Section III A Time of Unrest	Culture
Past to Present: Movie Technology and Attendance	Science, Technology, and Society
Chapter 24 Review	
Chapter 25 The Great Depression and the New Deal (1929–1940)	
Section I The Stock Market Crash	Individuals, Groups, and Institutions
Build Your Skills: Use a Line Graph	Time, Continuity, and Change
Section II Hard Times at Home	People, Places, and Environments
Points of View: The Role of Government in the Economy	Production, Distribution, and Consumption
Section III The New Deal	Power, Authority, and Governance
Chapter 25 Review	
Unit 8 Portfolio Project Debate: The Role of Government	Power, Authority, and Governance
UNIT 9 AMERICA BECOMES A WORLD LEADER	

NCSS Correlation

CONTENTS	NCSS THEMES
Chapter 26 World War II (1939–1945)	
Section I The Road to War	Power, Authority, and Governance
Build Your Skills: Recognize Propaganda	Individual Development and Identity
Section II The World at War	Power, Authority, and Governance
Past to Present: Women in the Workforce	Time, Continuity, and Change
Section III Winning the War	People, Places, and Environments
Chapter 26 Review	
Chapter 27 The Cold War (1945–1960)	
Section I The Cold War Begins	Power, Authority, and Governance
Build Your Skills: Read a Time-Zone Map	Time, Continuity, and Change
Section II The Korean War and the Red Scare	Power, Authority, and Governance
Section III The Changing Nation	Global Connections
Connect History & Medicine: Jonas Salk and the Polio Vaccine	Science, Technology, and Society
Section IV Life in the Fifties	Culture
Chapter 27 Review	
Chapter 28 The Kennedy Years (1961–1963)	
Section I The Communist Threat	Power, Authority, and Governance
Build Your Skills: Analyze Public Opinion Polls	Individual Development and Identity
Section II The New Frontier	Global Connections
Section III The Civil Rights Movement	Civic Ideals and Practices
Points of View: The Early Civil Rights Movement	Civic Ideals and Practices
Chapter 28 Review	
Chapter 29 The Johnson Years (1963–1968)	
Section I The Great Society	Production, Distribution, and Consumption
Build Your Skills: Present an Oral Report	Individual Development and Identity
Section II Equal Rights	Civic Ideals and Practices
Section III Conflict in Vietnam	Power, Authority, and Governance

CONTENTS	NCSS THEMES
Chapter 29 Review	
Unit 9 Portfolio Project An American Scrapbook	Culture
UNIT 10 MODERN AMERICA	
Chapter 30 Turbulent Times (1968–1979)	
Section I The End of the Vietnam War	People, Places, and Environments
Build Your Skills: Evaluate Information	Culture
Past to Present: Reporting Wars	Science, Technology, and Society
Section II Nixon's Administration	Power, Authority, and Governance
Section III Domestic Crises	People, Places, and Environments
Chapter 30 Review	
Chapter 31 New Challenges for the Nation (1980–Present)	
Section I The Reagan Years 1981–1989	Power, Authority, and Governance
Build Your Skills: Improve Your Test-Taking Skills	Science, Technology, and Society
Section II A Changing World 1987–1993	Time, Continuity, and Change
Connect History & the Environment: Exxon Valdez *Oil Spill*	Science, Technology, and Society
Section III Americans Respond to Crises 1992–Present	People, Places, and Environments
Chapter 31 Review	
Chapter 32 Looking to the Future (1990– Present)	
Section I Advances in Technology and Science	Science, Technology, and Society
Build Your Skills: Develop a Multimedia Presentation	Time, Continuity, and Change
Section II Life in the Twenty-First Century	Production, Distribution, and Consumption
Points of View: Technology in the Classroom	Science, Technology, and Society
Section III The Future of Our Planet	Global Connections
Chapter 32 Review	
Unit 10 Portfolio Project Visual Essay	Science, Technology, and Society

Contents

Terms to Know

Name ______________________ Date ______________

Terms to Know

Chapter 1

Vocabulary Review

Terms to Know

A. Match each term with its definition. Write the correct letter on the line.

_____	**1.** an apartment-like adobe dwelling; Spanish word for village	**a.** drought
_____	**2.** a large land area and population controlled by a single ruler or group	**b.** culture
_____	**3.** a person who moves about in search of food	**c.** civilization
_____	**4.** a well-developed way of life of a people in one place and time	**d.** pueblo
_____	**5.** a long period without rainfall	**e.** empire
_____	**6.** all of a group's arts, beliefs, and ways of doing things	**f.** nomad

B. Write *T* on the line if the statement is true. Write *F* if the statement is false.

_____ **7.** A natural resource is something that holds spiritual powers.

_____ **8.** Agriculture is the art or science of raising crops.

_____ **9.** To irrigate is to supply water to dry land for growing crops.

_____ **10.** A clan is a temple in which religious ceremonies are held.

_____ **11.** Dry farming is a method of farming that makes use of all the water available in a dry land.

_____ **12.** To migrate is to move from one place to another.

Name ______________________________ Date ______________

Chapter 2

Terms to Know

Vocabulary Review

Terms to Know

A. Match each term with its definition. Write the correct letter on the line.

_____	**1.** a journey made for a specific purpose	**a.** plantation
_____	**2.** to control the direction of a boat or ship	**b.** navigate
_____	**3.** an instrument used to calculate the position of the stars	**c.** kinship
_____	**4.** a large farm requiring many workers	**d.** expedition
_____	**5.** family relationships	**e.** astrolabe

B. Circle the letter of the correct definition for each term.

6. tax

a. money paid to a government
b. a trade route
c. a group of landowners
d. a tree that grows on savannas

7. colony

a. a tool used for navigation at sea
b. a settlement in a distant land that is governed by another country
c. an area of tall grass
d. an ocean voyage

8. commerce

a. exploration
b. planting and harvesting crops
c. slavery
d. the buying and selling of goods

9. caravan

a. a kingdom
b. a group of travelers with pack animals
c. a vast desert region
d. a large area of land controlled by a noble

Name ______________________ Date ______________

Terms to Know

Vocabulary Review

A. Complete each sentence with a term from the box.

sanitation	mission	cash crop	indentured servant

1. A ______________________ is grown to be sold rather than used by a farmer.

2. A settlement built by a church for religious work was known as a ______________________.

3. An ______________________ is a person who agrees to work for another for a certain period of time until a debt is paid.

4. Many slaves were crowded onto ships where there was no ______________________, or way to dispose of waste.

B. Circle the letter of the correct definition for each term.

5. encomienda system

- **a.** how Spanish explorers decided what route to take
- **b.** the trading system set up by colonists in the Southwest
- **c.** the system in which Native Americans were forced to work for Spanish landowners
- **d.** the system Native Americans used to keep track of land

6. joint-stock company

- **a.** a group of Dutch settlers that started Wall Street
- **b.** a group of investors that shares both risk and profit
- **c.** a group of wealthy landowners that loaned money to farmers
- **d.** a group of merchants that shipped cargo to the Americas

7. conquistador

- **a.** the god of the Aztec Empire
- **b.** the Incan who helped Pizarro kidnap Atahualpa
- **c.** the Native American who led the Spaniards to gold
- **d.** the Spanish term for conqueror, or one who gains control by winning a war

8. charter

- **a.** a type of boat built to carry colonists to the Americas
- **b.** a law giving Spain the right to take Native Americans as slaves
- **c.** an official document in which rights are given by a government to a person or company
- **d.** a treaty between Native Americans and French colonists

Name ______________________________ Date ______________

Chapter 4

Terms to Know

Vocabulary Review

A. Match each term with its definition. Write the correct letter on the line.

_____ **1.** a member of a religious group that wanted to simplify the practices of the Church of England

_____ **2.** a Dutch landowner in the colony of New Netherland

_____ **3.** a colony owned and managed by one or more individuals

_____ **4.** a religious traveler to a new land; a founder of Plymouth Colony

_____ **5.** a colony directly under the rule of a king or queen

_____ **6.** growing only enough crops to meet the needs of one household

_____ **7.** a Puritan who wished to break away, or separate, from the Church of England

a. subsistence farming

b. proprietary colony

c. patroon

d. Puritan

e. royal colony

f. Pilgrim

g. Separatist

B. Circle the term in each group that is not related to the others.

8. economy	freedom	production
9. unpopulated	backcountry	slavery
10. war	settler	immigration
11. debtor	owe	religion
12. persecute	shipbuilding	punish

Name ______________________________ Date ______________

Terms to Know

Vocabulary Review

A. Complete each sentence with a term from the box.

apprentice	libel	overseer	slave code

1. The person who was in charge of enslaved people was called the ______________________.

2. A ______________________ was a set of laws that limited the activities of enslaved people.

3. An ______________________ is someone who works with a master crafts person for period of time to gain a specific skill.

4. John Peter Zenger was put on trial for ______________________, or making false written statements that hurt a person's reputation.

B. Match each term with its definition. Write the correct letter on the line.

_____ **5.** to buy goods from another country

_____ **6.** to exchange one product or service for another

_____ **7.** an economic system that stresses increasing national wealth by selling more than buying in foreign trade

_____ **8.** to sell goods to another country

a. barter

b. export

c. import

d. mercantile system

Name ______________________________ Date ______________

Chapter 6

Terms to Know

Vocabulary Review

Terms to Know

A. Match each term with its definition. Write the correct letter on the line.

_____ **1.** a surprise attack from a hidden position		**a.** emigrate
_____ **2.** a person selected to act and speak in place of others		**b.** ally
_____ **3.** a nation, group, or people who are friendly with other people for a common goal		**c.** representative
_____ **4.** to give up or surrender land		**d.** ambush
_____ **5.** leave one country to settle in another country		**e.** cede

B. Complete each sentence with a term from the box.

Parliament	assembly	monarch	militia

6. James II was a ____________________ in England who struggled with Parliament for more power.

7. The lawmaking branch of government that came to represent the people of England was ____________________.

8. A ____________________ is a group of citizen-soldiers who volunteer when needed.

9. The elected group that made laws for a colony was its ____________________.

Name ______________________ Date ______________

Terms to Know

Chapter 7

Vocabulary Review

Terms to Know

A. Match each term with its definition. Write the correct letter on the line.

_____ **1.** a formal statement of opinion		**a.** proclamation
_____ **2.** the brutal killing of a large number of people		**b.** resolution
_____ **3.** a formal statement		**c.** massacre
_____ **4.** the region just beyond a settled area		**d.** declaration
_____ **5.** an official announcement		**e.** Patriot
_____ **6.** a person who supported independence from Great Britain		**f.** frontier

B. Complete each sentence with a term from the box.

minuteman	boycott	repeal
revenue	traitor	petition

7. Great Britain taxed the colonists to raise ______________ needed to pay the war debt.

8. Parliament decided to ______________ the Stamp Act after the Boston Massacre.

9. A ______________ was a member of the colonial militia who hoped to be ready for battle at all times.

10. New England merchants agreed to stop importing British products as part of a ______________ against those products.

11. The First Continental Congress sent a ______________ asking King George III for help in getting Parliament to repeal the tax laws.

12. A person who acts against his or her country is a ______________.

Name ______________________________ Date ______________

Chapter 8

Terms to Know

Vocabulary Review

A. Complete each sentence with a term from the box.

mercenary	Loyalist	casualty	inflation

1. A Hessian was a ______________________ from Germany who fought for the British in exchange for money.

2. A ______________________ was an American colonist who did not want to declare independence from Great Britain.

3. A sharp increase in the price of goods and services is known as ______________________.

4. A soldier who was wounded, captured, missing, or killed in battle was a ______________________ of the war.

B. Match each term with its definition. Write the correct letter on the line.

_____ **5.** a place where troops are stationed and weapons and ammunition are stored

_____ **6.** a long, drawn-out attack

_____ **7.** a government that receives its power from the people, who elect its leaders

_____ **8.** a person who is not a member of the military

a. siege

b. garrison

c. civilian

d. republic

Name ______________________________ Date ______________

Terms to Know

Vocabulary Review

A. Match each term with its definition. Write the correct letter on the line.

_____	**1.** the power of self-government	**a.** executive branch
_____	**2.** a union of countries or states for a common purpose	**b.** checks and balances
_____	**3.** land owned by the government	**c.** arsenal
_____	**4.** the lawmaking branch of the federal government	**d.** sovereignty
_____	**5.** a system to keep one part of a government from becoming stronger than other parts	**e.** constitution
_____	**6.** a building used to store weapons and ammunition	**f.** confederation
_____	**7.** to reject a law	**g.** veto
_____	**8.** the law-interpreting branch of the federal government	**h.** judicial branch
_____	**9.** the basic laws and plan of a nation's government	**i.** public domain
_____	**10.** to approve	**j.** ordinance
_____	**11.** a change or an addition	**k.** ratify
_____	**12.** a group of people from each state who perform the official duty of electing the President and Vice President	**l.** amendment
_____	**13.** the law-enforcing branch of the federal government	**m.** legislative branch
_____	**14.** a law	**n.** electoral college

Name ______________________________ Date ______________

Chapter 10

Terms to Know

Vocabulary Review

A. Complete each sentence with a term from the box.

inauguration	alliance	impressment	Cabinet

1. President Washington formed a ______________ to help him address the many issues facing the new nation.

2. George Washington was sworn in as the nation's first President in a ceremony known as an ______________.

3. American leaders grew angry over the British practice of ______________.

4. An ______________ is an agreement between two or more people, groups, or nations to cooperate with one another.

B. Match each term with its definition. Write the correct letter on the line.

_____ **5.** not taking one side or the other — **a.** precedent

_____ **6.** a person who moves into a country from another country — **b.** Union

_____ **7.** the United States of America — **c.** implied power

_____ **8.** an example for the future — **d.** nullify

_____ **9.** a tax on imported goods — **e.** unconstitutional

_____ **10.** to cancel — **f.** tariff

_____ **11.** something that goes against the U.S. Constitution — **g.** census

_____ **12.** a power that is not stated in the Constitution — **h.** neutral

_____ **13.** an official population count — **i.** immigrant

Name ______________________ Date ______________

Terms to Know

Chapter 11

Vocabulary Review

Terms to Know

A. Complete each sentence with a term from the box.

anthem	embargo	radical

1. Some people considered Jefferson a ______________ because he had new ideas about how the United States should be governed.

2. "The Star-Spangled Banner" was first written as a poem and later became the country's national ______________.

3. Congress signed an ______________ in 1807, which ordered U.S. ship owners to stop trading with European countries.

B. Circle the letter of the correct definition for each term.

4. judicial review

a. a court review to determine whether a law is constitutional
b. any law that the Supreme Court decides is unconstitutional
c. the process by which the President appoints a Chief Justice
d. the belief that if the government left people alone, they would create a better society

5. tribute

a. an order to stop trade
b. money paid for protection
c. to be held hostage
d. an act to declare war

6. nationalism

a. a song of praise
b. a military hero in the War of 1812
c. a desire for independence
d. a pride in one's country

Name ______________________________ Date ________________

Chapter 12

Terms to Know

Vocabulary Review

A. Match each term with its definition. Write the correct letter on the line.

_____ **1.** unofficial advisors to President Andrew Jackson

_____ **2.** the social, cultural, and natural conditions that influence a community

_____ **3.** government appointments of friends by the winning party of an election

_____ **4.** to move a person or group of people

a. relocate

b. "kitchen cabinet"

c. spoils system

d. environment

B. Circle the letter of the correct definition for each term.

5. doctrine

a. a set of beliefs or principles
b. a formal contract
c. a list of goals
d. an official proclamation

6. canal

a. a barge that moved goods from one part of the country to another
b. a man-made bridge to move goods from one place to another
c. a waterway dug across land for ships to travel through
d. a large, steam-powered boat

7. sectionalism

a. concern for the interests of a certain region or area
b. concern for the interests of other nations
c. concern for the interests of the nation as a whole
d. concern only for oneself

Name ______________________________ Date ______________

Terms to Know

Chapter 13

Vocabulary Review

Terms to Know

A. Match each term with its definition. Write the correct letter on the line.

_____ **1.** the making of many items in a short period of time

_____ **2.** a machine that removes seeds from cotton fibers

_____ **3.** identical parts that can be substituted for each other

_____ **4.** escape routes used by enslaved African Americans to reach freedom in the North

_____ **5.** cloth

a. interchangeable parts

b. Underground Railroad

c. mass production

d. textile

e. cotton gin

B. Circle the letter of the correct definition for each term.

6. planter

- **a.** the profits earned from growing cotton
- **b.** a machine to collect cotton seeds
- **c.** a person who owns and operates a plantation
- **d.** a person who works on a plantation

7. factory

- **a.** a shop that sold goods to farmers
- **b.** a building with workers and machines in which manufacturing takes place
- **c.** a machine that allowed the British factories to spin and weave cloth at amazing speeds
- **d.** a type of cloth

8. spiritual

- **a.** an expressive religious song
- **b.** a cabin in which enslaved Africans lived
- **c.** an African folk tale
- **d.** an African folk craft

Name ______________________ Date ______________

Chapter 14

Terms to Know

Vocabulary Review

A. Match each term with its definition. Write the correct letter on the line.

_____ **1.** a perfect society

_____ **2.** an emphasis on the value, rights, and power of the individual

_____ **3.** a community where people live and work together using shared resources

_____ **4.** the view that favors people born in a country over immigrants who come to that country

_____ **5.** the belief that people learn truth and knowledge from their experiences with God and nature

_____ **6.** having to do with the country

a. rural

b. nativism

c. transcendentalism

d. utopia

e. commune

f. individualism

B. Complete each sentence with a term from the box.

revival	urban	abolition
reformer	temperance	

7. Preachers in the 1840s led a ______________________ that urged people to live according to God's laws.

8. In the early 1800s, more people began moving to ______________________ areas.

9. The ______________________ movement worked to outlaw alcoholic beverages.

10. A ______________________ is a person who wants to improve society.

11. The ______________________ of slavery dominated reform efforts until the passage of the Thirteenth Amendment.

Name ______________________ Date ______________

Terms to Know

Vocabulary Review

A. Circle the letter of the correct definition for each term.

1. prospector

- **a.** a fur trapper
- **b.** a person who looks for gold or other valuable ores
- **c.** a religious missionary
- **d.** someone who fights for freedom

2. boomtown

- **a.** a town with two governments
- **b.** a mining camp that grew into a town almost overnight
- **c.** a town that prospers
- **d.** a temporary town set up along the Oregon Trail

3. presidio

- **a.** a religious mission
- **b.** an area thought to have gold
- **c.** a mining camp
- **d.** a Spanish fort

4. annexation

- **a.** the search for wealth
- **b.** a battle over land
- **c.** the act of adding to or taking possession of
- **d.** a claim of independence

B. Complete each sentence on the lines below.

5. The sharing of an area of land by two or more countries was known as

______________________.

6. The belief that the United States had the right to extend from the Atlantic Ocean to the Pacific Ocean was known as ______________________.

7. A person who went to California in 1849 seeking gold was known as a

______________________.

8. A ______________________ was a fur trapper or trader who went west to live in or near the mountains.

9. A person who received a contract to bring settlers to Texas in the 1800s was called an ______________________.

Name ______________________ Date ______________

Chapter 16

Terms to Know

Vocabulary Review

Use the clues below to complete the crossword puzzle.

Across

1. a war between people of the same country
4. control by the people
5. to withdraw from or leave
9. a rebellion against established authority

Down

2. a veto of a portion but not all of a proposed law
3. the Confederate States of America
6. to free
7. a person whose opinions are very different from those of most people
8. temporary
10. a person who has run away

Name ________________________________ Date ________________

Terms to Know

Vocabulary Review

A. Write *T* on the line if the statement is true. Write *F* if the statement is false.

_____ **1.** During the Civil War, a border state was a state that separated the United States from Canada.

_____ **2.** Censorship is the control of free expression.

_____ **3.** A blockade was a type of fort that Confederates built to protect women and children.

_____ **4.** An ironclad warship is a metal or metal-covered steam-driven warship.

B. Circle the letter of the correct definition for each term.

5. strategy

- **a.** a map of enemy territory
- **b.** a plan
- **c.** a type of weapon
- **d.** a route through mountains

6. trench warfare

- **a.** soldiers using long, pipe-like weapons in combat
- **b.** soldiers fighting from hilltops and mountains
- **c.** soldiers fighting from long ditches dug in the ground
- **d.** soldiers using homemade weapons made from metal

7. total war

- **a.** a war against civilians and resources as well as against armies
- **b.** the enlistment of all men and boys over the age of 16
- **c.** the use of guerrilla strategies to overcome an enemy
- **d.** the combined use of civilian soldiers and enlisted men to win a battle

8. conscription

- **a.** the act of supplying women with arms to defend their homes
- **b.** the act of removing all goods for military use
- **c.** the act of banning certain people from the military
- **d.** the act of requiring people to serve in the military

9. habeas corpus

- **a.** the right of a citizen to ask a court to decide if a prisoner is being held lawfully
- **b.** a group of people who openly support the South
- **c.** the right to close a newspaper for criticizing the war
- **d.** a slow move toward emancipation

Name ________________________________ Date ________________

Chapter 18

Terms to Know

Vocabulary Review

Terms to Know

A. Match each term with its definition. Write the correct letter on the line.

_____ **1.** the process of charging a high public official, such as the President, with a crime

_____ **2.** unjust treatment of someone based on prejudice

_____ **3.** a series of laws passed in early Reconstruction to limit the freedoms of formerly enslaved African Americans

_____ **4.** a government pardon for an offense

_____ **5.** a Northerner who moved to the South after the Civil War for political gain

_____ **6.** laws that enforced segregation in the South

a. discrimination

b. carpetbagger

c. black codes

d. amnesty

e. impeachment

f. Jim Crow laws

B. Complete each sentence on the lines below.

7. Paying rent for farmland by giving part of the harvest to the landowner was called ______________________.

8. The ______________________ was created by Congress to help emancipated African Americans adjust to life as free people.

9. A white Southerner who supported the Republicans during Reconstruction was called a ______________________.

10. White Southerners who did not want to associate in public with African Americans supported ______________________.

11. During ______________________, the federal government looked for a way to reunite the former Confederate states with the rest of the country.

Name ____________________ Date ____________

Terms to Know

Chapter 19

Vocabulary Review

Terms to Know

A. Complete each sentence with a term from the box.

assimilate	cooperative	homesteader
platform	transcontinental	

1. A ____________ was a person who received land on which to build a house and farm.

2. A ____________ was an organization that was jointly owned by those who used its services.

3. The Dawes Act reduced the amount of land held by Native Americans and forced them to ____________ with the culture of the nation.

4. The ____________ railroad opened the West up to new settlement.

5. A ____________ is a statement of a political party's policies and beliefs.

B. Match each term with its definition. Write the correct letter on the line.

_____ **6.** the vast public grasslands in the West where cattle graze freely

_____ **7.** the death of a species

_____ **8.** an African American who moved to the Great Plains in the late 1800s

_____ **9.** a hired person who looks after cattle

_____ **10.** public land set aside for special use, as for Native Americans

a. Exoduster

b. cowhand

c. range

d. reservation

e. extinction

Name ________________________________ Date ____________________

Chapter 20

Terms to Know

Vocabulary Review

A. Match each term with its definition. Write the correct letter on the line.

_____ **1.** the act of keeping a person or group out		**a.** steerage
_____ **2.** a large open area beneath a ship's deck		**b.** corporation
_____ **3.** a method for producing a stronger type of steel		**c.** stock
_____ **4.** a large company usually formed by a group of investors		**d.** exclusion
_____ **5.** a share of ownership in a company		**e.** Bessemer process
_____ **6.** having a common racial, national, or cultural tradition		**f.** ethnic

B. Circle the letter of the correct definition for each term.

7. collective bargaining

- **a.** government discussions over new immigration policies
- **b.** community agreements about where to install electricity
- **c.** talks between a union and an employer about working conditions
- **d.** deals between corporations and investment bankers about paying back loans

8. patent

- **a.** a tool that helps divers lay telegraph cables across the floor of the Atlantic Ocean
- **b.** a grant that gives an inventor the sole right to make and sell an invention for a set period of time
- **c.** a document declaring a union's demands for safer and better working conditions
- **d.** a certificate stating that an immigrant has passed the health inspection at Ellis Island or Angel Island

9. monopoly

- **a.** complete control over a supply, service, or market
- **b.** a group of writers at the turn of the century who wrote about the poor
- **c.** sections of cities populated mainly by immigrants
- **d.** purposely producing a small amount of a product to increase its value

Name ______________________ Date ______________

Terms to Know

Chapter 21

Vocabulary Review

Terms to Know

A. Write *T* on the line if the statement is true. Write *F* if the statement is false.

_____ **1.** A trust is a giant corporation made up of a group of companies.

_____ **2.** Prohibition banned the making and selling of alcoholic drinks in the United States.

_____ **3.** The suffrage movement of the early 1900s fought to give children the right to vote.

_____ **4.** A tenement is an overcrowded, dirty, and unhealthy workplace.

_____ **5.** A writer who hides the problems in society is a muckraker.

_____ **6.** An election in which members of a political party vote to choose their candidates is a direct primary.

B. Circle the letter of the correct definition for each term.

7. sweatshop

a. the place where women vote
b. an unhealthy workplace where people are overworked
c. a tiny apartment in a city
d. the city jail

8. racism

a. a worry that large factories are not safe
b. a wish to campaign in an election
c. feelings against people because of their ethnic background or skin color
d. a decision to hire experts to run a city

9. Progressive

a. a person who believes in social progress through reform
b. a person who does not want to change society
c. a person who works to give power to political bosses
d. a person who does not want government to make social reforms

10. conservation

a. population rise in cities
b. creation of safer workplaces
c. protection of natural resources
d. protection of political bosses

Name ______________________________ Date ______________

Chapter 22

Terms to Know

Vocabulary Review

Terms to Know

A. Match each term with its definition. Write the correct letter on the line.

_____ **1.** a statement that follows logically from another statement	**a.** corollary
_____ **2.** a small country protected and controlled by a larger one	**b.** isthmus
_____ **3.** a narrow strip of land separating two larger land areas	**c.** protectorate
_____ **4.** the policy of staying out of the political affairs of other countries	**d.** isolationism

B. Complete each sentence with a term from the box.

sphere of influence	yellow journalism
diplomacy	imperialism

5. A region in which one nation has influence or control over other nations is a ______________________.

6. Publishing exaggerated or made-up news stories to attract readers and influence their ideas is known as ______________________.

7. During the late 1800s, many Americans supported the notion of ______________________ because they wanted the United States to build an overseas empire.

8. Conducting relations with the governments of foreign countries is known as ______________________.

Name ______________________ Date ______________

Terms to Know

Chapter 23

Vocabulary Review

Terms to Know

A. Match each term with its definition. Write the correct letter on the line.

_____ **1.** the payment for damages

_____ **2.** a competition to build weapons

_____ **3.** a loan from U.S. citizens to the government meant to be paid back with interest in several years

_____ **4.** the promotion of certain ideas to influence people's opinions

_____ **5.** a theory in which the economy is controlled by the government, and property is owned by everyone equally

a. arms race

b. propaganda

c. communism

d. reparation

e. war bond

B. Complete each sentence with a term from the box.

self-determination	armistice	pacifist
victory garden	mobilize	

6. When European countries declared war on each other, they had to ______________ thousands of troops.

7. When each of the Central Powers signed an ______________ and Germany surrendered, World War I finally ended.

8. As a way of showing their support for the war effort, some people grew their own food in a ______________.

9. President Wilson's peace plan, the Fourteen Points, supported ______________, or the right of people to decide on their own form of government.

10. A ______________ is a person who opposes war under any circumstance.

Name ______________________________ Date ______________

Chapter 24

Terms to Know

Vocabulary Review

A. Complete each sentence with a term from the box.

Harlem Renaissance	installment plan	quota
bootlegger		

1. Families could buy expensive items and pay for them over time using the ______________________.

2. The cultural movement during the 1920s in which the artistic work of African American writers, painters, and musicians blossomed became known as the ______________________.

3. A person who made or transported alcohol illegally was known as a ______________________.

4. In 1921, Congress passed a ______________________ to limit the number of people immigrating from Europe.

B. Match each term with its definition. Write the correct letter on the line.

_____	**5.** a row of factory workers who put together a product, part by part, as it passes by on a conveyor belt	**a.** fundamentalist
_____	**6.** the name given to the 1920s because of the new popularity of jazz music	**b.** assembly line
_____	**7.** a person who believes in a strict interpretation of the Bible or another religious book	**c.** Jazz Age
_____	**8.** to force someone to leave a country	**d.** deport

Name ______________________ Date ______________

Terms to Know

Chapter 25

Vocabulary Review

Terms to Know

A. Complete each sentence with a term from the box.

profit	tenant farmer	pension
relief	conservative	

1. A direct money payment to the unemployed is ______________________.

2. The money gained from a business or investment after expenses have been paid is called a ______________________.

3. A ______________________ pays for the right to farm someone else's land.

4. A ______________________ is a person who believes in limited government involvement in the economy.

5. An income for retired workers is called a ______________________.

B. Match each term with its definition. Write the correct letter on the line.

_____ **6.** a person who moves from place to place to find work, usually harvesting crops

_____ **7.** a community in which mostly Spanish-speaking people live

_____ **8.** a person who favors using government resources to bring about social and economic change

_____ **9.** projects paid for by the government for public use

_____ **10.** a long period of economic decline

a. liberal

b. migrant worker

c. depression

d. barrio

e. public works

Name ______________________ Date ______________

Chapter 26

Terms to Know

Vocabulary Review

Terms to Know

A. Write *T* on the line if the statement is true. Write *F* if the statement is false.

_____ **1.** A kamikaze is a Japanese warship used to fight against the U.S. Navy.

_____ **2.** The Holocaust was Hitler's policy of killing European Jews and others considered "unfit to live" during World War II.

_____ **3.** A dictator is a ruler who has complete power and authority.

_____ **4.** An atomic bomb is a nuclear weapon that causes large-scale destruction.

_____ **5.** Blitzkrieg is the German method of conducting war with speed and force.

B. Match each term with its definition. Write the correct letter on the line.

_____ **6.** an attempt to keep peace with an enemy by giving in to its demands

_____ **7.** a country in which one person or group has complete control

_____ **8.** a political system that emphasizes nationalism and is ruled by a dictator

_____ **9.** a place where political prisoners and members of religious and ethnic groups are sent

_____ **10.** a place in which people are confined, especially during a time of war

_____ **11.** the deliberate destruction of a group of people based on their race, culture, or beliefs

_____ **12.** to limit to small portions in order to make something last

a. fascism

b. concentration camp

c. ration

d. internment camp

e. totalitarian state

f. genocide

g. appeasement

Name ______________________________ Date ______________

Terms to Know

Chapter 27

Vocabulary Review

Terms to Know

A. Match each term with its definition. Write the correct letter on the line.

_____	**1.** an area that military forces cannot enter	**a.** space race
_____	**2.** a meeting between important leaders of nations	**b.** summit meeting
_____	**3.** a person who flees to a foreign country	**c.** superpower
_____	**4.** a conflict between countries, with no actual fighting	**d.** refugee
_____	**5.** a nation controlled by another country	**e.** baby boom
_____	**6.** the competition among countries to be the first in exploring space	**f.** demilitarized zone
_____	**7.** the increase in the birthrate after World War II	**g.** satellite
_____	**8.** one of the most powerful nations in the world	**h.** Cold War

B. Write *T* on the line if the statement is true. Write *F* if the statement is false.

_____ **9.** A generation gap is a difference in tastes and values between young people and their parents.

_____ **10.** A suburb is a community at the edge of a city.

_____ **11.** The iron curtain was an imaginary line separating North Korea and South Korea.

_____ **12.** Containment is a policy of preventing a country from expanding its power.

_____ **13.** McCarthyism is the practice of publicly accusing people of political disloyalty without regard for evidence.

_____ **14.** Perjury is the act of lying to a parent or relative.

Name ________________________________ Date ____________________

Chapter 28

Terms to Know

Vocabulary Review

A. Complete each sentence with a term from the box.

guerrilla war	sit-in	integrate	New Frontier

1. During the civil rights movement, people used a nonviolent form of protest called a ____________________ in which they would sit and refuse to leave a place.

2. In ____________________, small bands of fighters make surprise attacks.

3. President Kennedy's programs and goals for the future of the United States were known as the ____________________.

4. Civil rights activists worked to ____________________ or open schools and other places to people of all races.

B. Match each term with its definition. Write the correct letter on the line.

_____	**5.** to isolate	**a.** Peace Corps
_____	**6.** a person who is forced to live away from his or her home country	**b.** exile
_____	**7.** a protest against segregated buses and bus stations	**c.** quarantine
_____	**8.** a federal agency that sends trained volunteers to help developing countries	**d.** Freedom Ride

Name ____________________ Date ____________

Terms to Know

Chapter 29

Vocabulary Review

Terms to Know

Match each term with its definition. Write the correct letter on the line.

_____	**1.** a movement among African Americans to gain political and economic power		**a.** urban renewal
_____	**2.** to give a long speech in order to delay the vote on a bill in Congress		**b.** domino theory
_____	**3.** national health insurance for older Americans and people with certain disabilities		**c.** Medicare
_____	**4.** the belief that women's rights should be equal to men's rights		**d.** Great Society
_____	**5.** a sticky gasoline jelly used in bombs		**e.** napalm
_____	**6.** a program to rebuild run-down areas of cities		**f.** feminism
_____	**7.** public health program that pays medical expenses for low-income people		**g.** deferment
_____	**8.** a postponement, or a delaying, of having to serve in the armed forces		**h.** escalation
_____	**9.** President Johnson's goals and programs for the future of the United States		**i.** Black Power
_____	**10.** an increasing involvement		**j.** Medicaid
_____	**11.** the belief that if one country falls to communism, others nearby will fall, one after the other		**k.** filibuster

Name ______________________________ Date ____________________

Chapter 30

Terms to Know

Vocabulary Review

A. Match each term with its definition. Write the correct letter on the line.

_____ **1.** President Nixon's plan to train the South Vietnamese to fight the Vietnam War

_____ **2.** a person who is held captive until certain demands are met

_____ **3.** a temporary agreement to stop fighting

_____ **4.** easing tensions between unfriendly nations

a. truce

b. détente

c. Vietnamization

d. hostage

B. Circle the letter of the correct definition for each term.

5. recession

a. higher prices without economic growth
b. rising costs for goods and services
c. a decline in economic activity
d. an increase in economic activity

6. stagflation

a. an overall decline in economic activity
b. the economic condition of higher prices without economic growth
c. an overall increase in economic activity
d. a sign of a healthy economy

7. affirmative action

a. programs for reversing the effects of discrimination
b. segregation in public schools
c. protest march in support of desegregation
d. court action to desegregate schools

8. human rights

a. the basic freedoms that all people should have
b. the freedoms that belong only to people living in democratic societies
c. protests against segregation in public schools
d. improved work opportunities for minorities

Name ______________________________ Date ______________

Terms to Know

Vocabulary Review

A. Match each term with its definition. Write the correct letter on the line.

_____ **1.** the difference produced when the government spends more than it collects during a year

_____ **2.** the act of ridding a region or society of one or more ethnic groups

_____ **3.** the support of developing governments in foreign countries

_____ **4.** the use of violence or threats to achieve a goal

_____ **5.** lay off or fire workers to cut costs

_____ **6.** the loosening of government controls

a. downsize

b. nation-building

c. federal deficit

d. ethnic cleansing

e. terrorism

f. deregulation

B. Circle the letter of the correct definition for each term.

7. apartheid

a. a policy in South Africa of complete separation of the races
b. a system of trade between the United States and Kenya
c. a plan to irrigate and develop the arid land of Ethiopia
d. a policy of tolerance between Zambia, Mali, and the Congo

8. national debt

a. the total amount of money that each citizen owes the government
b. the amount of money other countries owe to the United States
c. the total amount of money the federal government owes to individuals, institutions, and itself
d. the amount of money European countries loaned the United States in 1984

9. grand jury

a. a jury of senators that represent the state the defendant comes from
b. a jury of Supreme Court judges that have served at least seven years
c. a jury that decides if the charges against a person are strong enough for a trial
d. a jury that presents the verdict of guilty or not guilty at a trial

Name ______________________________ Date ______________

Chapter 32

Terms to Know

Vocabulary Review

Terms to Know

A. Circle the letter of the correct definition for each term.

1. human genome

a. the genetic makeup of human beings
b. the act of working on genes to copy them
c. the gene connected to kidney disease
d. a gene that promotes good health

2. greenhouse effect

a. the rise in the temperature of Earth
b. the Earth's ozone layer
c. the process by which Earth is kept warm at all times
d. the process by which agriculture has changed due to warmer temperatures

3. clone

a. to take the cells of an organism apart
b. to replace an imperfect gene with a normal one
c. to find a cure for a disease
d. to make an exact copy of an organism by duplicating genetic material

B. Match each term with its definition. Write the correct letter on the line.

_____ **4.** the act of working on genes to change, or copy them	**a.** computer literate
_____ **5.** a condition in which countries are members of a world community	**b.** globalization
_____ **6.** having the basic skills needed to operate a computer	**c.** global warming
_____ **7.** the rise in the average temperatures of Earth over time	**d.** genetic engineering
_____ **8.** using two languages	**e.** bilingual

Contents

Review History

Name ______________________ Date ______________

Chapter 1

Review History

Comprehension Check

A. Choose the answer that best completes each of the following sentences. Circle the letter of the correct answer.

1. During the last Ice Age

- **a.** hunters crossed a land bridge from Asia into North America.
- **b.** the Maya built a great empire.
- **c.** Native Americans in Mexico learned to grow corn.
- **d.** early travelers constructed a bridge across the Bering Sea.

2. To transport farm products to the cities of their empire, the Incas

- **a.** used wooden boats.
- **b.** built many miles of roads.
- **c.** crossed the Great Plains.
- **d.** sailed along the Pacific Coast.

3. The Inuit were the first Native Americans to

- **a.** depend on the sea for their survival.
- **b.** live in villages that closely resembled one another.
- **c.** cross the Bering Strait to trade with other groups.
- **d.** hunt with bows and arrows.

4. The Toltec civilization

- **a.** was at its height before the Maya settled in Mexico.
- **b.** made major scientific advances.
- **c.** took over Maya lands.
- **d.** kept track of planting and harvesting cycles.

B. Complete each sentence on the lines below.

5. The people who built adobe structures in the desert cliffs of the American Southwest were the ______________________.

6. Native Americans of the Great Plains depended on the ______________________ for food, clothing, tools, and other uses.

7. The beginning of agriculture can be traced back to about 5000 B.C., when people began to plant ______________________.

8. The migration of early hunters into North America was made possible by the formation of huge ice sheets called ______________________.

9. The ______________________ civilization was one of the first civilizations to thrive on present-day Mexico's Gulf Coast.

Name ______________________ Date ______________

Review History

Comprehension Check

A. Write *T* on the line if the statement is true. Write *F* if the statement is false.

_____ **1.** The Native Americans whom Christopher Columbus met on the island of San Salvador called themselves Táino.

_____ **2.** The Crusades brought many changes to Europe, including new ideas, foods, and inventions.

_____ **3.** The English were the first Europeans to trade by sea with West Africa and Asia.

_____ **4.** Trade routes developed in Africa to exchange salt for gold.

_____ **5.** Christopher Columbus was the first European to arrive on the North American continent.

_____ **6.** Outside of Africa's trading centers, the main activity was farming.

_____ **7.** Mali was the largest and most powerful of the West African trading empires.

B. Complete each sentence on the lines below.

8. The three large trading empires in West Africa were ______________________

____.

9. The Portuguese explorer Bartolomeu Dias sailed south around the

______________________ and into the Indian Ocean.

10. In the late Middle Ages, European nations looked for new trade routes to

______________________.

11. The Silk Road was a trade route linking Europe and ______________________.

12. The Portuguese explorer who landed on the shore of present-day Brazil and claimed the land for Portugal was ______________________.

Name ______________________________ Date ________________

Chapter 3

Review History

Comprehension Check

A. Choose the answer that best completes each of the following sentences. Circle the letter of the correct answer.

1. One of Spain's goals in the Americas was to

a. establish a prison system for their criminals.

b. spread the Catholic faith.

c. negotiate a treaty with the Native Americans.

d. develop a nation of slave labor.

2. The explorations of Henry Hudson led to

a. a Dutch colony in North America.

b. the discovery of gold in the Gulf of Mexico.

c. a war between Spain and France.

d. the development of slavery in the Southwest.

3. West African society began to change in the mid-1400s because

a. many native people died from a famine that swept across the region.

b. the rulers of West Africa negotiated a treaty with the Spanish.

c. land was destroyed as a result of tribal warfare.

d. the Portuguese began trading with West African villages for slaves.

4. Enslaved Africans were taken to Jamestown in 1619 to

a. work in the homes of settlers.

b. form their own free society.

c. work as field hands on tobacco farms.

d. wait to be sent to the Caribbean.

B. Read each of the following sentences. Write *F* on the line if the statement is a fact. Write *O* if it is an opinion.

_____ **5.** The settlers of Jamestown would not have survived without John Smith's leadership.

_____ **6.** The Spanish conquistadors were greedy and cruel.

_____ **7.** During the 1500s and 1600s, more than 90 percent of the Native Americans in Mexico died of diseases spread from Europe and Africa.

_____ **8.** Many English indentured servants worked to pay off the cost of their trip to the Americas.

_____ **9.** After arriving in present-day Peru, Francisco Pizarro captured and killed the Inca ruler Atahualpa.

_____ **10.** The Spaniards should not have conquered the Incas and the Aztecs.

Name ______________________ Date ______________

Review History

Chapter 4

Comprehension Check

A. Read each pair of sentences. If the sentence gives the cause, write *C*. If the sentence gives the effect, write *E*.

1. a. _____ Puritans are persecuted in England because of their religious ideals.

b. _____ The Plymouth colony is established.

2. a. _____ The government of Virginia will not help poor farmers fight Native Americans for their land.

b. _____ Nathaniel Bacon leads a rebellion and burns Jamestown, Virginia.

3. a. _____ Roger Williams founds Rhode Island.

b. _____ The Massachusetts Bay Colony discriminates against people who do not practice Puritan beliefs.

4. a. _____ Small farmers in the northern part of Carolina distrust wealthy landowners settling the southern coast.

b. _____ In 1729, the colony is split into North Carolina and South Carolina.

B. Write *T* on the line if the statement is true. Write *F* if the statement is false.

_____ **5.** The rise in production of tobacco in Virginia brought more settlers into the colony and onto Native American land.

_____ **6.** The Mayflower Compact gave all male landowners in the Massachusetts Bay Colony the right to vote.

_____ **7.** After three years of fighting, Native Americans retrieved their land from colonists.

_____ **8.** The colony of New Jersey was established when the Duke of York gave former Dutch land to two of his friends.

_____ **9.** King George II allowed the colony of Georgia to be established because it would protect the other colonies from the Spaniards in Florida.

_____ **10.** King James placed Virginia under his control as a royal colony.

_____ **11.** William Penn believed in taking land that did not belong to him, so he often took land from the Native Americans.

Review History

Name ______________________ Date ______________

Chapter 5

Review History

Comprehension Check

A. Complete each sentence on the lines below.

1. In colonial society, ______________________ were important for spreading information about events in Europe.

2. Colonies in ______________________ turned to the sea and forests for natural resources.

3. The second part of the triangular trade route used to transport enslaved Africans was called the ______________________.

4. The newspaperman who was tried for libel for publishing articles that exposed the dishonesty of the governor of New York was ______________________.

5. The large uprising of enslaved people that took place in South Carolina in 1739 was called the ______________________.

6. The two fastest growing colonies in the Middle colonies were ______________________.

B. Write *T* on the line if the statement is true. Write *F* if the statement is false.

_____ 7. In the Middle colonies, farmers had large and very productive family farms.

_____ 8. Because of the large size of plantations in the Southern colonies, many workers were needed.

_____ 9. The religious movement led by Jonathan Edwards and other ministers was known as the Middle Passage.

_____ 10. The most famous Enlightenment philosopher in the American colonies was Benjamin Franklin.

_____ 11. The Navigation Acts were imposed by Great Britain to fund schools in the colonies.

Name ______________________________ Date ______________

Review History

Chapter 6

Comprehension Check

Review History

A. Answer the following questions on the lines below.

1. Why did the British Parliament want to overthrow King James II?

___

___

2. How was the right to vote limited in colonial America?

___

___

3. How did the Navigation Acts affect the colonists?

___

___

4. Why did France, Spain, and England have so many conflicts between them during the 1600s and 1700s?

___

___

5. Why did the French build Fort Le Boeuf east of Lake Erie?

___

___

B. Read the questions below. Choose one question and answer it in a paragraph on a separate sheet of paper.

6. In what ways was John Locke's contract theory of government similar to, or different from, the colonial style of self-government?

7. What happened in each of the three wars that took place in North America between 1689 and 1750?

8. What was the Albany Plan of Union, and what did it propose to do?

Name ______________________________ Date ______________

Chapter 7

Review History

Comprehension Check

A. Write *T* on the line if the statement is true. Write *F* if the statement is false.

_____ **1.** At the time of the First Continental Congress, most colonists were ready to declare independence from Great Britain.

_____ **2.** The Committee of Correspondence helped bring the colonists together by letting them know about British actions.

_____ **3.** The Intolerable Acts convinced some colonies to stop protesting British laws.

_____ **4.** The First Continental Congress was the first time people from several colonies met to write a letter to the British government protesting taxes.

B. Match each item with its description. Write the correct letter on the line.

_____	**5.** the first major battle of the War for Independence	**a.** Second Continental Congress
_____	**6.** acts that placed import taxes on common products made in Britain and shipped to the colonies	**b.** Stamp Act
_____	**7.** the delegates from this group decided to write the Declaration of Independence	**c.** Intolerable Acts
_____	**8.** a document that stated that the colonies were still loyal to the king	**d.** Battle of Bunker Hill
_____	**9.** an act that led many colonists to take up the cry "no taxation without representation"	**e.** Boston Massacre
_____	**10.** an act that was passed in 1764 and forced colonists to provide food and shelter to British soldiers	**f.** Olive Branch Petition
_____	**11.** an event that led to Parliament repealing most of the Townshend taxes	**g.** Townshend Acts
_____	**12.** laws that were meant to punish the people of Boston, Massachusetts	**h.** Quartering Act

Name ______________________ Date ______________

Review History

Chapter 8

Comprehension Check

A. Complete each sentence on the lines below.

1. After the defeat of the British at Saratoga, New York, the United States began to receive help from its new ally, ______________.

2. The peace agreement signed by the United States and Great Britain at the end of the Revolutionary War was the ______________.

3. The final battle of the Revolutionary War took place at ______________

4. In the West, Native Americans fought on the side of the ______________

B. Match each person with his description. Write the correct letter on the line.

____ **5.** a commander in the Continental navy who led the defeat of the British navy	**a.** Count de Rochambeau
____ **6.** the British general who was surrounded at Saratoga and finally surrendered	**b.** Benjamin Lincoln
____ **7.** the British general who was trapped at Yorktown by French and American forces	**c.** John Paul Jones
____ **8.** a frontiersman who brought an end to British raids on western settlements	**d.** George Rogers Clark
____ **9.** the American general at the Battle of Yorktown	**e.** Charles Cornwallis
____ **10.** the French general at the Battle of Yorktown	**f.** George Washington
____ **11.** the Iroquois leader who was one of Britain's greatest allies	**g.** John Burgoyne
____ **12.** the American general who surrendered his entire army of troops to the British at Charleston, South Carolina	**h.** Joseph Brant

Name ______________________________ Date ______________

Chapter 9

Review History

Comprehension Check

A. Choose the answer that best completes each of the following sentences. Circle the letter of the correct answer.

1. The Three-Fifths Compromise

- **a.** stated that five enslaved people would be counted as three free citizens.
- **b.** was proposed by Roger Sherman of Connecticut.
- **c.** called for three branches of government.
- **d.** was rejected by delegates.

2. Under the Articles of Confederation, one of the main powers of the federal government was to

- **a.** build the White House.
- **b.** raise money for an army.
- **c.** resolve disagreements among the states.
- **d.** establish state boundaries.

3. The idea that each state kept control of its own affairs was called

- **a.** checks and balances.
- **b.** sovereignty.
- **c.** public domain.
- **d.** ratification.

4. According to the Ordinance of 1784, the United States would

- **a.** expand by owning colonies.
- **b.** gain control of territory west of the Mississippi.
- **c.** add to the number of independent states in the country.
- **d.** not allow any territories to become states.

B. Complete each sentence on the lines below.

5. The agreement to divide the legislative branch into an upper house and a lower house was called ______________________.

6. The delegates at the Annapolis Convention agreed that the states needed to revise the ______________________.

7. Americans who supported the Constitution and wanted a strong federal government were called ______________________.

8. When the Massachusetts state government ignored farmers' requests to lower taxes, ______________________ broke out.

Name ______________________ Date ______________

Review History

Comprehension Check

A. Choose the answer that best completes each of the following sentences. Circle the letter of the correct answer.

1. The U.S. Constitution gives Congress the power to

- **a.** print money.
- **b.** choose the President.
- **c.** command the military.
- **d.** declare laws unconstitutional.

2. As Secretary of the Treasury, Alexander Hamilton's job was to

- **a.** make treaties with Native Americans.
- **b.** oversee the building of roads and canals.
- **c.** strengthen the new nation's economy.
- **d.** establish good relations with other countries.

3. The Federalists believed in

- **a.** state banks.
- **b.** a strong national government.
- **c.** industry based on independent farmers.
- **d.** a strict interpretation of the Constitution.

4. The XYZ Affair brought the United States to the brink of war with

- **a.** Spain.
- **b.** France.
- **c.** Great Britain.
- **d.** Native Americans.

B. Write *T* on the line if the statement is true. Write *F* if the statement is false.

_____ **5.** As part of the compromise over Hamilton's economic plan, the nation's capital was moved from New York City to Philadelphia.

_____ **6.** The Democratic-Republicans believed in a strict interpretation of the Constitution.

_____ **7.** Thomas Jefferson followed George Washington to become the nation's second President.

_____ **8.** The Sedition Act made it illegal for anyone to criticize Congress or the President.

_____ **9.** President Washington ordered an army to go to Pennsylvania to end the Whiskey Rebellion.

_____ **10.** The Judiciary Act of 1789 created the court system in the United States.

Name ______________________ Date ______________

Chapter 11

Review History

Comprehension Check

A. Complete each sentence on the lines below.

1. When the United States bought the ______________ from France, the area of the United States doubled.

2. The War Hawks hoped that winning a war against Great Britain would allow the United States to gain control of ______________.

3. Congress ordered all U.S. shipowners to stop trading with European countries by passing the ______________.

4. Americans received their first information about the territory they had purchased from the French as a result of the ______________.

5. Great Britain tried to invade the United States at New York City, New York, Washington, D.C., and New Orleans, Louisiana, during the last part of the ______________.

6. Native Americans tried to chase settlers out of the northern territories of the United States until General William Henry Harrison won the ______________.

7. To prevent the problem of a tie vote for President in the electoral college, Congress passed the ______________.

8. Thomas Jefferson won the presidency in the election of 1800 after ______________ gave him support.

B. Answer the following question. Write your answer in a paragraph on a separate sheet of paper.

9. When President Jefferson took office, there was trouble between the United States and pirates from the Barbary States of North Africa. What happened between the United States and the country of Tripoli when Thomas Jefferson became President?

Name ______________________ Date ______________

Review History

Comprehension Check

A. Write *T* on the line if the statement is true. Write *F* if the statement is false.

_____ **1.** John Quincy Adams was not a popular President, and many Americans thought that he was cold and insensitive.

_____ **2.** In the case *McCullough* v. *Maryland*, the Supreme Court ruled that only the federal government could control trade.

_____ **3.** The Monroe Doctrine asked the nations of Europe to colonize the lands of the Western Hemisphere.

_____ **4.** The Indian Removal Act of 1830 ordered Native Americans to move west of the Mississippi River.

B. Complete each sentence with a term from the box.

two-party system	Bank of the United States	American System
Whig Party	states' rights	Five Tribes

5. During the Nullification Crisis, many Southerners agreed with the idea of ______________________.

6. By 1820, the ______________________ in American politics had temporarily ended.

7. The ______________________ was a plan to make the nation more unified and better able to take care of itself.

8. Political leaders who did not agree with Andrew Jackson and the Democrats formed the ______________________.

9. The Cherokees were part of the group of Native Americans known together as the ______________________.

10. Andrew Jackson believed the ______________________ had too much power over the national economy.

Name ______________________________ Date ______________

Chapter 13

Review History

Comprehension Check

A. Choose the answer that best completes each of the following sentences. Circle the letter of the correct answer.

1. The leader of one of the best-known slave rebellions was

a. Eli Whitney.
b. Nat Turner.
c. Cyrus McCormick.
d. Samuel Morse.

2. In an effort to help farmers of the Great Plains, John Deere invented

a. the lightweight steel plow.
b. the mechanical reaper.
c. barbed wire.
d. the windmill.

3. Eli Whitney developed a machine called the

a. cotton mill.
b. Underground Railroad.
c. cotton gin.
d. mechanical clock.

4. One thing that helped increase the number of factories in the United States was the

a. aid of Great Britain.
b. slave system.
c. Tariff of 1816.
d. plantation system.

B. Write *T* on the line if the statement is true. Write *F* if the statement is false.

_____ **5.** Before the invention of the cotton gin, it took a worker a whole day to remove the seeds from just one pound of cotton.

_____ **6.** The development of the plantation system caused a rise in the number of enslaved people in the United States.

_____ **7.** Before the Industrial Revolution, many American colonists earned their living by farming.

_____ **8.** Samuel Morse invented the mechanical reaper to replace the slow method of harvesting by hand.

_____ **9.** Industrial growth was centered in the North because the North had better transportation systems and a more developed banking system.

_____ **10.** Enslaved people in the United States were not allowed to live in cities.

_____ **11.** Some African Americans tried to escape a life of slavery to be closer to family members that had been separated from them.

Review History

Name ______________________________ Date ______________

Review History

Comprehension Check

A. Write *T* on the line if the statement is true. Write *F* if the statement is false.

_____ **1.** Many people immigrated to the United States because of social unrest or food shortages in their home countries.

_____ **2.** Horace Mann felt that people should pay taxes to support a public education system.

_____ **3.** Paintings done during the Hudson River school movement were similar in style to European paintings.

_____ **4.** Members of the abolitionist and antislavery movements agreed that slavery should be ended but disagreed on how it should be done.

_____ **5.** Women's rights advocates believed women should be able to vote but not own property.

_____ **6.** Horace Mann lectured throughout the United States in support of nativism.

B. Choose the answer that best completes each of the following sentences. Circle the letter of the correct answer.

7. The growth of urban population led to all of the following problems except

a. overcrowding.
b. high unemployment.
c. increased deaths from disease.
d. fires due to wooden buildings.

8. Harriet Beecher Stowe wrote an influential antislavery novel titled

a. *Walden.*
b. *Uncle Tom's Cabin.*
c. *The Scarlet Letter.*
d. *Leaves of Grass.*

9. One group that hoped to limit immigration became known as the

a. Know-Nothing Party.
b. Abolitionists.
c. American Colonization Society.
d. Hudson River school.

10. Dorothea Dix worked successfully to improve conditions in

a. communes.
b. factories.
c. mental institutions.
d. other countries.

Name ________________________________ Date ____________________

Chapter 15

Review History

Comprehension Check

A. Write *T* on the line if the statement is true. Write *F* if the statement is false.

_____ **1.** The 1848 Treaty of Guadalupe Hidalgo allowed Mexico to keep California for five more years.

_____ **2.** The main task of Spanish missionaries in North America was to convert Native Americans to Christianity.

_____ **3.** Many people wanted Texas to join the United States so the slaveholding states would outnumber the free states.

_____ **4.** The belief in Manifest Destiny prompted many Americans to push for an end to slavery.

_____ **5.** The United States and Great Britain agreed that joint occupation of the Oregon Territory would end when one country had a larger population in the territory than the other.

_____ **6.** The struggle between slaveholding and free states ended when California was admitted to the United States.

_____ **7.** Sam Houston was elected president of the Republic of Texas.

_____ **8.** Joseph Smith led nearly 2,000 Mormons westward along the Oregon Trail in 1864.

_____ **9.** In 1830, the Mexican government passed a law to stop American immigration to Texas.

B. Number the following events in the order in which they occurred. The first one is done for you.

_____ **10.** Californians adopt a Constitution and ask to be admitted to the United States.

_____ **11.** Mexican troops rush through the walls of the Alamo.

_____ **12.** The United States and Mexico sign the Treaty of Guadalupe Hidalgo.

_____ **13.** California is admitted to the United States as the thirty-first state.

__1__ **14.** Mexico wins its independence from Spain.

Review History

Name ______________________________ Date ______________

Review History

Chapter 16

Comprehension Check

A. Write *T* on the line if the statement is true. Write *F* if the statement is false.

_____ **1.** In 1859, John Brown attacked Harpers Ferry in an effort to begin a slave rebellion.

_____ **2.** The Missouri Compromise applied only to land that had been part of the Louisiana Purchase.

_____ **3.** *Uncle Tom's Cabin* was a novel praising the slave system.

_____ **4.** The Crittenden Compromise was an attempt to bring the seceded states back into the Union.

_____ **5.** According to the idea of popular sovereignty, the people of a territory could vote to settle the issue of slavery.

_____ **6.** The Civil War began when Abraham Lincoln was elected President of the United States.

_____ **7.** Northerners were upset about the Fugitive Slave Law because it forced them to be part of the slave system even though they did not support it.

_____ **8.** The Confederacy was created by delegates from the seven states that voted to leave the Union.

B. Complete each sentence on the lines below.

9. The four candidates in the election of 1860 were ______________________

____

10. Violence broke out in Kansas in the mid-1850s when ______________________

____

11. The first state to secede from the Union was ______________________

____

12. In the Dred Scott case, the Supreme Court ruled that slaves were considered

____

Review History

Name ______________________________ Date ________________

Chapter 17

Review History

Comprehension Check

A. Number the events below in the order in which they occurred.

_____ **1.** The Confederacy wins the Battle of Bull Run.

_____ **2.** President Lincoln is re-elected by a landslide.

_____ **3.** Confederates defeat the Union army at Fredericksburg, Virginia.

_____ **4.** Virginia, Arkansas, Tennessee, and North Carolina secede from the Union.

_____ **5.** The Union wins the Battle of Antietam.

B. Complete each sentence on the lines below.

6. President Lincoln formally signed the ______________________ on January 1, 1863.

7. General Lee Surrendered on April 9, 1865, at ______________________, a village in Virginia.

8. Charles Francis Adams, who represented the United States in Great Britain, convinced ______________________ to stop selling ships to the Confederacy.

9. Until June 1864, ______________________ soldiers received less pay than other soldiers.

10. The Union's law allowed people to pay a fee of $300 to avoid being ______________________ to serve in the military.

11. The Union army hoped to create a ______________________ that would cut off all trading and supply routes between the South and foreign countries.

12. In June 1864, General Grant planned a major attack on ______________________, an important railroad center just south of Richmond, Virginia.

Name ______________________ Date ______________

Review History

Comprehension Check

A. Read each of the following sentences. Write *F* on the line if the statement is a fact. Write *O* if it is an opinion.

_____ **1.** The Republican Congress did not agree with President Johnson's plan for Reconstruction.

_____ **2.** African Americans were granted too many rights after the Civil War.

_____ **3.** President Johnson should have been removed from office because he disagreed with the Fourteenth Amendment to the Constitution.

_____ **4.** President Lincoln's Ten Percent Plan was the best plan for Reconstruction.

_____ **5.** By law, Confederate leaders were not allowed to serve in elected office during Reconstruction.

_____ **6.** Many Republicans in Congress did not support President Lincoln's plan for Reconstruction.

B. Write *T* on the line if the statement is true. Write *F* if the statement is false.

_____ **7.** No African Americans were elected to state or federal office during Reconstruction.

_____ **8.** President Andrew Johnson was brought up on impeachment charges for violating the Tenure of Office Act.

_____ **9.** Reconstruction ended because the southern states had finally stopped discriminating against African Americans.

_____ **10.** Poll taxes and the "grandfather clause" provided a legal way for southern governments to discriminate against African American voters.

_____ **11.** In the Compromise of 1877, southern states agreed to accept Rutherford Hayes as the newly elected President in exchange for the removal of federal troops from their lands.

_____ **12.** The Freedmen's Bureau had its greatest success in setting up schools.

_____ **13.** The 1876 election between Samuel Tilden and Rutherford B. Hayes ended up being one of the closest in history.

Name ______________________________ Date ____________________

Chapter 19

Review History

Comprehension Check

A. Read each pair of sentences. If the sentence gives the cause, write *C*. If the sentence gives the effect, write *E*.

1. a. _____ Some Native Americans will not move to reservations.
b. _____ Native Americans battle government troops.

2. a. _____ Transcontinental railroad lines are completed.
b. _____ Regions of the West are opened up to new settlement.

3. a. _____ Native Americans lose their land, and many are forced onto reservations.
b. _____ The Homestead Act grants large amounts of land to settlers.

4. a. _____ The city of Denver, Colorado, is founded.
b. _____ Gold and silver are discovered near Cherry Creek, Colorado.

5. a. _____ The government allows gold miners into the Black Hills of the Dakotas.
b. _____ General Custer is defeated at the Battle of Little Bighorn.

6. a. _____ The Dawes Act is passed by Congress.
b. _____ Each Native American family would receive 160 acres of reservation land to own.

B. Write *T* on the line if the statement is true. Write *F* if the statement is false.

_____ **7.** Most settlers did not have any difficulty making a living by farming prairie land.

_____ **8.** Many of the Native American uprisings resulted from the government requirement that they move to reservations.

_____ **9.** Railroad companies and miners created the Populist Party and voted to elect government officials who were friendly toward farmers.

_____ **10.** Only a small number of the miners who searched for gold during the gold rush actually became rich.

_____ **11.** The transcontinental railroad decreased conflicts between Native Americans and settlers.

Name ______________________ Date ______________

Review History

Chapter 20

Comprehension Check

Review History

A. Write *true* or *false* on the line below each sentence. If the sentence is false, rewrite it to make it true. Use a separate sheet of paper if you need more space.

1. Most new immigrants settled in the countryside and bought farmland with the help of the government.

____

2. Andrew Carnegie raised the salary of his employees because he believed that poverty was unnatural.

____

3. Many women became switchboard operators after Alexander Graham Bell invented the telephone.

____

4. The Chinese Exclusion Act banned all Chinese immigrants from working on the railroads.

____

5. In the late 1800s, most labor strikes were unsuccessful, and the government supported the corporations instead of the unions.

____

6. Most Asian immigrants entered the United States at Ellis Island in New York.

____

7. In ethnic communities, immigrants from different cultures and nationalities lived in close contact with one another.

____

B. How did the development of the Bessemer process affect the railroad industry's demand for steel? Write your answer in a paragraph on a separate sheet of paper.

Name ______________________________ Date ______________

Chapter 21

Review History

Comprehension Check

A. Choose the answer that best completes each of the following sentences. Circle the letter of the correct answer.

1. The Interstate Commerce Act

a. called for states to print time schedules for trains.

b. called for railroads that traveled through more than one state to set "reasonable and just" rates.

c. banned trading between states.

d. let states tax items moved by railroad.

2. The Seventeenth Amendment gave people the right to

a. earn minimum wage.

b. fire the President.

c. trade with Canadians.

d. elect U.S. senators directly.

3. Run-down apartment buildings where many people lived were called

a. suburbs.

b. tenements.

c. factories.

d. mines.

4. The Pendleton Civil Service Act

a. set up a system for filling some government jobs based on ability.

b. took all land away from Native Americans.

c. made bribes illegal.

d. gave Canada all the land owned by Native Americans.

B. Complete each sentence on the lines below.

5. The ____________________ stopped most Chinese immigration into the United States.

6. The National American Women's Suffrage Association fought to get women the right to ____________________.

7. The Federal Reserve Act changed the ____________________ in the United States.

8. The Keating-Owen Act prohibited the shipment of goods made by ____________________ across state lines.

9. Congress created the ____________________ in 1903 to settle problems between workers and business owners.

Name ______________________________ Date ______________

Review History

Comprehension Check

A. Read the main idea below. Place a check by the sentences that support the main idea.

Main idea: From the mid-1800s to the early 1900s, the United States expanded its influence throughout the world.

_____ **1.** The United States began trading with Japan in the mid-1850s.

_____ **2.** Theodore Roosevelt was elected President of the United States after the Spanish-American War.

_____ **3.** In 1867, the United States purchased Alaska.

_____ **4.** Francisco "Pancho" Villa led a revolt in Mexico.

_____ **5.** As a result of the Spanish-American War, the United States brought many Caribbean and Pacific countries under its control.

_____ **6.** The United States annexed Hawaii on July 7, 1898.

B. Choose the answer that best completes each of the following sentences. Circle the letter of the correct answer.

7. In 1900, the Boxers led a rebellion to

a. discourage trade in China.
b. protest the building of the Panama Canal.
c. rid China of all foreigners.
d. protest the paying of taxes.

8. The leader who helped organize the Rough Riders was

a. Alfred Mahan.
b. Theodore Roosevelt.
c. Commodore Matthew Perry.
d. John Hay.

9. In 1901, the United States forced Cuba to adopt the

a. Foraker Act.
b. Platt Amendment.
c. Teller Amendment.
d. Philippine Government Act.

10. President Taft's foreign policy became known as

a. dollar diplomacy.
b. moral diplomacy.
c. big-stick diplomacy.
d. good-neighbor diplomacy.

11. After the 1903 revolt in Panama, the new Panamanian government

a. gave the United States land to build the Panama Canal.
b. made Panama a protectorate.
c. paid taxes to the United States.
d. sent warships to the United States.

12. The policy that allowed any nation to trade in China was called the

a. Closed Door policy.
b. sphere of influence.
c. Open Door policy.
d. Boxer Rebellion.

Name ______________________________ Date ______________

Chapter 23

Review History

Comprehension Check

A. Write *T* on the line if the statement is true. Write *F* if the statement is false.

_____ **1.** Germany's invasion of France was the event that triggered the beginning of World War I.

_____ **2.** In his 1916 presidential campaign, President Wilson argued that the United States should immediately enter the war.

_____ **3.** In the Selective Service Act, men of a certain age were required to register for the draft.

_____ **4.** Airplanes were used during World War I to help pilots locate enemy lines.

_____ **5.** In the early 1900s, many African Americans moved north to find jobs in war industries and factories.

_____ **6.** Russia withdrew from World War I after fighting began on the eastern front.

B. Complete each sentence on the lines below.

7. The ______________________ sent speakers across the nation to explain why Americans were fighting overseas.

8. Pilots in World War I who shot down five or more enemy planes were known as ______________________.

9. The name given to U.S. forces fighting in Europe was the ______________________.

10. Congress rejected a treaty that would have let the United States join the ______________________.

11. In the United States, two thirds of the cost of World War I was paid by ______________________.

Name ______________________________ Date ______________

Review History

Comprehension Check

A. Complete each sentence on the lines below.

1. The most famous scandal of Warren Harding's presidency was the ____________________ Scandal.

2. It was the job of ____________________ to convince Americans that they needed to buy more material goods.

3. The ____________________, which was ratified in 1920, guaranteed that women could not be denied the right to vote.

4. The Eighteenth Amendment was ratified in 1919 and made it illegal to manufacture, sell, or buy ____________________.

5. Babe Ruth, Ty Cobb, and Lou Gehrig were famous ____________________.

B. Write *T* on the line if the statement is true. Write *F* if the statement is false.

_____ **6.** One benefit of making cars on an assembly line was that they were made to be more gas efficient.

_____ **7.** W. E. B. DuBois fought for equal rights for African Americans by founding the NAACP.

_____ **8.** Some people feared the U.S. government would be taken over by Canada.

_____ **9.** The trial of Sacco and Vanzetti showed that some Americans were suspicious of the Ku Klux Klan.

_____ **10.** During his presidency, John Calvin Coolidge focused on strengthening the economy.

_____ **11.** The Cotton Club, in New York City, was where people went to hear musicians such as Duke Ellington and Ethel Waters.

Name ______________________________ Date ____________________

Chapter 25

Review History

Comprehension Check

A. Match each item with its description. Write the correct letter on the line.

_____ **1.** act that provided monthly pensions for retired people over the age of 65

_____ **2.** organization that provided loans to farm cooperatives and purchased surplus crops

_____ **3.** novel by John Steinbeck about a family fleeing the Dust Bowl

_____ **4.** act that placed high tariffs on foreign goods

_____ **5.** campaign slogan of Franklin Roosevelt that promised an end to the Great Depression

_____ **6.** name given to the day the stock market crashed on October 29, 1929

a. Hawley-Smoot Tariff Act

b. "New Deal"

c. Social Security Act

d. *The Grapes of Wrath*

e. Federal Farm Board

g. Black Tuesday

B. Complete each sentence on the lines below.

7. The residents of shantytowns, who hoped President Herbert Hoover would send them relief, often named their communities

______________________.

8. Under the ______________________, dams were built along the Tennessee River to stop flooding and produce electricity.

9. The National Labor Relations Act guaranteed the rights of ______________________ to join unions and negotiate with their employers.

10. The Sunday evening radio broadcasts in which President Roosevelt described his policies to the public became known as ______________________.

Name ______________________ Date ______________

Review History

Comprehension Check

A. Write *T* on the line if the statement is true. Write *F* if the statement is false.

_____ **1.** Germany was one of the countries that suffered the most after World War I.

_____ **2.** Benito Mussolini came to power in Spain after World War I.

_____ **3.** Joseph Stalin turned the Soviet Union into a totalitarian state in which he placed businesses and farms under government control.

_____ **4.** Adolf Hitler was not interested in Czechoslovakia because Great Britain and France had already claimed it.

B. Match each item with its description. Write the correct letter on the line.

_____	**5.** location where Allied leaders met to make plans for the end of the war	**a.** Hiroshima
_____	**6.** program that offered planes, tanks, and other equipment to the Allied nations as a loan	**b.** Pearl Harbor
_____	**7.** the largest land battle in World War II that involved American forces	**c.** Atlantic Charter
_____	**8.** an agreement stating that every nation that was controlled by the Axis Powers should have the right to choose its own government through free elections	**d.** United Nations
_____	**9.** site of a key victory for the United States over the Japanese	**e.** Battle of the Bulge
_____	**10.** site of the unexpected Japanese attack on the U.S. Pacific Fleet	**f.** Midway Island
_____	**11.** city in Japan where the United States dropped an atomic bomb	**g.** Yalta
_____	**12.** a world peace organization that would replace the League of Nations	**h.** Lend-Lease Act

Name ______________________________ Date ______________

Chapter 27

Review History

Comprehension Check

A. Number the following events in the order in which they occurred. The first one is done for you.

_____ **1.** The *Brown* v. *Board of Education of Topeka* decision is made.

_____ **2.** North Koreans surge across the 38th parallel and invade South Korea.

_____ **3.** The Montgomery bus boycott takes place.

_____ **4.** The Little Rock school crisis begins.

__1__ **5.** Communists establish the People's Republic of China.

_____ **6.** The Korean War ends.

B. Complete each sentence on the lines below.

7. During the ____________________, President Truman ordered U.S. pilots to deliver food, fuel, and medical supplies to West Berlin.

8. The ____________________ was established when President Truman asked Congress to help Greece and Turkey defend themselves against Communists.

9. One of the greatest achievements by African Americans in the years after World War II was in ____________________.

10. In response to NATO, the Soviet Union organized the ____________________.

11. An increased fear of communism and the Soviet Union led to the ____________________ in the United States.

12. NASA was developed because many Americans worried that the United States had fallen behind the Soviet Union in developing ____________________.

Name ______________________________ Date ______________

Review History

Chapter 28

Comprehension Check

Review History

A. Complete each sentence on the lines below.

1. The ______________________ was a protest against segregated buses and bus stations in the South.

2. One of the leaders of protests and campaigns for civil rights throughout the South was ______________________.

3. The 1960 election was the first time two candidates debated on ______________________.

4. A ______________________ almost occurred when Soviet ships were on their way to Cuba with missiles.

5. The Bay of Pigs invasion was an attempt to overthrow the Cuban government, which was led by ______________________.

B. Write *T* on the line if the statement is true. Write *F* if the statement is false.

_____ **6.** After President Kennedy died, Vice President Lyndon B. Johnson was sworn in as the new President.

_____ **7.** The Student Nonviolent Coordinating Committee worked to reduce segregation in the South and to register African Americans to vote.

_____ **8.** The 1960 presidential election was one of the closest in U.S. history.

_____ **9.** During Kennedy's administration, the Supreme Court made many decisions that took rights away from individuals.

_____ **10.** The Peace Corps was one of President Kennedy's most successful programs.

_____ **11.** President Kennedy put an end to most of the previous administration's Cold War policies.

_____ **12.** President Kennedy planned to have an American on Mars by the end of the 1960s.

Name ______________________________ Date ____________

Chapter 29

Review History

Comprehension Check

Review History

A. Complete each sentence with a term from the box.

Higher Education Act	Voting Rights Act	Indians of All Tribes
Viet Cong	Tet Offensive	Gulf of Tonkin Resolution

1. The ____________________ gave President Johnson the power to wage war in Vietnam without formally declaring war.

2. The ____________________ provides student loans and gives money to universities for research.

3. Members of ____________________ took control of Alcatraz Island to bring national attention to their cause.

4. When the ____________________ was passed in 1965, states could no longer make voters pay a poll tax or take a literacy test.

5. Communist supporters in South Vietnam were known as the ____________________.

6. The ____________________ prompted many Americans to question U.S. involvement in the Vietnam War.

B. Write *T* on the line if the statement is true. Write *F* if the statement is false.

_____ **7.** Freedom Summer was a campaign by African American and white volunteers to register African Americans in the South to vote.

_____ **8.** The Immigration and Nationality Act allowed more people from Asia, Latin America, and Eastern Europe to come to the United States.

_____ **9.** Despite the growing unpopularity of the Vietnam War, President Johnson decided to run for re-election in 1968.

Name ______________________________ Date ______________

Review History

Chapter 30

Review History

Comprehension Check

A. Match each item with its description. Write the correct letter on the line.

_____ **1.** the government institution formed during the Nixon administration to help protect the nation's air and water

_____ **2.** village in South Vietnam where hundreds of unarmed people were killed on March 16, 1968

_____ **3.** the act that declared that the President should consult with Congress before committing U.S. armed forces to conflicts overseas

_____ **4.** an agreement between Israel and Egypt made during the Carter administration

a. Camp David Accords

b. Environmental Protection Agency

c. My Lai

d. War Powers Act

B. Complete each sentence on the lines below.

5. The assassination of Robert Kennedy during the 1968 presidential campaign led to the Democratic Party's nomination of ______________________.

6. Richard Nixon resigned as President on August 9, 1974, rather than facing ______________________.

7. In 1979, Iranians stormed the U.S. embassy and took American hostages because they wanted ______________________.

8. On July 20, 1969, a major milestone occurred in space exploration when ______________________.

9. A ______________________ occurs when government spending is equal to or less than government income.

Name ______________________ Date ______________

Chapter 31

Review History

Comprehension Check

Review History

A. Number the following groups of events in the order in which they occurred. The first one is done for you.

1. _____ **a.** Serbian troops kill or expel Muslims and Croats from their villages.
__1__ **b.** Croats, Muslims, and Serbs begin fighting for control of Bosnia.
_____ **c.** The Dayton Peace Agreement is signed.
_____ **d.** The United States and its allies launch air attacks against the Serbs.

2. __1__ **a.** George W. Bush becomes the forty-third President of the United States.
_____ **b.** Operation Enduring Freedom begins.
_____ **c.** The Taliban and al Qaeda are driven from power.
_____ **d.** Hijackers fly two planes into the Twin Towers of the World Trade Center.

B. Write *T* on the line if the statement is true. Write *F* if the statement is false.

_____ **3.** President Reagan gave tax cuts to the poor and increased spending on social programs.

_____ **4.** President Bush sent U.S. troops to Panama to help Manuel Noriega put down an uprising.

_____ **5.** In the election of 1984, Geraldine Ferraro was the first woman to run for Vice President on the ticket of a major political party.

_____ **6.** President Clinton continued President Bush's efforts to pass a free trade agreement between the United States and its neighbors.

_____ **7.** A group of foreign terrorists were charged with the crime of placing a bomb beneath the World Trade Center in 1993.

_____ **8.** George W. Bush received the majority of the popular votes in the election of 2000.

Name ______________________________ Date ______________

Review History

Comprehension Check

A. Complete each sentence with a term from the box.

health insurance	NAFTA	fossil fuels
tax cuts	healthcare	World Wide Web

1. In 2001, President Bush proposed federal ____________________ to help the nation's sagging economy grow.

2. A large source of carbon dioxide comes from the burning of ____________________, such as oil and gas.

3. The ____________________ enables people to send pictures and sound over the Internet.

4. A growing problem that the United States must solve in the twenty-first century is providing affordable ____________________ to Americans.

5. In 1994, ____________________ eliminated trade barriers between the United States, Canada, and Mexico.

6. As the population in America gets older and technology improves, numerous jobs are expected in the field of ____________________.

B. Complete the chart with information from your textbook.

Technological and Scientific Advances	Global Concerns
7.	**10.**
8.	**11.**
9.	**12.**

Contents

Build Your Skills

Name ______________________________ Date ______________

Build Your Skills

Chapter 1

Read a Timeline

Study the timeline below. Then, answer the questions that follow.

700 A.D. Maya civilization is at its height.

800 A.D. Mississippian civilization develops in the Mississippi River valley.

1000 A.D. Incas begin building an empire.

1325 A.D. Aztecs build Tenochtitlán in Mexico.

1570 A.D. Five Native American groups combine to form Iroquois League.

500 A.D. | 1000 A.D. | 1500 A.D. | 2000 A.D.

1. How many years are shown on the timeline?

____

2. How many years does each interval of the timeline represent?

____

3. Did the Inca Empire develop before or after the Iroquois League was formed?

____

4. How many years separate the height of the Maya civilization and the building of Tenochtitlán?

____

5. Did the Mississippian civilization develop before or after the Inca Empire?

____

6. When was the Iroquois League formed?

____

Build Your Skills

Name ________________________ Date ____________

Chapter 2

Build Your Skills

Read a Historical Map

Study the historical map below. Then, answer the questions that follow.

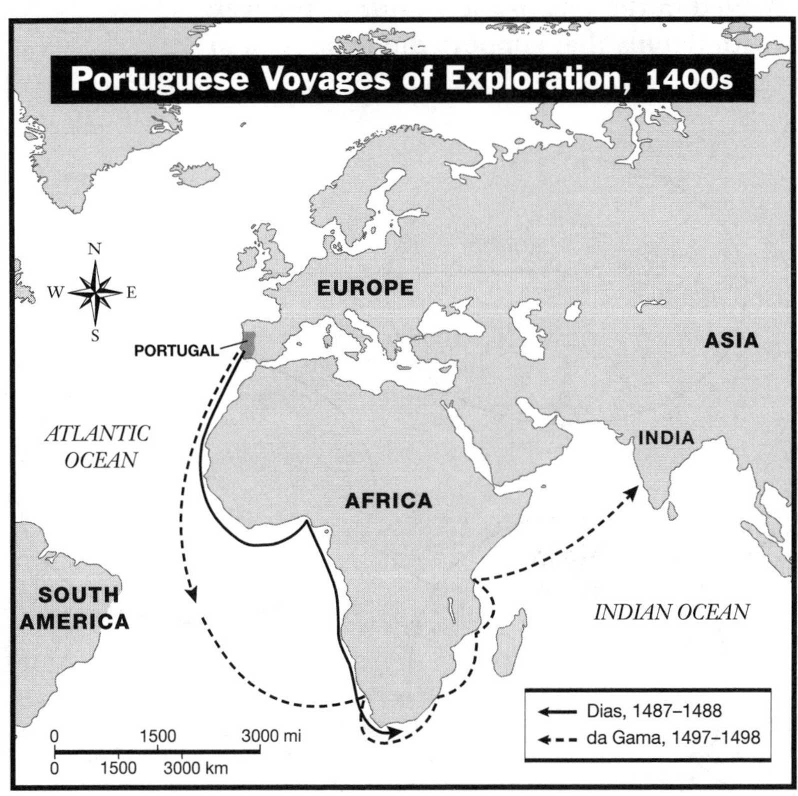

1. What information does the title of the map provide?

____

2. What information is given in the map key?

____

3. Describe the voyages of Bartolomeu Dias and Vasco da Gama.

____

____

4. In which ocean did both explorers begin their voyages?

____

Name ______________________ Date ______________

Build Your Skills

Identify the Main Idea

Select a section from Chapter 3 of your textbook. Write the main idea of the section you selected in the box in the center of the web. Then, fill in the six ovals with details that support the main idea of the section you selected.

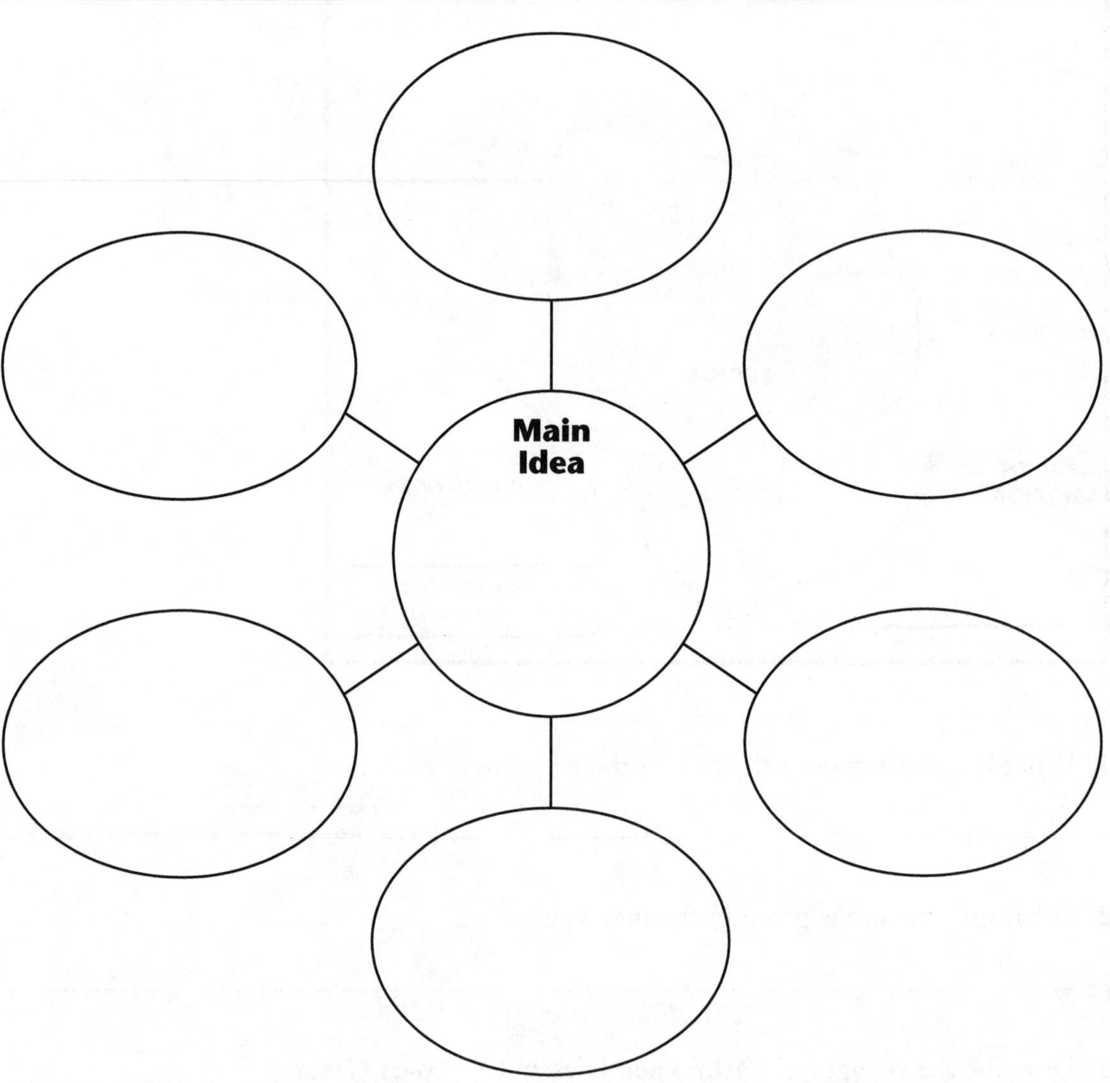

Name ______________________ Date ______________

Chapter 4

Build Your Skills

Interpret a Bar Graph

Study the bar graph below. Then, answer the questions that follow.

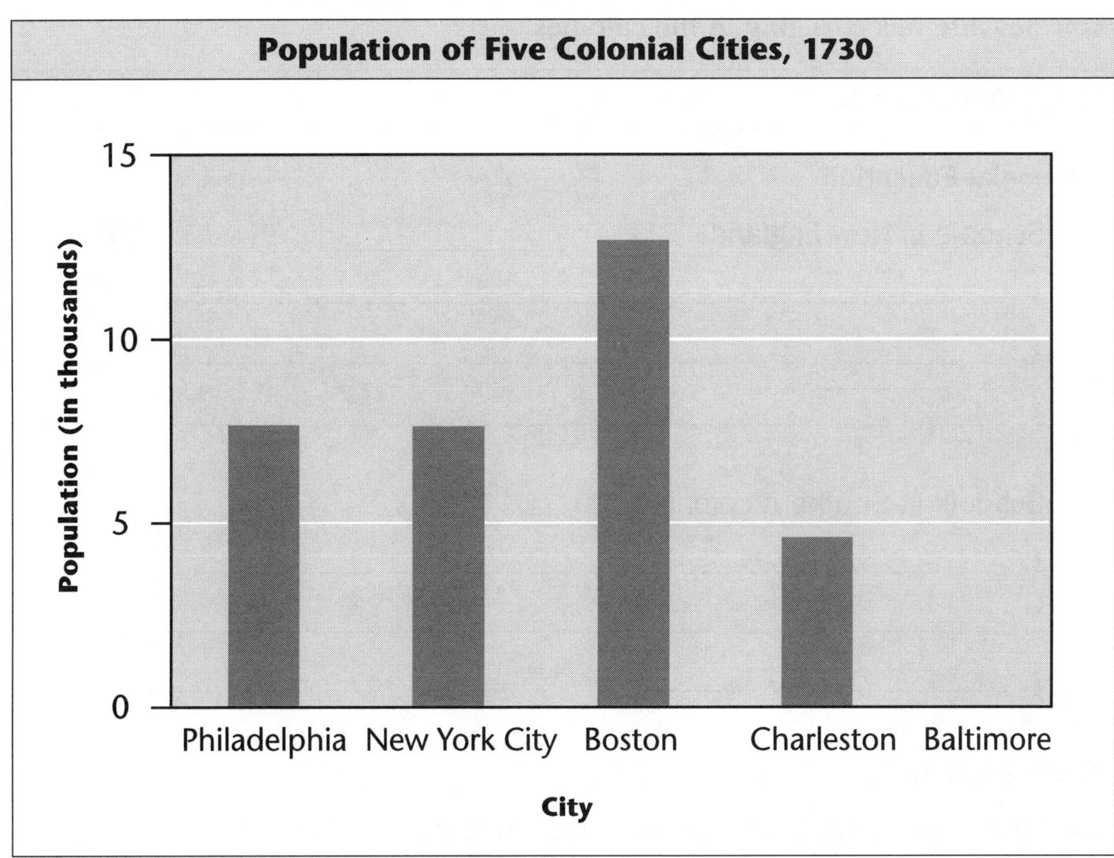

1. Which city had the largest population in 1730?

____

2. Which city had about half the population of New York City?

____

3. Why do you think Baltimore does not have a population listed for 1730?

____

____

4. How many people lived in Charleston in 1730?

____

Name ______________________ Date ______________

Build Your Skills

Chapter 5

Take Notes and Outline

During the first half of the eighteenth century, all aspects of colonial life were developing and changing. Complete the outline below to show how life was changing in the colonies.

Topic: Colonial Life

I. Colonial Education

A. Schools in New England

1. ______________________

2. ______________________

3. ______________________

B. Schools in Southern colonies

1. ______________________

2. ______________________

3. ______________________

II. Slave Codes

A. Laws took rights away from enslaved Africans

1. ______________________

2. ______________________

3. ______________________

B. People born into slavery

1. ______________________

2. ______________________

C. Slave codes reinforced

1. ______________________

2. ______________________

Build Your Skills

Name ______________________ Date ______________

Chapter 6

Build Your Skills

Understand Cause and Effect

Complete the chart below by writing causes and effects of events from the French and Indian War.

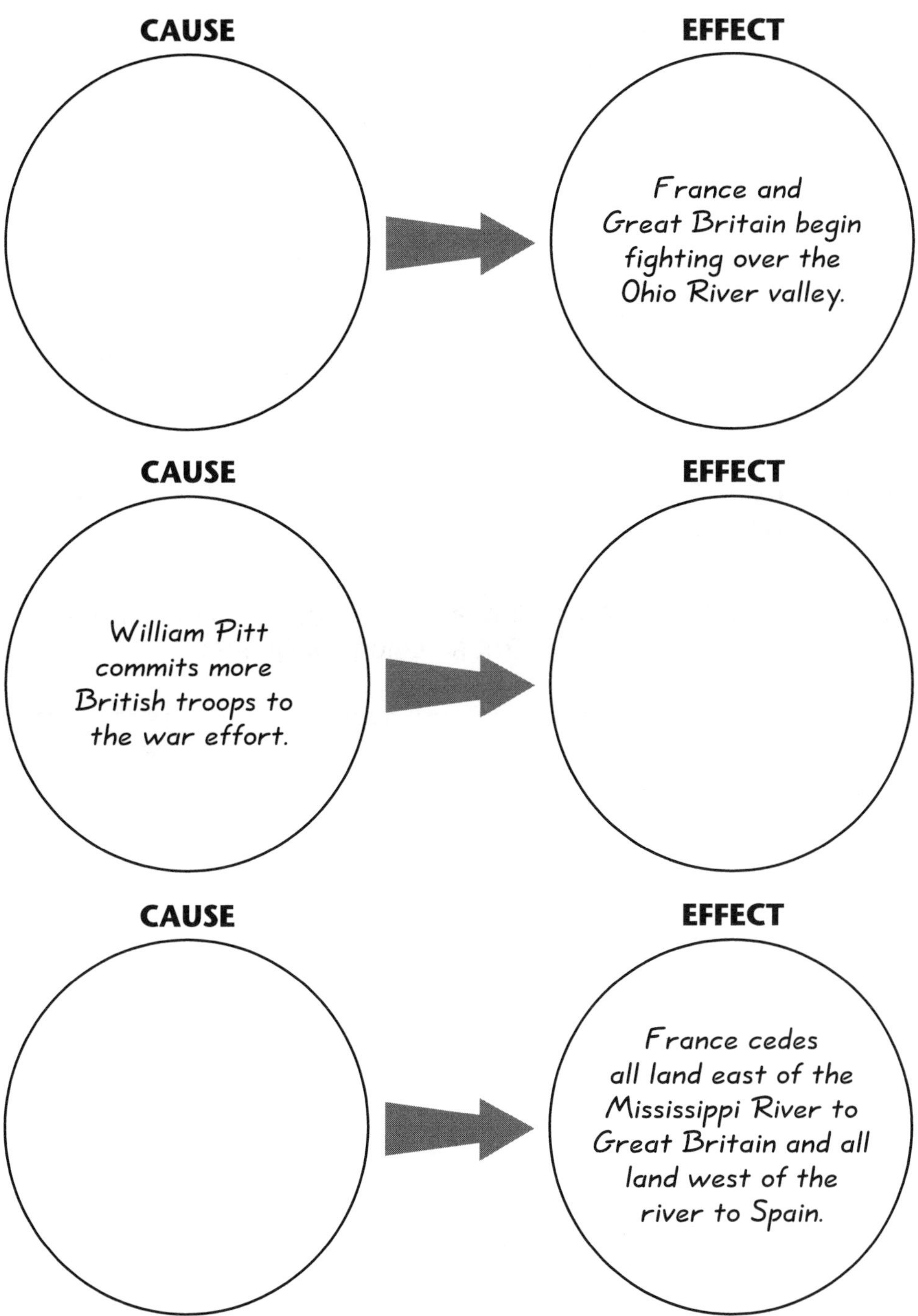

Build Your Skills

Name ______________________ Date ______________

Build Your Skills

Chapter 7

Read Tables and Charts

Read the table below. Then, answer the questions that follow.

Effects of Parliament Acts	
ACT	**EFFECT**
Sugar Act (1764)	Placed taxes on imports of sugar, cloth, and coffee
Stamp Act (1765)	Placed taxes on all printed documents
Townshend Acts (1767)	Placed taxes on imports of glass, paint, paper, lead, and tea
Intolerable Acts (1774)	Closed the port of Boston to trade; sent more troops to Boston
Quebec Act (1774)	Made lands north of the Ohio River a part of the British colony of Quebec

1. What was the effect of the Stamp Act?

____

2. Which act was passed in 1765?

____

3. In what year were two acts passed?

____

4. In what order are the acts listed on the chart?

____

Build Your Skills

Name ______________________________ Date ______________

Chapter 8

Build Your Skills

Read a Military Map

Study the map below. Then, answer the questions that follow.

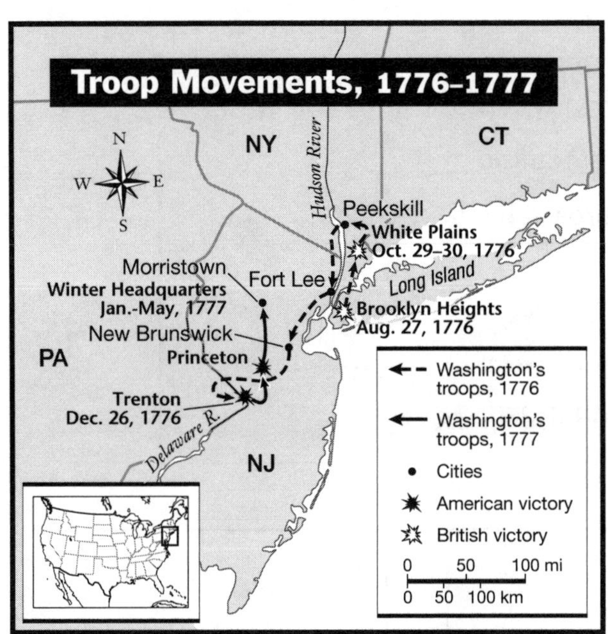

1. Beginning at Brooklyn Heights, New York, through which cities did Washington and his troops travel?

____

2. Where did Washington and his troops spend the winter of 1777?

____

3. Which of the battles shown on the map did the Americans win?

____

4. Which of the battles shown on the map did the British win?

____

5. When were Washington and his troops at Trenton, New Jersey?

____

Build Your Skills

Name ______________________ Date ______________

Build Your Skills

Chapter 9

Make a Flowchart

Complete the flowchart below to show events leading up to the creation of the U.S. Constitution. Write the events listed in the box below in the order in which they occurred.

Daniel Shays leads farmers in a rebellion against the government.

The delegates agree to the Great Compromise.

The Articles of Confederation are approved by the Second Continental Congress.

The Constitution is signed by the delegates.

The Ordinance of 1784 is created by Congress.

Delegates meet at the State House in Philadelphia.

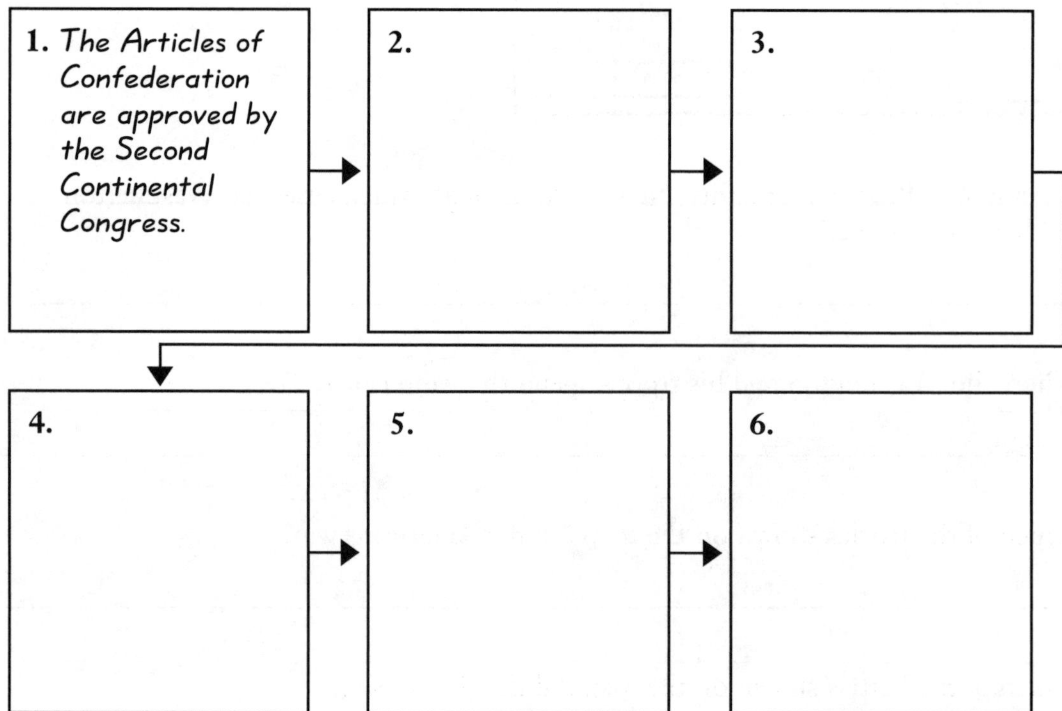

Build Your Skills

Name ______________________ Date ______________

Chapter 10

Build Your Skills

Use Primary and Secondary Sources

A. Fill in the chart below to show which type of source you would use to answer each question. Explain why you would choose that type of source.

QUESTION:	How did Thomas Jefferson and Alexander Hamilton feel about each other's view of government?	Why was George Washington's presidency so significant?
Which type of source would you use?		
Why?		

B. Think of one fact you would like to know about Thomas Jefferson. Use the Internet or your school library to find a primary or secondary source containing that information.

Name ______________________ Date ______________

Build Your Skills

Chapter 11

Interpret Political Cartoons

Study the political cartoon below. Then, answer the questions that follow.

In this cartoon, King George III, Ruler of Great Britain (left), and Napoleon I, emperor of France (right), attack each other with sticks. They empty Thomas Jefferson's pockets at the same time.

1. How is King George III shown in this cartoon?

____

____

2. How is Napoleon I shown in this cartoon?

____

____

3. What is Thomas Jefferson doing in this cartoon?

____

____

4. How does the creator of the cartoon show Jefferson's feelings about the war between Britain and France?

____

____

Name ______________________________ Date ______________

Chapter 12

Build Your Skills

Draw Conclusions

A. Complete the chart below by writing four details about why Napoleon agreed to sell the Louisiana Territory to the United States. The first one is done for you. Then, write a conclusion about the Louisiana Purchase.

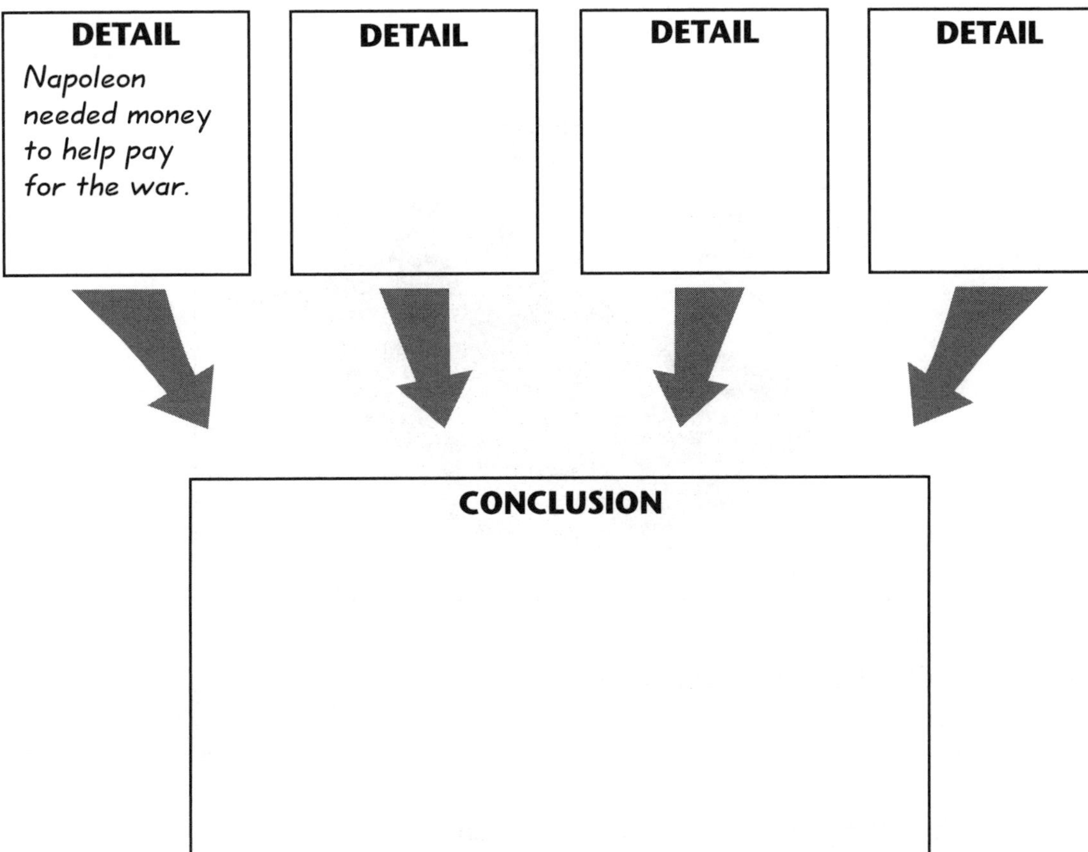

B. Write a paragraph about the events leading up to the Louisiana Purchase. Write your paragraph on a separate sheet of paper.

Build Your Skills

Name ______________________ Date ______________

Build Your Skills

Chapter 13

Use a Circle Graph

Look at the circle graph below. Then, answer the questions that follow.

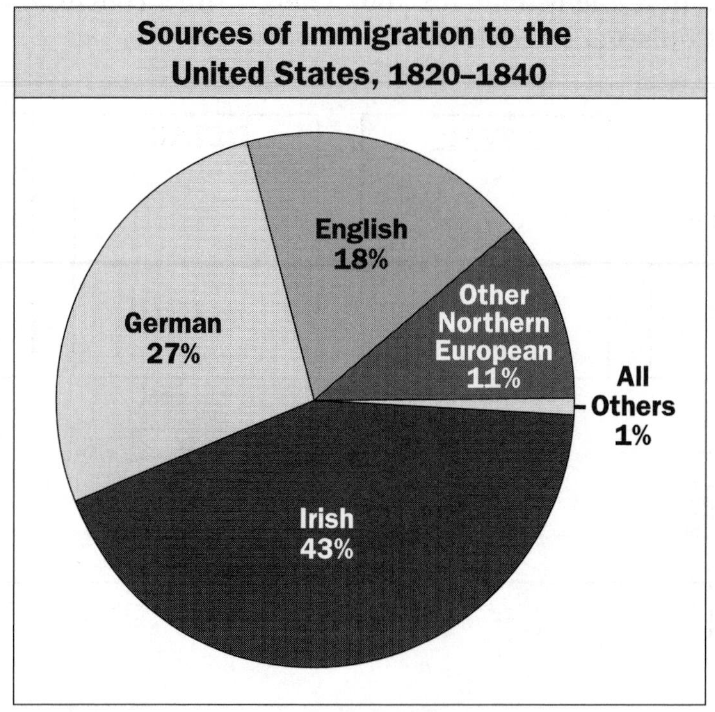

1. What does the whole circle represent?

____

2. What do the different parts of the circle represent?

____

3. What is the combined percentage of immigrants from Germany and Ireland?

____

4. What conclusions can you draw about immigration to the United States between 1820 and 1840?

____

Build Your Skills

Name ______________________ Date ______________

Chapter 14

Build Your Skills

Make Inferences

Complete the chart below by making inferences on what life might have been like in the United States during the 1800s. In the first column, write facts from the text. In the second column, write facts from your experience or from other information you have learned. In the third column, write inferences that you have made. Some of the chart is filled in for you.

Facts From the Text	Facts From Your Experience	Inferences
The growth of cities created a need for better education.	*Colleges and universities exist throughout the country.*	*One of the opportunities offered by cities was public education.*
Women in the 1800s fought for equal rights.	*Women still face inequality in society today.*	
More people began moving to the cities and towns.	*Cities are filled with theaters, museums, libraries, and other cultural centers.*	
Many people fought for the abolition of slavery.		

Build Your Skills

Name ______________________ Date ______________

Build Your Skills

Chapter 15

Distinguish Fact From Opinion

Read the following passage by newspaper editor John O'Sullivan on the eve of the War with Mexico. Decide which statements in the passage are facts and which are opinions. In the chart below, list the facts in the first column and the opinions in the second column.

> "In the case of California . . . the Anglo-Saxon [white race] foot is already at its borders . . . marking its trail with schools, colleges, courts and representative halls, mills and meetinghouses. A population will soon be in actual occupation of California, over which it will be idle for Mexico to dream of dominion. They will necessarily become independent. . . . And they will have a right to independence. . . ."

Build Your Skills

Facts	Opinions

Name ______________________ Date ______________

Chapter 16

Build Your Skills

Classify Information

Before the Civil War, Northerners and Southerners had different points of view about issues and events. Complete the chart below by writing in the northern and southern views of these issues and events.

Issue or Event	Northern Views	Southern Views
A. John Brown's attack on Harpers Ferry		
B. Abraham Lincoln is elected President		
C. Southern states form Confederate States of America		
D. Confederate forces attack Fort Sumter		

Build Your Skills

Name ______________________ Date ______________

Build Your Skills

Chapter 17

Predict Consequences

A. Complete the graphic organizer below. In the top boxes, write three facts about the South's advantages in the war. The first one is done for you. In the bottom box, predict a consequence based on this information.

FACT	FACT	FACT
The South had better leadership during the early years of the war.		

CONSEQUENCE

B. Write a paragraph explaining how the information you wrote in the graphic organizer led to the consequence you predicted. Write your paragraph on a separate sheet of paper.

Build Your Skills

Name ______________________ Date ______________

Build Your Skills

Compare and Contrast

In the circle on the left, write the experiences of African American men in the South before Reconstruction. In the circle on the right, write the experiences of African American men in the South during Reconstruction. In the center section, write the experiences that were the same during both periods.

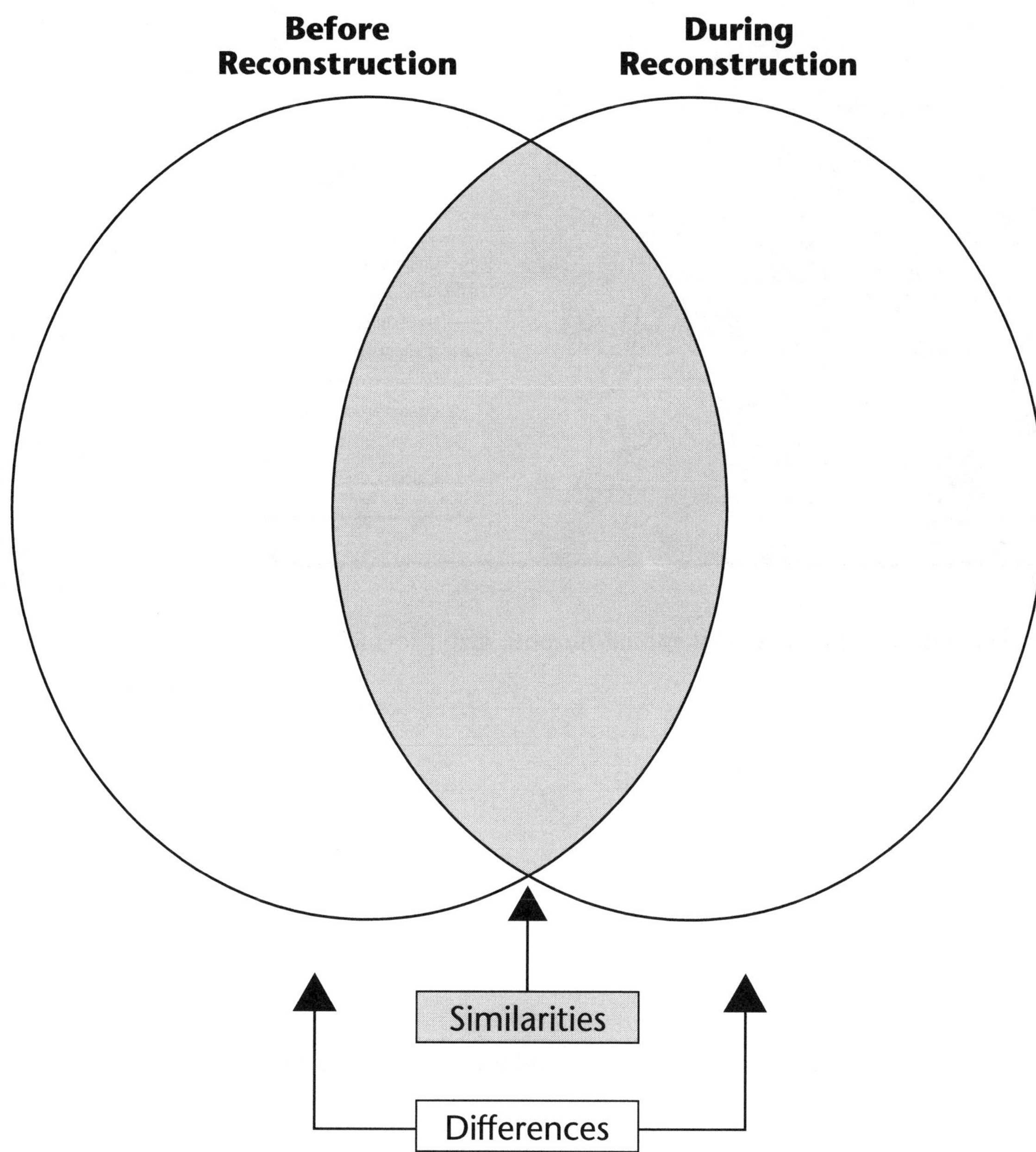

Name ______________________ Date ______________

Build Your Skills

Read a Special-Purpose Map

Study the map below. Then, answer the questions that follow.

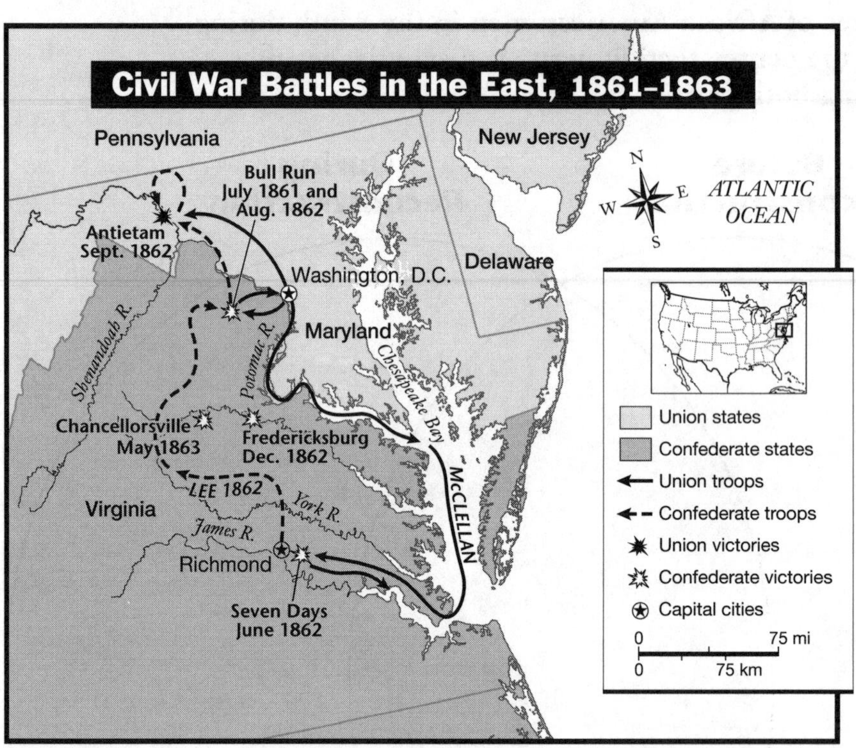

1. What information does this special-purpose map provide?

____

2. When was the Battle of Antietam?

____

3. Which capital cities are shown on this map?

____

4. Which of the battles shown on the map did the Confederates win?

____

Name ______________________________ Date ____________

Chapter 20

Build Your Skills

Choose a Research Topic

A. Complete the chart below. Add some narrow topics for each broad topic listed.

Broad Topic	Narrow Topics
Big Business	
Labor Unions	
Immigration	

B. Select one of the narrow topics and research your choice. Write a three-paragraph report based on your research. Write your report on a separate sheet of paper.

Build Your Skills

Name ______________________________ Date ______________

Build Your Skills

Chapter 21

Make Generalizations

During the late 1800s and early 1900s, many people were aware of the nation's social problems. In each box on the left, write a fact about how people and groups took actions to address these social problems. In the box on the right, write a generalization about the facts. The first fact has been filled in for you.

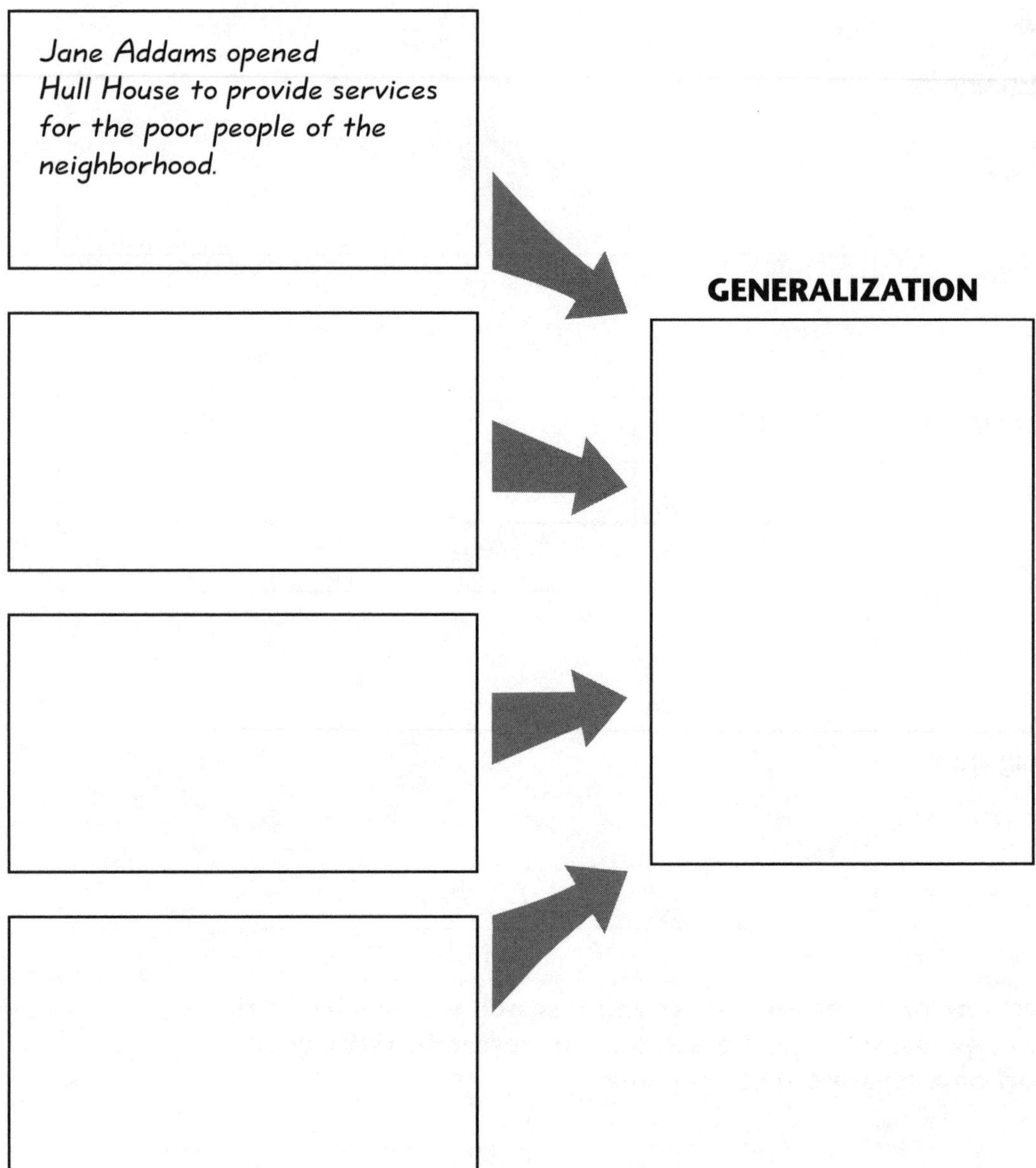

Build Your Skills

Name ______________________ Date ______________

Chapter 22

Build Your Skills

Use a Library

Complete the chart below. Visit a library to find two sources you could use to prepare a report on each topic listed. Research which type of source provides the best information for each topic on U.S. expansion.

Topic	Sources
Annexation of Hawaii	
Open Door Policy	
Roosevelt Corollary	
Philippine Government Act	
Panama Canal	

Build Your Skills

Name ______________________ Date ______________

Build Your Skills

Chapter 23

Conduct Research on the Internet

Use the Internet to find out about each topic listed in the chart below. Include at least two Web sites that contain information about each topic. Explain why each Web site is a reliable resource.

Topic	Web Address	Content	Reliability
Woodrow Wilson			
Lusitania			
Captain Eddie Rickenbacker			
Espionage Act of 1917			

Build Your Skills

Name ______________________ Date ______________

Build Your Skills

Analyze Visuals

Look at the visual on this page. Then, answer the questions that follow.

1. What item suggests that this photograph was taken during the 1920s?

____

2. Why do you think people in the photograph are so curious about the item?

____

3. What adjective describes the mood of the photograph?

____

4. What can you tell from the photograph about technology during the 1920s?

____

Name ______________________ Date ______________

Build Your Skills

Chapter 25

Use a Line Graph

Look at the graph on this page. Then, answer the questions that follow.

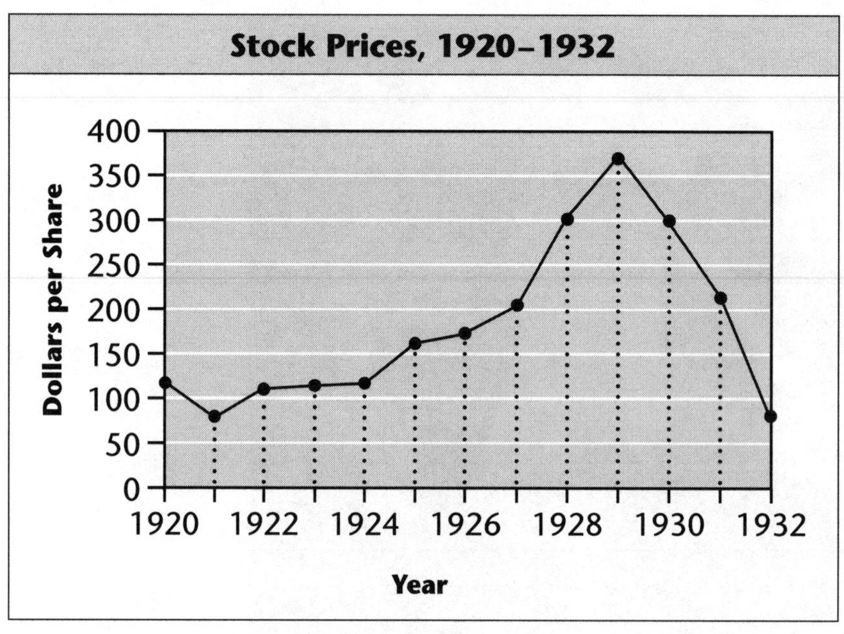

1. What does the graph show?

____

2. How many dollars per share was stock worth in 1922?

____

3. In what year were the stocks worth the most dollars per share?

____

4. How many dollars per share was stock worth in 1928?

____

5. What trend do you see reflected in the graph?

____

Build Your Skills

Name ______________________ Date ______________

Chapter 26

Build Your Skills

Recognize Propaganda

During the war, many Americans had mixed opinions about women working in factories. Look at the poster below. Then, answer the questions that follow.

1. List three adjectives that describe the woman in the poster.

____

2. Why did you choose these adjectives to describe the woman in the poster?

____

3. What is the purpose of this poster?

____

4. What effect do you think this poster had on women during World War II?

____

Build Your Skills

Name ______________________ Date ______________

Build Your Skills

Read a Time-Zone Map

Look at the time-zone map on this page. Then, answer the questions that follow.

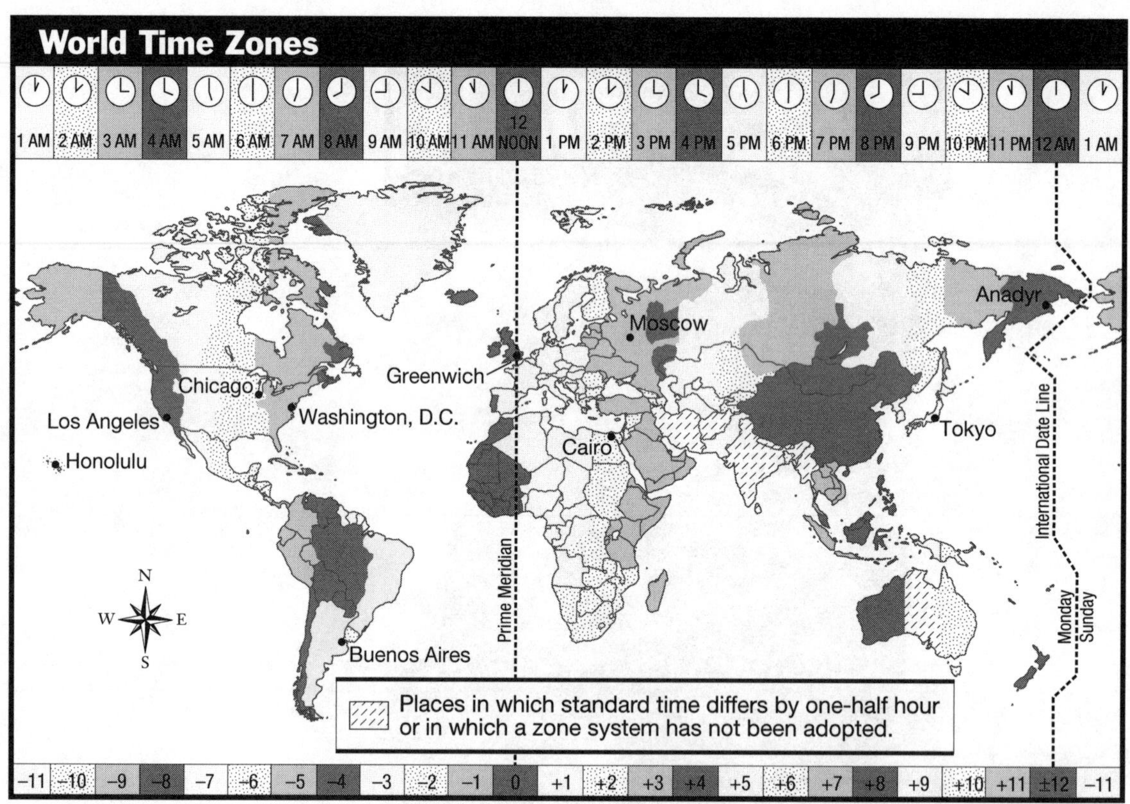

1. If it is 10 A.M. in Chicago, what time is it in Los Angeles?

____

2. Which cities on the map lie east of the Prime Meridian?

____

3. If it is 5 P.M. in Toyko, what time is it in Cairo?

____

4. If it is noon in Washington, D.C., in which city is it 7 P.M.?

____

Name ______________________ Date ______________

Chapter 28

Build Your Skills

Analyze Public Opinion Polls

Before John F. Kennedy became President of the United States, Americans had never elected a Roman Catholic President. Read the public opinion poll below to find out how Americans felt about a Roman Catholic President. Then, answer the questions that follow.

Would you vote for a Roman Catholic presidential candidate?	Yes	No	No Opinion
February 1999	94%	4%	2%
April–May 1983	92	5	3
July 1978	91	4	5
July 1965	87	10	3
August 1961	82	13	5
July–August 1958	69	24	7
February 1937	60	30	10

1. Between February 1937 and February 1999, did the percentage of people who said that they would vote for a Roman Catholic presidential candidate increase or decrease?

____

2. Between February 1937 and February 1999, did the percentage of people who said that they would not vote for a Roman Catholic presidential candidate increase or decrease?

____

3. Between what years did the percentage of people who said that they would vote for a Roman Catholic presidential candidate change the most?

____

4. Between what years did the percentage of people who said that they would vote for a Roman Catholic presidential candidate change the least?

____

Name ______________________________ Date ______________

Build Your Skills

Chapter 29

Present an Oral Report

While Lyndon B. Johnson was President, many groups worked for equal rights for Americans. Complete the notecard below. Write information you would use to present an oral report on the struggle for equality in the United States.

The Struggle for Equality in the United States

- *Women's Rights*
  - *Women's groups push for the Equal Rights Amendment.*
  -
  -
- *Mexican American Rights*
  - *Mexican Americans want more bilingual education.*
  -
  -
- *Native American Rights*
  - *American Indian Movement seizes headquarters of Federal Bureau of Indian Affairs.*
  -
  -

Build Your Skills

Name ______________________________ Date ______________

Chapter 30

Build Your Skills

Evaluate Information

Look at the campaign buttons on this page. Then, answer the questions that follow.

1. Which words, images, or phrases on the Ford button are used to sway voters?

____

____

2. Which words, images, or phrases on the Carter button are used to sway voters?

____

____

3. Which button do you feel is more effective? Explain why in a paragraph on the lines below?

____

____

____

____

____

Build Your Skills

Name ______________________________ Date ______________

Build Your Skills

Improve Your Test-Taking Skills

Read the essay topics below the chart. For each topic, identify the key direction word used. Write the key word on the line below each topic.

DIRECTION WORDS	WHAT TO DO
Compare	Show how things are alike.
Contrast	Show how things are different.
Define	Tell what something means.
Discuss	Present your ideas.
Illustrate	Give examples.
Evaluate	Give good and bad points; then draw a conclusion.

1. Compare the political goals of Presidents Ronald Reagan, George H. W. Bush, and Bill Clinton.

   ____

2. In the 1980s and 1990s, the United States intervened in several world events. Discuss two of these events.

   ____

3. Evaluate the positive and negative effects of President Ronald Reagan's economic plan on the United States.

   ____

4. Define what the Americans With Disabilities Act meant to Americans.

   ____

5. Contrast President Reagan's and President Clinton's approaches to foreign policy.

   ____

Name ________________________________ Date ________________

Chapter 32

Build Your Skills

Develop a Multimedia Presentation

Complete the chart below by writing four types of media that could be used to make a presentation on global warming. Then, write how you would use each type of media.

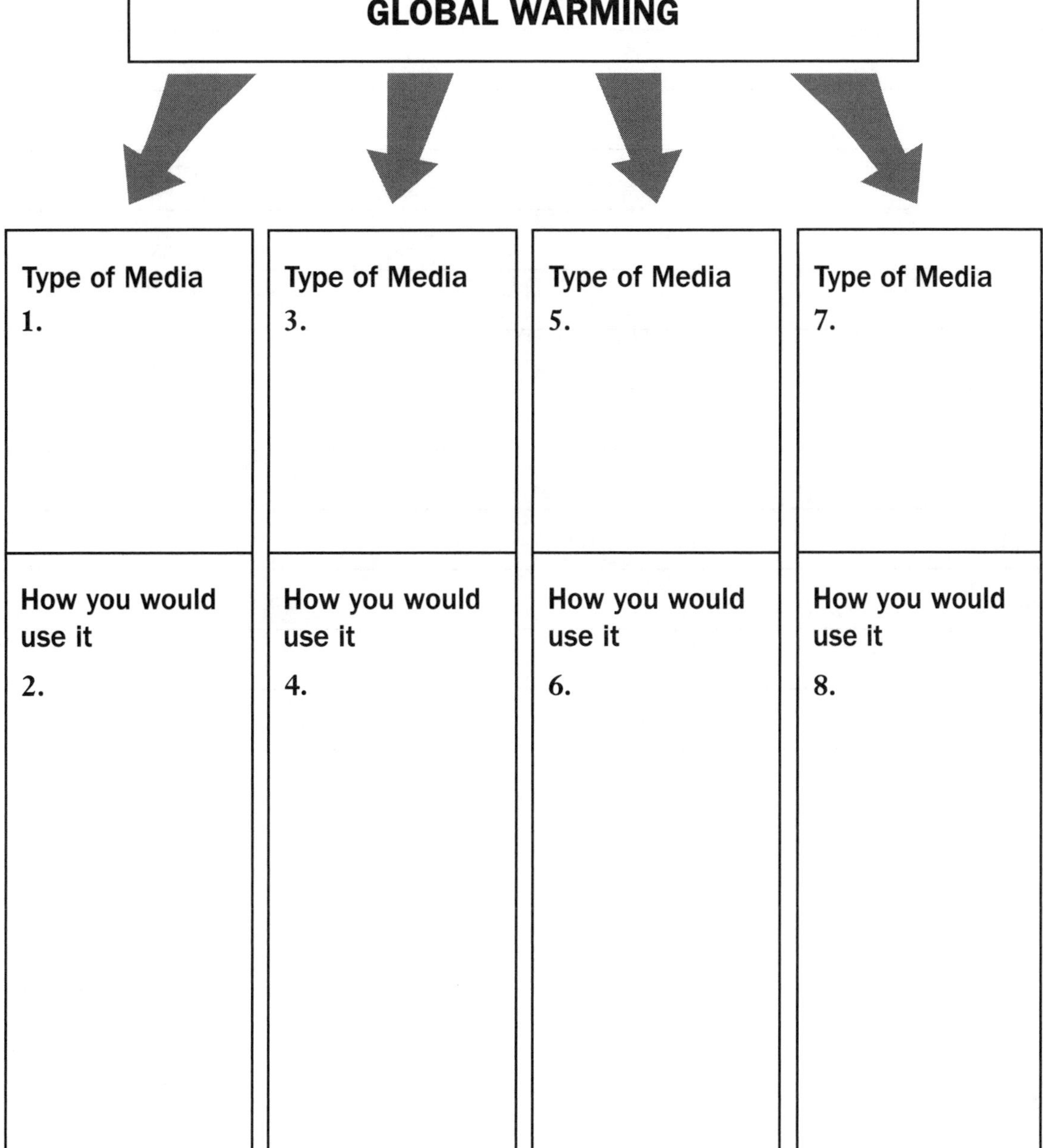

Build Your Skills

Teacher's Notes

Contents

Assessment

About Assessment

The worksheets in this section provide cumulative assessment and preparation for standardized tests. The following worksheets are located in the **Assessment** section:

- **Chapter Tests** assess the concepts and content of each of the 32 chapters in the Student Edition. Each test is two pages long. The material in these tests is provided in a variety of formats, such as sentence completion, matching, multiple choice, and open-ended response. Each chapter test also contains an essay question.
- The **Midterm Exam** assesses the concepts of Chapters 1–18 of the Student Edition. The test is eight pages long. It is divided into three parts. Part A contains multiple-choice questions. Part B contains document-based questions. Part C contains an essay question.
- The **Final Exam** assesses the concepts of Chapters 19–32 of the Student Edition. The test is eight pages long. It is divided into three parts. Part A contains multiple-choice questions. Part B contains document-based questions. Part C contains an essay question.

Both the Midterm Exam and Final Exam gauge student understanding of content and prepare students for standardized tests. You can find a scantron® sheet on page 302 of this book that can be used along with these exams. If students are familiar with this answer form, they will be more successful when taking standardized tests. Each test can be given in sections or can be given altogether to assess the year's work.

Name ______________________________ Date ____________________

Chapter 1

Assessment

Chapter Test

A. Match each item with its description. Write the correct letter on the line.

_____	**1.** group that created one of the greatest empires of the early American cultures	**a.** Inuit
_____	**2.** Pueblo groups in the Southwest who had to learn to grow their crops in dry land	**b.** maize
_____	**3.** seeds planted by people in Mexico in about 5000 B.C.	**c.** Tenochtitlán
_____	**4.** a place early hunters from Asia crossed to get to North America	**d.** flint
_____	**5.** the first Native Americans to hunt with bows and arrows	**e.** Plains peoples
_____	**6.** the Aztec capital city that was built in the middle of a lake	**f.** Hopis and Zunis
_____	**7.** the group that arrived in Mexico and took over Maya lands	**g.** Algonquins and Iroquois
_____	**8.** location of Cuzco, the center of the Inca Empire	**h.** Adena-Hopewells
_____	**9.** a type of stone Native Americans sharpened to make tools and weapons	**i.** Mississippians
_____	**10.** the two main groups of Native Americans in the Northeast	**j.** Andes Mountains
_____	**11.** groups that moved often to follow buffalo herds	**k.** Maya
_____	**12.** a group whose burial mounds contain artifacts that reveal how they lived	**l.** Toltec
_____	**13.** one of the earliest groups in the eastern region to use large-scale agriculture	**m.** Bering Land Bridge

Name ______________________ Date ______________

Assessment

Chapter Test *continued*

B. Write *T* on the line if the statement is true. Write *F* if the statement is false.

_____ **14.** Native Americans in the Pacific Northwest built their villages near the coastline.

_____ **15.** The Maya were outstanding farmers and scientists.

_____ **16.** Salmon fishing was important to Native Americans living along the Pacific coast.

_____ **17.** The Pueblos did not have to learn to grow crops on dry land.

_____ **18.** In early Native American communities, men worked close to home gathering plants and caring for the children.

_____ **19.** At the end of the Ice Age, many large animals died from climate changes and from hunting by humans.

C. Choose one of the following essay topics. Write your answer in a paragraph on the lines below and on a separate sheet of paper if you need more space.

20. a. How did the development of agriculture change people's way of life in early America?

b. In what ways were animals important to the survival of different groups of Native Americans?

Name ______________________________ Date ______________

Chapter 2

Assessment

Chapter Test

A. Match each item with its description. Write the correct letter on the line.

_____	**1.** prince in Portugal who wanted his nation to control trade with Asia	**a.** Norsemen
_____	**2.** earliest known African trading empire	**b.** Silk Road
_____	**3.** religious wars fought between Christian and Muslim people	**c.** Mansa Musa
_____	**4.** leader of the Catholic Church who wanted to drive Muslims out of the Holy Land	**d.** Táino
_____	**5.** trading kingdom that used Timbuktu as a center of learning	**e.** Songhai
_____	**6.** wealthy king who made a journey from Mali to the Middle East	**f.** caravel
_____	**7.** type of ship developed by the Portuguese	**g.** Marco Polo
_____	**8.** French explorer who drew detailed maps of the entire North American coastline	**h.** Pope Urban II
_____	**9.** dangerous trade route across land from Europe to eastern Asia	**i.** Jacques Cartier
_____	**10.** sailors from Scandinavia who reached the shores of North America before Columbus's voyage	**j.** Ghana
_____	**11.** Native Americans whom Columbus named "Indians"	**k.** Giovanni Verrazano
_____	**12.** Italian explorer who published an account of his trip and the riches in China	**l.** Crusades
_____	**13.** French explorer who tried to establish a settlement along the St. Lawrence River in 1535	**m.** Prince Henry

Name ______________________________ Date ______________

Assessment

Chapter 2

Chapter Test *continued*

B. Read each of the following sentences. Write *F* on the line if the statement is a fact. Write *O* if it is an opinion.

_____ **14.** Portugal's success in trading with Africa encouraged other nations to explore overseas.

_____ **15.** Christopher Columbus was the greatest of the early explorers.

_____ **16.** Africa is a continent with contrasting climates.

_____ **17.** Europeans benefited more than Muslims from increased trade.

_____ **18.** In the fifteenth century, the largest and most powerful trading empire in West Africa was Songhai.

_____ **19.** Slavery was considered an acceptable form of punishment in the West African empires.

Assessment

C. Choose one of the following essay topics. Write your answer in a paragraph on the lines below and on a separate sheet of paper if you need more space.

20. a. How did West Africa's land and climate influence farming in the region?

b. How did Portuguese sailors combine old and new methods to become outstanding ocean travelers?

____

____

____

____

____

____

____

____

____

____

____

Name ________________________ Date ______________

Chapter 3

Assessment

Chapter Test

A. Match each item with its description. Write the correct letter on the line.

_____	**1.** Spanish adventurer who defeated the Inca Empire	**a.** Hernándo Cortés
_____	**2.** a settlement built by a church for religious work	**b.** Roanoke
_____	**3.** the oldest permanent European-founded city in the United States	**c.** Francisco Pizarro
_____	**4.** first European to explore the land of present-day Florida	**d.** Robert de La Salle
_____	**5.** the first permanent English settlement in North America	**e.** Northwest Passage
_____	**6.** the French colony that was founded along the banks of the St. Lawrence River	**f.** mission
_____	**7.** leader of a fleet of Spanish ships that sailed from Cuba to the Gulf of Mexico in search of gold	**g.** Jamestown
_____	**8.** settlement off the coast of present-day North Carolina where colonists disappeared and were never seen again	**h.** Quebec
_____	**9.** an explorer who claimed the entire Mississippi River valley for France	**i.** Juan Ponce de León
_____	**10.** French explorer who founded the settlement of Quebec	**j.** encomienda system
_____	**11.** arrangement by which Spanish settlers received a group of laborers from the native population	**k.** Samuel de Champlain
_____	**12.** a water route through North America to Asia	**l.** St. Augustine

Name ______________________ Date ______________

Assessment

Chapter 3

Chapter Test *continued*

B. Write *T* on the line if the statement is true. Write *F* if the statement is false.

_____ **13.** The Aztecs drove the Spaniards away with cannons, guns, and swords.

_____ **14.** Henry Hudson was hired by Dutch merchants to find the Northwest Passage.

_____ **15.** The Spanish Armada was a small fleet of ships that defeated England in 1588.

_____ **16.** European traders forced millions of West Africans to go to the Americas on slave ships.

_____ **17.** The French and Dutch colonies of North America prospered by trading furs with Native Americans.

_____ **18.** Most colonists in New Spain treated Native Americans as equals.

_____ **19.** The settlement at Roanoke was a successful colony.

C. Choose one of the following essay topics. Write your answer in a paragraph on the lines below and on a separate sheet of paper if you need more space.

20. a. Discuss how the European settlers treated the West Africans and Native Americans similarly.

b. Describe some of the hardships the first settlers of Jamestown faced.

Name ______________________ Date ______________

Chapter 4

Assessment

Chapter Test

A. Choose the answer that best completes each of the following sentences. Circle the letter of the correct answer.

1. The colony of Pennsylvania

a. began as a refuge for people persecuted because of religion.
b. relied heavily on plantation farming.
c. was founded by Roger Williams.
d. was a Southern colony.

2. William Penn's model city was called

a. Philadelphia.
b. New Amsterdam.
c. Boston.
d. Charleston.

3. A proprietary colony is a colony

a. run by a single religious group.
b. started and governed by a group of wealthy landowners.
c. ruled by the king of England.
d. established and managed by one person or group.

4. The Carolina colony was eventually split into

a. North Carolina and South Carolina.
b. North Carolina and Georgia.
c. Virginia and Florida.
d. South Carolina and Virginia.

5. In 1618, the Virginia Company changed its policy about ownership of land to

a. allow religious freedom.
b. end slavery.
c. increase immigration.
d. limit immigration.

6. The patroons were

a. a religious group that broke away from the Catholic Church.
b. Dutch landowners in the colony of New Netherland.
c. Swedish indentured servants living near Delaware.
d. Native Americans who rebelled against English colonists in Georgia.

Assessment

Chapter Test *continued*

7. The principal crop in Virginia and Maryland was
   a. indigo.
   b. tobacco.
   c. cotton.
   d. corn.

B. Write *T* on the line if the statement is true. Write *F* if the statement is false.

_____ 8. Most Puritans fled England because they were seeking wealth and good farming land.

_____ 9. Many conflicts between settlers and Native Americans were due to struggles over land.

_____ 10. The English were the first Europeans to settle in the Middle colonies.

_____ 11. The Powhatan began attacking colonial settlements in Virginia to halt the settlers' progress.

_____ 12. William Penn paid Native Americans for their land and maintained good relations with them.

_____ 13. The Toleration Act of 1649 allowed for freedom of all religions in the Massachusetts Bay Colony.

_____ 14. King James made Virginia a royal colony because he feared that the House of Burgesses might gain too much power.

_____ 15. It was difficult to produce crops in the Southern colonies because of the dry, poor soil.

_____ 16. Roger Williams founded Rhode Island because he did not agree with the Massachusetts Bay Colony's strict Puritan laws.

C. Choose one of the following essay topics. Write your answer in a paragraph on a separate sheet of paper.

17. a. Compare and contrast the economies of the New England colonies and the Southern colonies.

    b. Explain both the positive and negative aspects of tobacco farming in Virginia and Maryland.

Name ______________________ Date ______________

Chapter 5

Assessment

Chapter Test

A. Complete each sentence on the lines below.

1. The ______________ were a series of laws passed by the English government to limit colonial trade.

2. The first nonreligious college to be established in the colonies was the ______________.

3. The product of ______________ was made in North Carolina and used to waterproof ships.

4. The Great Awakening movement caused many people to join a ______________ for the first time.

5. The ______________ set up both primary and secondary schools in their towns to teach students to be good Christians.

6. Most enslaved Africans in the American colonies lived on plantations in the ______________.

7. The mercantile system is based upon the idea that a country becomes wealthy through ______________.

8. One of the effects of the ______________ was that it helped to unify the colonies because people everywhere took part in it.

9. A major difference between the economies of the New England and Southern colonies was ______________.

10. John Locke was a leader of the ______________ in Europe.

Assessment

B. Write *T* on the line if the statement is true. Write *F* if the statement is false.

_____ **11.** There were no nonreligious colleges in the American colonies.

_____ **12.** All African people living in the colonies were enslaved.

_____ **13.** The shipbuilding industry never thrived in the port cities of the New England colonies.

_____ **14.** Some American colonists refused to follow the trade regulations of the Navigation Acts.

_____ **15.** African people who completed the voyage to the Americas were sold to plantation owners or other slave traders.

_____ **16.** Some colonial women assisted their husbands in the family business.

_____ **17.** Colonial newspapers were tightly controlled by the British government.

_____ **18.** The harsh climate and poor soil in the Middle colonies made farming difficult.

_____ **19.** The Middle colonies had good relations with Native Americans.

C. Choose one of the following essay topics. Write your answer in a paragraph on the lines below and on a separate sheet of paper if you need more space.

20. a. Discuss how the slave codes affected the children of enslaved people.

b. Discuss the lives of women in the colonies.

____

____

____

____

____

____

____

____

Name ______________________________ Date ________________

Chapter 6

Assessment

Chapter Test

A. Complete each sentence with a term from the box.

England	English Bill of Rights	Parliament
council	"power of the purse"	assembly
Iroquois	governor	self-government

1. The government of each colony included a ______________________ of wealthy men who helped the governor approve or disapprove laws.

2. The ______________________ was a lawmaking body that was elected by and represented the voters in each colony.

3. The colonial American government was patterned after the government of ______________________.

4. Each colony was led by a ______________________, who most often was selected by the English king or by the proprietor who owned the colony.

5. The ______________________ were one of the Native American groups that did not ally themselves with the French.

6. When colonial assemblies used their ______________________, they took control of taxes and government spending.

7. During the 1700s, the colonists became used to ______________________ because England was more concerned about war in Europe.

8. The Magna Carta and the ______________________ limited the power of the English monarchs.

9. The first legislative, or lawmaking, body to represent the people of England was ______________________.

Assessment

B. Write *T* on the line if the statement is true. Write *F* if the statement is false.

_____ **10.** The French and Indian War ended as soon as the British captured Quebec.

_____ **11.** Native Americans gained power as a result of the French and Indian War.

_____ **12.** British soldiers, colonial militiamen, and Native American fighters joined together to defeat the French in the French and Indian War.

_____ **13.** In the Treaty of Paris, the French gave all lands east of the Mississippi River to Britain.

_____ **14.** George Washington lost his first battle against the French at the beginning of the French and Indian War.

_____ **15.** The first war between France and England began in 1689 and was known as King William's War.

_____ **16.** Many colonists ignored the new trade laws passed by Parliament.

_____ **17.** New France covered a larger area of land than all of the English colonies combined.

C. Choose one of the following essay topics. Write your answer in a paragraph on the lines below and on a separate sheet of paper if you need more space.

18. a. Why were there fewer French settlers than British settlers in America, even though France held much more territory?

b. What happened to the Native Americans who had been involved in the French and Indian War?

____

____

____

____

____

____

Name ______________________ Date ______________

Chapter 7

Assessment

Chapter Test

A. Number the following groups of events in the order in which they occurred. The first one is done for you.

1. _____ **a.** The First Continental Congress meets in Philadelphia.
__1__ **b.** Parliament passes the Sugar Act.
_____ **c.** Parliament repeals the Stamp Act.
_____ **d.** Stamp Act Congress meets in New York City.
_____ **e.** Parliament passes a series of laws known as the Intolerable Acts.

2. __1__ **a.** Parliament passes the Townshend Acts.
_____ **b.** The Boston Massacre takes place.
_____ **c.** The Second Continental Congress meets in Philadelphia.
_____ **d.** The battles at Lexington and Concord take place.
_____ **e.** The Battle of Bunker Hill takes place.

Assessment

B. Answer each question on the lines below.

3. How did Great Britain try to control the colonists after the French and Indian War?

____

____

4. What did the colonists mean when they said "no taxation without representation"?

____

____

5. What happened at the Boston Tea Party?

____

____

Assessment

Chapter Test *continued*

6. What did the Tea Act do?

____

____

7. How did the colonists respond to the Intolerable Acts?

____

____

8. Why did colonists object to the new courts that Parliament started in the colonies?

____

____

9. What did Thomas Paine say about King George in *Common Sense*?

____

____

C. Choose one of the following essay topics. Write your answer in a paragraph on the lines below and on a separate sheet of paper if you need more space.

10. a. What are three things colonists did to protest the Acts of Parliament?

b. What happened during the Second Continental Congress?

____

____

____

____

____

____

____

Name ______________________ Date ______________

Chapter 8

Assessment

Chapter Test

A. Answer each question on the lines below.

1. What problems were faced by the people of the new United States after the Revolutionary War?

2. Why was there a shortage of money during and after the Revolutionary War?

3. What was the most important ideal of the new government?

4. What effect did France have on the outcome of the war?

5. What happened at the Battle of Yorktown?

6. What happened at the Battle of Brooklyn Heights?

7. What happened at the Battle of Saratoga?

Name ______________________ Date ______________

Assessment

Chapter 8

Chapter Test *continued*

8. What did Benjamin Franklin, John Adams, and John Jay do at the end of the Revolutionary War?

____

____

B. Number the following group of events in the order in which they occurred. The first one is done for you.

9. ____ **a.** The British march into Philadelphia.

____ **b.** Continental soldiers defeat British forces at Saratoga.

____ **c.** Washington and his troops cross the Delaware River in a surprise attack against Hessian troops.

__1__ **d.** The Continental army retreats from defeat at the Battle of Brooklyn Heights.

____ **e.** Congress prints Continentals to help fund the war.

10. ____ **a.** Washington and his troops destroy the power of the Iroquois Confederacy.

____ **b.** The Americans and French defeat Cornwallis at Yorktown.

____ **c.** American troops are forced to surrender at Charleston, South Carolina.

____ **d.** France signs two treaties with the United States to help with the war effort.

__1__ **e.** The American army retreats to Valley Forge.

C. Choose one of the following essay topics. Write your answer in a paragraph on a separate sheet of paper.

11. a. What were the differences between the Continental army and the British army at the beginning of the Revolutionary War?

b. Did the new U.S. government fulfill the ideal of freedom and equality for all? Why or why not?

Assessment

Name ______________________________ Date ________________

Chapter 9

Assessment

Chapter Test

A. Match each item with its description. Write the correct letter on the line.

_____	**1.** this delegate's plan called for two houses in the legislative branch	**a.** Roger Sherman
_____	**2.** the ten amendments that were added to the Constitution in 1791	**b.** Articles of Confederation
_____	**3.** a plan that proposed that the number of representatives for a state be based on that state's population	**c.** John Locke
_____	**4.** a treaty that gave Americans independence from Great Britain	**d.** *The Federalist Papers*
_____	**5.** a regulation that suggested that the United States not keep colonies	**e.** Ordinance of 1784
_____	**6.** a plan that proposed equal representation for all states in a one-house Congress	**f.** veto
_____	**7.** a seventeenth-century Englishman who believed that people should be able to remove a government that does not protect their rights	**g.** Northwest Territory
_____	**8.** a document that created a federal government made up only of a congress	**h.** New Jersey Plan
_____	**9.** a name given to people who opposed the Constitution	**i.** Antifederalists
_____	**10.** to refuse to enact a law	**j.** Virginia Plan
_____	**11.** famous essays written to urge people to support the Constitution	**k.** Treaty of Paris
_____	**12.** duties and rules that were designed to keep one part of government from becoming stronger than any other	**l.** checks and balances
_____	**13.** area of land north of the Ohio River and east of the Mississippi River	**m.** Bill of Rights

B. Write *T* on the line if the statement is true. Write *F* if the statement is false.

_____ **14.** George Washington believed he should be king of the United States.

_____ **15.** The Federalists supported a strong federal government.

_____ **16.** Daniel Shays led farmers in a rebellion against the federal government.

_____ **17.** The President enforced laws under the Articles of Confederation.

_____ **18.** The first ten amendments to the Constitution are known as the Bill of Rights.

_____ **19.** Only five states sent representatives to the Annapolis Convention.

C. Choose one of the following essay topics. Write your answer in a paragraph on the lines below and on a separate sheet of paper if you need more space.

20. a. Compare and contrast the views of the Federalists and the Antifederalists.

b. Discuss the similarities between the Articles of Confederation and the Constitution.

____

____

____

____

____

____

____

____

____

____

Name ______________________________ Date ______________

Chapter 10

Assessment

Chapter Test

A. Match each item with its description. Write the correct letter on the line.

_____ **1.** leader of the Constitutional Convention in 1787

_____ **2.** a law that organized the nation's court system

_____ **3.** a man who believed in placing as much power as possible with the states

_____ **4.** a group of people holding similar views on the policies a government should follow

_____ **5.** a revolt by farmers in western Pennsylvania

_____ **6.** a battle that resulted in white settlers gaining greater control of northwest lands

_____ **7.** an agreement that tried to ease hostility between the United States and Great Britain

_____ **8.** a belief that states have the power to overrule federal law

_____ **9.** a group of presidential advisors that included the Secretary of Treasury

_____ **10.** a group that settles disagreements over the meaning of laws

a. political party

b. Judiciary Act

c. states' rights

d. Whiskey Rebellion

e. Cabinet

f. George Washington

g. Battle of Fallen Timbers

h. Thomas Jefferson

i. Supreme Court

j. Jay's Treaty

Assessment

B. Number the following groups of events in the order in which they occurred. The first one is done for you.

11. _____ **a.** XYZ Affair occurs.

_____ **b.** John Adams wins the presidency.

_____ **c.** Congress passes Alien Acts.

__1__ **d.** The treaty of Greenville is signed.

Name ________________________ Date ____________

Assessment

Chapter Test *continued*

12. _____ **a.** Vermont joins the Union.
 _1_ **b.** George Washington is sworn in as President.
 _____ **c.** U.S. forces win the Battle of Fallen Timbers.
 _____ **d.** Kentucky joins the Union.

C. Choose one of the following essay topics. Write your answer in a paragraph on the lines below and on a separate sheet of paper if you need more space.

13. a. How did Alexander Hamilton and Thomas Jefferson differ in their views of the Constitution?

b. Describe George Washington's views on political parties and foreign affairs.

Name ______________________ Date ______________

Chapter 11

Assessment

Chapter Test

A. Write *true* or *false* on the line below each sentence. If the sentence is false, replace the underlined word or phrase with one that makes it true.

1. Thomas Jefferson <u>won</u> a majority of electoral votes in the election of 1800.

   ____

2. <u>Lewis and Clark</u> led an expedition along the Arkansas River to explore the Spanish Territory.

   ____

3. Native Americans and soldiers from <u>Great Britain</u> fought together to drive U.S. settlers away from the Northwest Territory.

   ____

4. France sold the Louisiana Territory to the United States to raise money for its war against <u>Great Britain</u>.

   ____

5. The Embargo Act of 1807 was an attempt to protect American ships from being captured by <u>Barbary pirates</u>.

   ____

6. Thomas Jefferson was the first U.S. President who did not belong to the <u>Federalist Party</u>.

   ____

7. Chief Justice John Marshall decided that <u>the Supreme Court</u> did not have the right to decide cases involving federal officials.

   ____

8. <u>John Adams</u> sent a team of explorers, led by Lewis and Clark, to survey the Louisiana Territory.

   ____

9. Congress repealed the Embargo Act of 1807, and passed a law allowing American ships to trade with any country in the world.

____

10. The Treaty of Ghent ended the war of 1812.

____

11. Native Americans helped the United States defeat the British at New Orleans at the end of the War of 1812.

____

B. Read each of the following sentences. Write *F* on the line if the statement is a fact. Write *O* if it is an opinion.

_____ **12.** In the election of 1800, Democratic-Republicans accused John Adams of wanting to be King of America.

_____ **13.** William Marbury should not have become a federal judge.

_____ **14.** Thomas Jefferson ran in the election of 1800.

_____ **15.** Aaron Burr was a dangerous man and should not have been nominated for Vice President.

_____ **16.** The Shawnee leader Tecumseh wanted to drive all settlers out of the Northwest Territory.

_____ **17.** The United States should have declared war on Britain in 1807.

_____ **18.** The central government of the United States should be large and powerful.

C. Choose one of the following essay topics. Write your answer in a paragraph on a separate sheet of paper.

19. a. How did the election of Thomas Jefferson create a trend for transferring power from one political party to another?

b. Who were the American War Hawks, and why did they want to go to war with Great Britain in 1812?

Name ______________________ Date ______________

Chapter 12

Assessment

Chapter Test

A. Match each item with its description. Write the correct letter on the line.

_____	**1.** opened in 1825 and connected the Hudson River to Buffalo, New York	**a.**	James Monroe
_____	**2.** a measure proposed by President Jackson to frighten nullification supporters	**b.**	Indian Removal Act
_____	**3.** Jackson's Vice President who was so angry about the Force Bill that he quit as Vice President	**c.**	Oklahoma
_____	**4.** person who proposed the American System to Congress	**d.**	Erie Canal
_____	**5.** a plan that ordered Native Americans to give up their lands east of the Mississippi River in exchange for land west of the Mississippi River	**e.**	Force Bill
_____	**6.** President during the Era of Good Feelings	**f.**	John Calhoun
_____	**7.** a group of Florida Native Americans who fought the U.S. government	**g.**	Henry Clay
_____	**8.** the head of the Bank of the United States	**h.**	Seminoles
_____	**9.** present-day state known earlier as "Indian Territory"	**i.**	Nicholas Biddle
_____	**10.** crisis that weakened the U.S. economy	**j.**	Panic of 1837

B. Number the following groups of events in the order in which they occurred. The first one is done for you.

11. _____ **a.** Trail of Tears

_____ **b.** Indian Removal Act

__1__ **c.** Erie Canal opens

_____ **d.** Bank of the United States closes

12. _____ **a.** *Gibbons* v. *Ogden* ruling

__1__ **b.** James Monroe elected President

_____ **c.** Monroe Doctrine declared

_____ **d.** United States takes control of Florida

C. Choose one of the following essay topics. Write your answer in a paragraph on the lines below and on a separate sheet of paper if you need more space.

13. a. How did Andrew Jackson change American politics?

b. How did the presidential election of 1824 help bring an end to the Era of Good Feelings?

____

____

____

____

____

____

____

____

____

____

____

Name ______________________________ Date ______________

Chapter 13

Assessment

Chapter Test

A. Match each item with its description. Write the correct letter on the line.

_____ **1.** laws that limited the rights of enslaved African Americans

_____ **2.** invention that replaced the slow method of harvesting crops by hand

_____ **3.** the first steam-operated railway for passengers and freight

_____ **4.** the industrial pioneer who built a giant textile factory near Boston

_____ **5.** the person who led a slave revolt in Charleston, South Carolina

_____ **6.** men and women who helped and guided runaways on the Underground Railroad

_____ **7.** the person who designed and built a cotton-spinning machine using only his memory of British textile mills

_____ **8.** the person who developed and completed the first practical telegraph

_____ **9.** the first steam-powered boat that sailed on the Hudson River in 1807

_____ **10.** large area in the South where cotton was grown

_____ **11.** a building with workers and machines in which manufacturing takes place

_____ **12.** a religious song through which slaves expressed their beliefs

a. mechanical reaper

b. Denmark Vesey

c. *Clermont*

d. "conductors"

e. Samuel F. B. Morse

f. slave codes

g. spiritual

h. Samuel Slater

i. Baltimore and Ohio Railroad

j. Cotton Kingdom

k. Francis Lowell

l. factory

Name ______________________________ Date ______________

Assessment

Chapter Test *continued*

B. Number the events below in the order in which they occurred. The first one is done for you.

_____ **13.** Gabriel Prosser and a group of enslaved African Americans try to take over Richmond, Virginia.

_____ **14.** Congress bans the importation of enslaved Africans to the South.

_____ **15.** John Deere invents the lightweight steel plow.

__*1*__ **16.** Samuel Slater, a young British textile mechanic, arrives in the United States.

_____ **17.** Eli Whitney invents the cotton gin.

C. Choose one of the following essay topics. Write your answer in a paragraph on the lines below and on a separate sheet of paper if you need more space.

18. a. Why do you think improvements in transportation occurred during the same time as the Industrial Revolution in the United States?

b. Why did so many Southerners support slavery?

____

____

____

____

____

____

____

____

____

____

____

____

____

Name ______________________________ Date ______________

Chapter 14

Assessment

Chapter Test

A. Match each item with its description. Write the correct letter on the line.

_____	**1.** the person who opened one of the first schools for women in Troy, New York	**a.** Second Great Awakening
_____	**2.** group that suggested enslaved African Americans return to Africa after slavery was ended	**b.** American Party
_____	**3.** the person who founded the abolitionist newspaper, *The Liberator*, in Boston	**c.** American Colonization Society
_____	**4.** group that began as a secret society to try to limit immigration	**d.** William Lloyd Garrison
_____	**5.** a painting movement that featured beautiful scenes from nature	**e.** Crawford Long
_____	**6.** the person who worked to create a public school system	**f.** Horace Mann
_____	**7.** the person who developed the use of ether as a drug that causes loss of feeling in parts of the body	**g.** individualism
_____	**8.** the person who wrote one of the first biographies of George Washington	**h.** Ralph Waldo Emerson
_____	**9.** an emphasis on the value, rights, and power of the individual	**i.** Emma Willard
_____	**10.** a religious movement that began because religion was losing its influence in American life	**j.** Hudson River school
_____	**11.** writer of a novel about the cruelty of slavery	**k.** Washington Irving
_____	**12.** a great believer in transcendentalism who argued that people must trust themselves above all else	**l.** Harriet Beecher Stowe

B. Read each pair of sentences. If the sentence gives the cause, write *C*. If the sentence gives the effect, write *E*.

13. a. _____ More people began moving into cities.

b. _____ Disease and unclean conditions became common in cities.

14. a. _____ The United States became more diverse.

b. _____ Immigrants moved to the United States to escape problems at home.

15. a. _____ Widespread public education produced a more educated society.

b. _____ Philadelphia, New York City, and Boston began supporting symphony orchestras.

16. a. _____ Americans were filled with the spirit of reform.

b. _____ Groups fought to change conditions in mental institutions and prisons.

17. a. _____ Women turned their attention to demanding more rights in society.

b. _____ Married women gained more power at home as decision makers.

18. a. _____ Abolitionists spoke against slavery in newspapers.

b. _____ The abolition movement grew stronger.

19. a. _____ Creative literature became more common in the United States.

b. _____ The growth of cities allowed more people to become writers.

C. Choose one of the following essay topics. Write your answer in a paragraph on a separate sheet of paper.

20. a. Describe the abolition movement, including the goals of the people involved and how the people worked for those goals.

b. Discuss the women's rights movement, including the goals of the people involved and how the people worked to achieve those goals.

Name ______________________ Date ______________

Chapter 15

Assessment

Chapter Test

A. Choose the answer that best completes each of the following sentences. Circle the letter of the correct answer.

1. The California gold rush prompted a wave of immigrants from

a. China.
b. Ireland.
c. Germany.
d. France.

2. The rallying cry "Remember the Alamo!" is associated with the

a. War with Mexico.
b. California gold rush.
c. Battle of San Jacinto.
d. Mormon migration.

3. The Mormons migrated westward to

a. convert Native Americans.
b. escape persecution.
c. search for gold.
d. avoid paying taxes.

4. In 1846, ownership of the Oregon Territory was shared by the United States and

a. Spain.
b. France.
c. Mexico.
d. Great Britain.

5. One of the states that was created from land won from Mexico was

a. Montana.
b. Colorado.
c. North Dakota.
d. South Dakota.

6. The United States gained nearly half of Mexico's territory in the

a. annexation of Texas.
b. annexation of California.
c. Gadsden Purchase.
d. Treaty of Guadalupe Hidalgo.

7. Missions became less necessary when
   a. the gold rush of 1849 began.
   b. Texas gained its independence from Mexico.
   c. Mexico took control of California.
   d. the United States purchased California.

B. Match each item with its description. Write the correct letter on the line.

_____	8. led the Mormons westward along the Oregon Trail	a. California
_____	9. the thirty-first state to enter the Union	b. Santa Fe Trail
_____	10. elected president of the Republic of Texas in 1836	c. Brigham Young
_____	11. President who led the United States into war with Mexico	d. Alamo
_____	12. pathway to the West opened by William Becknell in 1821	e. Antonio López de Santa Anna
_____	13. carpenter who discovered gold while building a sawmill near San Francisco	f. James K. Polk
_____	14. man who became president of Mexico in 1883 and was determined to control Texas	g. John Marshall
_____	15. the United States claimed this was the Texas border with Mexico	h. Rio Grande
_____	16. site of a historic battle during the Texas Revolution	i. Sam Houston

C. Choose one of the following essay topics. Write your answer in a paragraph on a separate sheet of paper.

17. a. Do you think the settlers in Texas were justified in revolting against Mexican rule?

    b. How might Native Americans have felt about the concept of Manifest Destiny?

Name ______________________________ Date ______________

Chapter 16

Assessment

Chapter Test

A. Match each item with its description. Write the correct letter on the line.

_____	**1.** the law requiring Northerners to capture escaped slaves and return them to slaveholders in the South	**a.** Compromise of 1850
_____	**2.** candidate who ran against Abraham Lincoln in the 1858 Illinois Senate race	**b.** Dred Scott
_____	**3.** a plan that included admitting California into the Union as a free state	**c.** Fugitive Slave Law
_____	**4.** temporary president of the Confederate States of America	**d.** Missouri Compromise
_____	**5.** political party that was formed to prevent a Republican majority in the 1860 election	**e.** Fort Sumter
_____	**6.** case in which the decision stated that slaves were property and could be taken anywhere by their owners	**f.** Jefferson Davis
_____	**7.** novel that helped people understand that slavery was a social problem	**g.** Stephen Douglas
_____	**8.** site of the first conflict between Confederate and Union forces	**h.** *Uncle Tom's Cabin*
_____	**9.** plan that maintained the balance of power between the North and the South	**i.** Constitutional-Union Party
_____	**10.** political party that was formed in 1854 and opposed the expansion of slavery into any territory	**j.** Republican Party

Assessment

Chapter Test *continued*

B. Read each of the following sentences. Write *F* on the line if the statement is a fact. Write *O* if it is an opinion.

_____ **11.** The six states that seceded from the Union after South Carolina were Mississippi, Florida, Alabama, Georgia, Louisiana, and Texas.

_____ **12.** Runaway slaves deserved to be returned to their owners in the South.

_____ **13.** John Brown was a hero who died for a worthy cause.

_____ **14.** The southern and northern Democrats were divided over the issue of slavery.

_____ **15.** The violence that took place in the Kansas Territory earned it the nickname Bleeding Kansas.

_____ **16.** Major Robert Anderson should have surrendered Fort Sumter to the Confederates in April of 1861.

_____ **17.** The Compromise of 1850 proved that Henry Clay was a great leader.

_____ **18.** Abraham Lincoln received 40 percent of the popular vote in the election of 1860.

_____ **19.** Many people in the Republican Party wanted to free enslaved people and have them achieve social equality.

C. Choose one of the following essay topics. Write your answer in a paragraph on the lines below and on a separate sheet of paper if you need more space.

20. a. Discuss two events that led to the breakup of the Union.

b. Discuss two ways that Congress managed to maintain a balance between slaveholding and free states.

____

____

____

____

____

Name ______________________________ Date ______________

Chapter 17

Assessment

Chapter Test

A. Match each item with its description. Write the correct letter on the line.

_____	**1.** village where General Lee surrendered	**a.** Anaconda Plan
_____	**2.** Union plan to divide the Confederacy and cut off its supplies	**b.** Bull Run
_____	**3.** site of the first battle of the Civil War	**c.** American Red Cross
_____	**4.** site of General Sherman's famous "march to the sea"	**d.** Robert E. Lee
_____	**5.** battle that took place on September 17, 1862, which was the bloodiest day of the war	**e.** Copperheads
_____	**6.** person who demanded that African Americans in the North be allowed to fight in the war	**f.** Gettysburg
_____	**7.** organization founded by Clara Barton, a Union nurse	**g.** Frederick Douglass
_____	**8.** person who struck the Union army in a series of attacks known as the Seven Days Battles	**h.** Antietam
_____	**9.** battle site where President Lincoln made a famous speech	**i.** Appomattox
_____	**10.** name given to a group of Democrats who openly supported the South	**j.** Georgia

B. Circle the letter of the correct answer to each question.

11. Which of the following was not an important technological advance used in the war?

a. telegraphs
b. hot-air balloons
c. grenades
d. railroads

Assessment

12. What news helped President Lincoln win the election of 1864?
    a. the Gettysburg Address
    b. news of important war victories
    c. the Emancipation Proclamation
    d. the end of the war

13. How was General Grant's war strategy different from those of previous Union generals?
    a. He believed in attacking quickly and always moving forward.
    b. He used ironclad ships.
    c. He used trench warfare.
    d. He only attacked when reinforcements had arrived.

14. Why did the Union want to capture the Mississippi River?
    a. because it contained important resources
    b. so they could maneuver more easily
    c. to divide the Confederacy in two
    d. to get more food and water

15. What was one advantage the Union held over the Confederacy?
    a. more experience in war
    b. the support of Great Britain and France
    c. a much larger population
    d. more capable generals

16. Why did many people who were not soldiers come to witness the Battle of Bull Run?
    a. to fight in battle
    b. to watch an easy victory
    c. to provide first aid to wounded soldiers
    d. to motivate the soldiers

C. Choose one of the following essay topics. Write your answer in a paragraph on a separate sheet of paper.

17. **a.** What reasons might President Lincoln have given to convince people to vote for him in 1864?

    b. Discuss the advantages and disadvantages both the Union and the Confederacy had before the war.

Name ______________________ Date ______________

Chapter 18

Assessment

Chapter Test

A. Match each item with its description. Write the correct letter on the line.

_____ **1.** law that made it illegal for the President to fire a Cabinet member without Senate approval

_____ **2.** a series of laws that enforced the separation of African American and white people in public places

_____ **3.** amendment to the Constitution that defined who a U.S. citizen was

_____ **4.** amendment to the Constitution that was passed in 1864 and abolished slavery in the United States

_____ **5.** the presidential candidate in the 1868 election who won easily

_____ **6.** the seventeenth President of the United States

_____ **7.** system of work that made it possible for African Americans and white people who had little or no money to rent land

_____ **8.** agreement that named Rutherford Hayes as President and stated that federal troops in the South would be removed

_____ **9.** amendment to the Constitution that stated that the right to vote could not be denied to any person based on race

_____ **10.** the Radical Republicans' plan for reuniting the North and the South

_____ **11.** bill passed by Congress that gave citizenship to all people born in the United States except Native Americans

a. Fourteenth Amendment

b. Ulysses Simpson Grant

c. Compromise of 1877

d. Andrew Johnson

e. Jim Crow laws

f. Tenure of Office Act

g. Civil Rights Act of 1866

h. Thirteenth Amendment

i. sharecropping

j. Fifteenth Amendment

k. Wade-Davis Bill

Assessment

Chapter Test *continued*

B. Answer the questions on the lines below.

12. Why did the Compromise of 1877 result in the end of Reconstruction?

____

____

13. Why was President Lincoln's Reconstruction plan named the Ten Percent Plan?

____

____

14. Why was President Lincoln's Ten Percent Plan never put into effect?

____

____

15. Why did Congress pass the Fourteenth Amendment?

____

____

16. What were the goals of the white Southerners who formed secret societies like the Ku Klux Klan?

____

____

C. Choose one of the following essay topics. Write your answer in a paragraph on a separate sheet of paper.

17. a. What actions did Lincoln take that strengthened the federal government and expanded the powers of the presidency?

b. In what ways did white Southerners try to avoid obeying laws that granted civil rights to African Americans?

Name ______________________ Date ______________

Chapter 19

Assessment

Chapter Test

A. Answer the questions on the lines below.

1. What changes did Native Americans experience during settlement of the West?

____

____

2. How did the railroad companies make life difficult for wheat farmers?

____

____

3. What were the three major industries in the West during the late 1800s?

____

____

4. What did the invention of barbed wire in 1874 have to do with the end of the cattle drives?

____

____

5. Before the transcontinental railroads were built, what did most Americans think the region west of the Mississippi River was like?

____

____

6. How did the Pacific Railway Act encourage the building of railroads?

____

____

7. How did the railroad companies encourage settlement of the West?

____

____

B. Circle the letter of the correct answer to each question.

8. Who were the Exodusters?

a. African American settlers
b. European settlers
c. Texans
d. all of the above

9. Which of the following was an organization that helped prairie farmers?

a. Grange
b. Farmers' Alliance
c. Populist Party
d. all of the above

10. What law broke up the reservations and reduced the amount of land held by Native Americans?

a. Homestead Act
b. Dawes Act
c. Interstate Commerce Act
d. none of the above

11. Why did ranchers begin fencing in their property in 1874?

a. frequent raids by Native Americans
b. loss of cattle that wandered away
c. the invention of barbed wire
d. the invention of stronger fences

12. What battle marked the beginning of a period of warfare on the Plains?

a. Sand Creek, Colorado
b. Wounded Knee, South Dakota
c. Little Big Horn, Wyoming
d. none of the above

C. Choose one of the following essay topics. Write your answer in a paragraph on a separate sheet of paper.

13. a. Explain how cowhands did their job.

b. Explain what happened to Chief Sitting Bull between the years of 1868 and 1890.

Name ______________________ Date ______________

Chapter 20

Assessment

Chapter Test

A. Complete the cause/effect chart with sentences from the box.

Anti-Chinese riots break out in California.
Isaac Singer invents the sewing machine.
Bottles are invented that seal out air.
Persecution, hunger, and war take place in many countries.
Manufacturing, transportation, and communications are improved.
Steel production increases.
Workers are often killed on the job.
Railway workers' wages are cut by 10 percent.

Cause	Effect
The Bessemer process is developed.	**1.**
2.	Many people immigrate to the United States.
Electricity is introduced in the United States.	**3.**
4.	More clothing becomes mass produced.
5.	Fruits and vegetables can be packaged safely for long-term storage.
The fast pace of factories makes working there unsafe.	**6.**
7.	A strike completely shuts down train service in the East.
Nativists in the West fear losing their jobs to Asian workers.	**8.**

Assessment

Assessment

Chapter Test *continued*

B. Write *T* on the line if the statement is true. Write *F* if the statement is false.

_____ **9.** Labor unions formed to bargain for higher pay, a shorter workday, and a safer workplace.

_____ **10.** Most immigrants who entered the country before 1890 were able to assimilate easily into American culture.

_____ **11.** The telegraph played a key role in developing the Bessemer process.

_____ **12.** Nativists were concerned about the growing population of immigrants in the United States.

_____ **13.** Most corporations sell stocks in order to keep investors from receiving the corporation's profits.

_____ **14.** The Chinese Exclusion Act of 1882 banned Asian groups from entering the United States.

_____ **15.** A patent is a grant that gives an inventor the sole right to make and sell an invention.

_____ **16.** Kerosene, one of the first products to be refined from oil, was used for powering steamships.

_____ **17.** Most factory workers worked in uncomfortable conditions but made a lot of money.

_____ **18.** During the Gilded Age, business owners were becoming wealthy while factory workers remained quite poor.

_____ **19.** Henry Ford built the first Model T automobile in 1908.

C. Choose one of the following essay topics. Write your answer in a paragraph on a separate sheet of paper.

20. a. Compare and contrast two experiences of eastern European immigrants and Asian immigrants.

b. Discuss how workers fought against poor working conditions and low pay. Were workers generally successful in improving working conditions? Explain your answer.

Name ______________________________ Date ______________

Chapter 21

Assessment

Chapter Test

A. Match each item with its description. Write the correct letter on the line.

_____	**1.** people who believed the government should be involved in making major social reforms	**a.** Pendleton Civil Service Act
_____	**2.** a center started by Jane Addams to help poor and disadvantaged immigrants	**b.** Adamson Act
_____	**3.** a law that required people applying for certain government jobs to pass a test before they could be hired	**c.** W.E.B. Du Bois
_____	**4.** laws that limited the rights of African Americans	**d.** Clayton Antitrust Act
_____	**5.** law that helped railway workers by limiting their workday to eight hours	**e.** Upton Sinclair
_____	**6.** writer of a book about the unclean conditions of meat-processing factories	**f.** Hull House
_____	**7.** the ban on the making and sale of alcohol from 1919 to 1933	**g.** Prohibition
_____	**8.** person who led reformers of the Niagara Movement to come up with a plan for ending racism	**h.** Jim Crow laws
_____	**9.** a leader in fighting for women's rights	**i.** Progressives
_____	**10.** a law that banned unfair trade practices and protected unions	**j.** Susan B. Anthony

Assessment

Name ____________________ Date ____________

Assessment

Chapter Test *continued*

B. Write *T* on the line if the statement is true. Write *F* if the statement is false.

_____ **11.** President Theodore Roosevelt believed government should be active in making people's lives better.

_____ **12.** The Chinese Exclusion Act led to many Chinese people becoming citizens of the United States.

_____ **13.** Muckrakers were coal miners from South Carolina.

_____ **14.** The Sixteenth Amendment gave Congress the power to collect income taxes from people, families, and businesses.

_____ **15.** President Woodrow Wilson passed many important laws to help control business trusts and monopolies.

_____ **16.** President Theodore Roosevelt helped to resolve the Pennsylvania mine workers strike by forcing the owners to talk to the miners.

_____ **17.** In the years after the Civil War, there was little discrimination against African Americans.

_____ **18.** Boss William Marcy Tweed worked hard to rid New York City of corrupt politicians.

_____ **19.** Theodore Roosevelt ran as a third-party candidate in the 1912 presidential election.

C. Choose one of the following essay topics. Write your answer in a paragraph on the lines below and on a separate sheet of paper if you need more space.

20. a. In what ways did Jim Crow laws limit the rights of African Americans?

b. What were some of the problems muckrakers wrote about to convince the public to make reforms?

____

____

____

____

____

Name ______________________________ Date ______________

Chapter 22

Assessment

Chapter Test

A. Match each item with its description. Write the correct letter on the line.

_____ **1.** publisher of emotional stories of Spanish cruelty during the Spanish-American War

_____ **2.** a statement that follows logically from another statement

_____ **3.** Hawaiian ruler who fought against U.S. control of the Hawaiian Islands

_____ **4.** revolt by a secret society that was against foreign influence in China

_____ **5.** amendment stating that after the war was over, control of Cuba would be given to the Cubans without interference from the United States

_____ **6.** a narrow strip of land separating two larger land areas

_____ **7.** Mexican rebel leader who raided border towns between Texas and Mexico

_____ **8.** Cuban rebel leader who fought to gain Cuba's independence from Spain

_____ **9.** policy that included the use of economic power to influence countries

_____ **10.** battleship that was sent to Havana to help protect Americans there

a. Queen Liliuokalani

b. Teller Amendment

c. Francisco "Pancho" Villa

d. William Randolph Hearst

e. José Martí

f. dollar diplomacy

g. corollary

h. USS *Maine*

i. Boxer Rebellion

j. isthmus

Assessment

Chapter Test *continued*

B. Write *T* on the line if the statement is true. Write *F* if the statement is false.

_____ **11.** After winning the Spanish-American War, the United States granted the Philippines its independence.

_____ **12.** Some Americans who supported imperialism felt that the United States had a moral duty to colonize and impose its culture upon the people with whom it traded.

_____ **13.** The first battle of the Spanish-American War took place in the Philippine Islands.

_____ **14.** Upon taking office, President Woodrow Wilson continued the foreign policy practices of Theodore Roosevelt and William Howard Taft.

_____ **15.** In 1917, the Jones Act granted U.S. citizenship to Puerto Ricans.

_____ **16.** During Millard Fillmore's presidency, trade was opened between Japan and the United States.

_____ **17.** El Caney was the site of a Spanish victory during the Spanish-American War.

_____ **18.** Russia gave Alaska to the United States as a gift.

_____ **19.** General Valeriano Weyler was sent to Cuba and forced many people into prisonlike camps.

C. Choose one of the following essay topics. Write your answer in a paragraph on the lines below and on a separate sheet of paper if you need more space.

20. a. How were the Latin American policies of President Roosevelt, President Taft, and President Wilson different?

b. Why might some people argue that the United States went against its democratic principles by engaging in imperialism?

____

____

____

____

____

Name ______________________________ Date ______________

Chapter 23

Assessment

Chapter Test

A. Match each item with its description. Write the correct letter on the line.

_____	**1.** money to pay for the cost of war damages	**a.** propaganda
_____	**2.** law that fined or jailed people for speaking or writing against the government	**b.** isolationists
_____	**3.** agency that supported daylight saving time to conserve energy	**c.** reparation
_____	**4.** airships that carried weapons and were used on spy missions	**d.** Kaiser Wilhelm II
_____	**5.** the German leader who built up his nation's army until it was the largest in Europe	**e.** President Wilson
_____	**6.** the spreading of certain ideas to boost Americans' support of the war	**f.** self-determination
_____	**7.** the candidate who won a narrow victory in the election of 1916	**g.** Sedition Act
_____	**8.** people who believed the United States should stay out of Europe's problems	**h.** Fourteen Points
_____	**9.** the right of people to decide on their own form of government	**i.** Fuel Administration
_____	**10.** President Woodrow Wilson's peace plan, which included freedom of the seas and free trade	**j.** zeppelins

B. Number the following groups of events in the order in which they occurred. The first one is done for you.

11. _____ **a.** Germany's foreign minister sends a telegram urging Mexico to join the war.

__1__ **b.** President Wilson wins re-election.

_____ **c.** The United States declares war on Germany.

_____ **d.** Allies defeat German forces in France's Belleau Wood.

12. _____ **a.** President Wilson wins re-election.

_____ **b.** Archduke Franz Ferdinand is assassinated.

_____ **c.** Congress rejects the League of Nations.

__1__ **d.** Great Britain, France, and Russia form the Triple Entente.

_____ **e.** German troops invade France.

C. Choose one of the following essay topics. Write your answer in a paragraph on the lines below and on a separate sheet of paper if you need more space.

13. a. Explain how different events helped Americans decide to declare war on Germany.

b. Describe how new technology and new ways of fighting were used during World War I.

____

____

____

____

____

____

____

____

____

____

Name ______________________________ Date ______________

Chapter 24

Assessment

Chapter Test

A. Match each item with its description. Write the correct letter on the line.

_____	**1.** first woman to swim across the English Channel from France to England	**a.** John Calvin Coolidge
_____	**2.** President who believed that government and business should work together as partners	**b.** labor unions
_____	**3.** gangster who went into business transporting and selling alcohol illegally	**c.** Herbert Hoover
_____	**4.** writer of a book about what can happen when people are too interested in becoming rich	**d.** Harlem Renaissance
_____	**5.** groups that worked to get better wages for workers	**e.** Al Capone
_____	**6.** a cultural movement of African American writers, painters, and musicians	**f.** F. Scott Fitzgerald
_____	**7.** founder of the NAACP	**g.** Ku Klux Klan
_____	**8.** first person to fly across the Atlantic Ocean alone	**h.** Gertrude Ederle
_____	**9.** Vice President who took over when Warren Harding died	**i.** Charles Lindbergh
_____	**10.** group of anti-Catholic and anti-Jewish members	**j.** W. E. B. Du Bois

B. Choose the answer that best completes each of the following sentences. Circle the letter of the correct answer.

11. During the economic boom, the income of the average American

a. increased.
b. remained about the same.
c. decreased.
d. doubled.

Assessment

Chapter Test *continued*

12. More Americans had time to read books and magazines partly because
- **a.** unemployment was high.
- **b.** they took long vacations.
- **c.** they saved time by using new appliances.
- **d.** they lost interest in other activities.

13. *The Jazz Singer* was different from other movies because it
- **a.** was a silent movie.
- **b.** had spoken words.
- **c.** featured an African American actor.
- **d.** was in color.

14. Prohibition led to an increase in
- **a.** religion.
- **b.** interest in music.
- **c.** nativism.
- **d.** crime.

15. Many people accused of being Communists were
- **a.** deported.
- **b.** executed.
- **c.** found guilty at trial.
- **d.** found innocent at trial.

16. In the Scopes trial, a teacher was charged with
- **a.** being a Communist.
- **b.** teaching Darwin's theory of evolution.
- **c.** starting a race riot.
- **d.** selling bootleg whiskey.

C. Choose one of the following essay topics. Write your answer in a paragraph on a separate sheet of paper.

17. a. Describe how new inventions changed life for many Americans in the 1920s.

b. Explain problems some groups faced from people who feared or disliked them in the 1920s.

Name ________________________________ Date ____________________

Chapter 25

Assessment

Chapter Test

A. Read each pair of sentences. If the sentence gives the cause, write *C*. If the sentence gives the effect, write *E*.

1. a. _____ Many people took risks in the stock market by buying on margin.

b. _____ People lost their life savings when the stock market crashed.

2. a. _____ Drought and dust clouds destroyed the crops in the Great Plains.

b. _____ Three million people were forced off their lands.

3. a. _____ Violence broke out when President Hoover sent troops to drive the veterans away.

b. _____ A group of World War I veterans marched to Washington, D.C., to demand early payment of their bonuses.

4. a. _____ European countries raised their tariffs, and trade decreased.

b. _____ President Herbert Hoover signed the Hawley-Smoot Tariff Act, which placed high tariffs on foreign goods.

5. a. _____ By the election of 1932, President Hoover was unpopular with many Americans because they blamed him for their hardship.

b. _____ Franklin D. Roosevelt was elected President.

6. a. _____ The Tennessee Valley Authority was created under the New Deal.

b. _____ Dams that stopped flooding of farmland and produced electricity were built.

7. a. _____ The Social Security Act was created, which provided monthly pensions to retired people over age 65.

b. _____ President Roosevelt got the idea from Francis Townsend to provide elderly people with a pension.

8. a. _____ Factories slowed production and needed fewer workers.

b. _____ Many people were laid off, and unemployment increased.

9. a. _____ Many Mexican immigrants lost their jobs and were forced to return to Mexico.

b. _____ Some Americans felt Mexican immigrants were taking away jobs from people who had lived in the United States for many years.

Assessment

Chapter Test *continued*

B. Write *T* on the line if the statement is true. Write *F* if the statement is false.

_____ **10.** President Franklin D. Roosevelt's three *R*s program stood for recreation, relaxation, and renewal.

_____ **11.** Conservatives criticized President Roosevelt's programs because they feared the government was getting too involved in people's lives.

_____ **12.** Shantytowns were clusters of luxurious, high-rise buildings built by the wealthy.

_____ **13.** When states could not provide aid to their residents, President Hoover sent surplus food and money to help the poor and unemployed.

_____ **14.** Eleanor Roosevelt shattered the traditional role of the First Lady by working as an active reformer.

_____ **15.** Many Americans listened to Roosevelt's radio broadcasts to calm their fears during the Depression.

_____ **16.** Segregation and discrimination against African Americans decreased during the Great Depression.

_____ **17.** Tenant farmers purchased their land for farming.

_____ **18.** President Roosevelt explained his policies to Americans in a weekly newspaper column.

_____ **19.** The New Deal finally ended the Great Depression.

C. Choose one of the following essay topics. Write your answer in a paragraph on a separate sheet of paper.

20. a. Why was Franklin D. Roosevelt able to defeat President Hoover by a landslide in the 1932 election?

b. Describe how the Great Depression impacted minorities and what advantages they gained under the New Deal.

Name ______________________________ Date ________________

Chapter 26

Assessment

Chapter Test

A. Number the following groups of events in the order in which they occurred. The first one is done for you.

1. _____ **a.** The Allies defeat Germany.
   __1__ **b.** Many Japanese Americans are moved to internment camps.
   _____ **c.** The Allies push German troops out of North Africa.
   _____ **d.** The United States drops the atomic bomb on Hiroshima and Nagasaki to end the war.

2. __1__ **a.** Adolf Hitler becomes the leader of Germany.
   _____ **b.** The United States begins lending military supplies to Great Britain.
   _____ **c.** The Japanese army invades northern China.
   _____ **d.** The Japanese bomb Pearl Harbor in Hawaii.

Assessment

B. Circle the letter of the correct answer to each question.

3. What was the result of the battle at Midway Island?
   a. an American win that gave U.S. forces the chance to attack Japan
   b. a Japanese win that pushed U.S. forces back to Guadalcanal
   c. an American win that gave U.S. forces the chance to attack Germany
   d. a German win that pushed U.S. forces back to Guadalcanal

4. Which of the following countries had a dictator to solve its problems after World War I?
   a. Italy
   b. Germany
   c. the Soviet Union (USSR)
   d. all of the above

5. What did France and Great Britain do after Germany demanded possession of the Sudetenland?
   a. They were angry and declared war on Germany.
   b. They allowed Hitler to keep the land because they did not want to enter another war.
   c. They called on the United States to bomb Germany for breaking the Treaty of Versailles.
   d. They ignored Germany's action and focused on rebuilding their economies.

Assessment

Chapter Test *continued*

6. What plan did the Allies decide to use against the Axis Powers?
   a. They split up their troops evenly between Asia and Europe.
   b. They chose an "Asia First" policy.
   c. They adopted a "Europe First" policy.
   d. They sent most of their troops to Italy to defeat Mussolini.

7. What was Hitler's "final solution"?
   a. using the Japanese army to take over all of Asia
   b. killing all Jews and others he considered "unfit to live"
   c. taking over Poland for the "master race"
   d. refusing to surrender to the Allied forces

8. Which of the following helped the Nazi Party rise to power in Germany?
   a. increased wealth in Germany
   b. the Nazi Party's promise of equal rights for all
   c. the Nazi Party's promise to start a world war
   d. increased unemployment in Germany

9. Why did Japan decide to invade northern China?
   a. to gain resources such as oil, iron, and coal
   b. to position itself to invade Russia
   c. because China had threatened to invade Japan
   d. because Japan hoped to take over the world

10. What did Japan do after the United States restricted exports of oil, steel, and iron to Japan?
    a. agreed to leave China
    b. looked for more resources at home
    c. invaded Southeast Asia
    d. increased trade with European countries

C. Choose one of the following essay topics. Write your answer in a paragraph on a separate sheet of paper.

11. a. Discuss the reasons why the United States emerged as a world power following World War II.

    b. Discuss the experiences of the Jewish people under Hitler's rule.

Name ______________________ Date ______________

Chapter 27

Assessment

Chapter Test

A. Match each person with his or her description. Write the correct letter on the line.

_____	**1.** chosen by Truman to lead U.S. forces in Korea	**a.** Harry Truman
_____	**2.** leader of an anti-Communist campaign in the United States	**b.** Mao Zedong
_____	**3.** Soviet leader after World War II	**c.** Rosa Parks
_____	**4.** U.S. official who was accused of passing information to Soviet agents	**d.** General Douglas MacArthur
_____	**5.** candidate who lost the 1948 presidential election	**e.** Thomas Dewey
_____	**6.** U.S. President after World War II	**f.** Joseph McCarthy
_____	**7.** African American woman who refused to give her seat on a bus to a white man	**g.** Joseph Stalin
_____	**8.** Montgomery minister who was asked to help with the bus boycott	**h.** Alger Hiss
_____	**9.** baseball player who was signed to the Brooklyn Dodgers in 1947	**i.** Jackie Robinson
_____	**10.** leader of the Communists in China	**j.** Martin Luther King Jr.

Assessment

B. Choose the answer that best completes each of the following sentences. Circle the letter of the correct answer.

11. President Harry Truman's legislative programs were known as the

a. New Deal.
b. Fair Deal.
c. Square Deal.
d. Good Deal.

12. The Berlin airlift came in response to the Soviet Union's blockade of

a. Paris.
b. London.
c. West Germany.
d. Poland.

13. The presidential successor to Harry Truman was
- **a.** Dwight Eisenhower.
- **b.** Richard Nixon.
- **c.** Joseph McCarthy.
- **d.** George Marshall.

14. The North Koreans wanted to unify Korea under a
- **a.** military dictatorship.
- **b.** Communist government.
- **c.** democratic government.
- **d.** Nazi government.

15. The Central Intelligence Agency
- **a.** worked to help foreign nations resist Communist takeover.
- **b.** placed Korea under Communist rule.
- **c.** worked to stop the testing of nuclear weapons.
- **d.** ruled that segregation on Alabama buses was unconstitutional.

16. One result of the growth of suburbs was that
- **a.** people drove longer distances to work.
- **b.** crime increased.
- **c.** people stopped using trains.
- **d.** more women went to work.

17. The *Brown* v. *Board of Education of Topeka* decision helped pave the way for
- **a.** desegregation of schools.
- **b.** more minority teachers.
- **c.** smaller class sizes.
- **d.** computers in every classroom.

C. Choose one of the following essay topics. Write your answer in a paragraph on a separate sheet of paper.

18. a. Do you agree or disagree with Martin Luther King Jr.'s view that nonviolence is the best way to fight injustice? Explain.

b. Why was the United States so concerned with stopping the spread of communism?

Name ______________________________ Date ______________

Chapter 28

Assessment

Chapter Test

A. Match each person with his description. Write the correct letter on the line.

_____	**1.** Soviet leader responsible for the building of the Berlin Wall	**a.** John Glenn
_____	**2.** African American student who wanted to enter the University of Mississippi	**b.** Earl Warren
_____	**3.** astronaut who became the first American to orbit Earth	**c.** Ho Chi Minh
_____	**4.** Vice President in the Kennedy administration	**d.** Lyndon B. Johnson
_____	**5.** leader who took power in Cuba in 1959	**e.** Yuri Gagarin
_____	**6.** Attorney General of the United States during John F. Kennedy's presidency	**f.** Lee Harvey Oswald
_____	**7.** politician who ran against President Kennedy in the 1960 election	**g.** James Meredith
_____	**8.** the person arrested for President Kennedy's murder	**h.** Nikita Khrushchev
_____	**9.** Dallas business owner who killed Lee Harvey Oswald	**i.** Robert Kennedy
_____	**10.** Chief Justice who headed a commission to study the assassination of President Kennedy	**j.** Fidel Castro
_____	**11.** Communist leader of North Vietnam	**k.** Jack Ruby
_____	**12.** Soviet cosmonaut who became the first person to orbit Earth	**l.** Richard Milhous Nixon

Name ______________________ Date ______________

Assessment

Chapter 28

Chapter Test *continued*

B. Read each pair of sentences below. If the sentence gives the cause, write *C*. If the sentence gives the effect, write *E*.

13. a. _____ City leaders in Birmingham decided to end segregation.

b. _____ Americans were angered by the police violence against protesters in Birmingham.

14. a. _____ Cuba asked for military and economic aid from the Soviet Union.

b. _____ On April 17, 1961, the United States supported an unsuccessful invasion in Cuba.

15. a. _____ The Montgomery bus boycott showed the success of nonviolent protests.

b. _____ People were inspired to fight segregation.

16. a. _____ Almost three million Germans escaped from Communist East Berlin.

b. _____ Nikita Khrushchev had the Berlin Wall built.

17. a. _____ Lyndon B. Johnson became President.

b. _____ President John F. Kennedy was assassinated.

C. Choose one of the following essay topics. Write your answer in a paragraph on the lines below and on a separate sheet of paper if you need more space.

18. a. Discuss how public opinion helped to end segregation in Birmingham, Alabama.

b. Discuss two events that occurred as a result of the Cuban Missile Crisis.

____

____

____

____

____

____

____

Assessment

Name ______________________________ Date ______________

Chapter 29

Assessment

Chapter Test

A. Answer each question on the lines below.

1. What was the purpose of Medicare?

____

____

2. What is the goal of the Department of Housing and Urban Development?

____

____

3. What change came after the *Miranda* v. *Arizona* case?

____

____

4. What did the Indians of All Tribes do to bring attention to its cause?

____

____

5. According to the domino theory, what did U.S. leaders feel would happen if Vietnam fell to communism?

____

____

6. What were many Americans convinced about after the Tet Offensive?

____

____

7. Why did many legislators vote against the Equal Rights Amendment?

____

____

B. Choose the answer that best completes each of the following sentences. Circle the letter of the correct answer.

8. The Communist rebels in South Vietnam were known as the

a. Vietminh.
b. Viet Cong.
c. Contras.
d. guerrillas.

9. The Great Society program that provided student loans was the

a. Civil Rights Act.
b. Higher Education Act.
c. Immigration and Nationality Act.
d. Elementary and Secondary Education Act.

10. In April 1968, the nation witnessed the death of

a. Malcolm X.
b. Lyndon Johnson.
c. Stokely Carmichael.
d. Martin Luther King Jr.

11. The author of *The Feminine Mystique* was

a. Betty Friedan.
b. Shirley Chisholm.
c. Lady Bird Johnson.
d. Rosa Parks.

12. The Civil Rights Act of 1964 outlawed segregation

a. in public places.
b. in all businesses.
c. at private universities.
d. in the military.

C. Choose one of the following essay topics. Write your answer in a paragraph on a separate sheet of paper.

13. a. How did television play a role in creating concerns among Americans about the Vietnam War?

b. What do you think was the most important Great Society program?

Name ______________________ Date ______________

Chapter 30

Assessment

Chapter Test

A. Read the following sentences. Write *F* on the line if the statement is a fact. Write *O* if it is an opinion.

_____ **1.** Most Americans believe that the United States should never have become involved in the Vietnam War.

_____ **2.** Desegregation and affirmative action have improved the opportunities for minorities and women in this country.

_____ **3.** During the 1970s, competition with Western Europe and Japan led to a period of recession in the American economy.

_____ **4.** If President Jimmy Carter's attempts to rescue the hostages in Iran had been successful, he would have been re-elected in 1981.

_____ **5.** President Nixon was an anti-Communist.

_____ **6.** The United States could have won the war in Vietnam if more Americans had supported the war.

Assessment

B. Circle the letter of the correct answer to each question.

7. What was the agreement reached in 1975 in which many countries agreed to respect human rights and honor post-World War II boundaries in Europe?

a. SALT
b. Helsinki Accords
c. Camp David Accords
d. détente

8. Which of the following did not contribute to President Jimmy Carter's defeat in the 1980 election?

a. Iranian hostage crisis
b. Camp David Accords
c. recession
d. energy crisis

9. Which of the following events took place during Richard Nixon's presidency?

a. the first celebration of Earth Day
b. astronauts walked on the moon's surface
c. a presidential visit to China
d. all of the above

Assessment

10. Which of the following Presidents had to deal with a troubled national economy during his administration?
   a. Jimmy Carter
   b. Richard Nixon
   c. Gerald Ford
   d. all of the above

11. Which of the following Presidents won the election of 1976?
   a. Jimmy Carter
   b. Richard Nixon
   c. Gerald Ford
   d. all of the above

12. Which foreign affairs policy of Richard Nixon did President Ford follow?
   a. WIN
   b. politics as usual
   c. détente
   d. affirmative action

13. What is a truce?
   a. a way to limit the President's power
   b. a law aimed at cleaning up the environment
   c. a decline in economic activity
   d. a temporary peace agreement

14. Why did President Ford pardon Richard Nixon?
   a. so that Nixon would be forced to stand trial
   b. to restore confidence in the White House
   c. to keep the Watergate scandal fresh in everyone's minds
   d. so that Ford would not be re-elected

C. Choose one of the following essay topics. Write your answer in a paragraph on a separate sheet of paper.

15. a. Discuss how learning about My Lai and the violence at Kent State and Jackson State universities affected how many Americans felt toward their government.

   b. Discuss the accomplishments made by the space program during the Nixon administration.

Name ______________________________ Date ____________________

Chapter 31

Assessment

Chapter Test

A. Match each item with its description. Write the correct letter on the line.

_____	**1.** the first woman to be appointed to the United States Supreme Court	**a.**	Moral Majority
_____	**2.** the headquarters of the U.S. Department of Defense	**b.**	Sandra Day O'Connor
_____	**3.** conservative group led by Reverend Jerry Falwell that promoted "family values"	**c.**	nation-building
_____	**4.** a worldwide network of terrorists run by Osama bin Laden	**d.**	Manuel Noriega
_____	**5.** an attack on Iraq by the United States and its allies	**e.**	John Hinckley Jr.
_____	**6.** the support of developing governments in foreign countries	**f.**	Pentagon
_____	**7.** person responsible for the assassination attempt on President Reagan	**g.**	Operation Desert Storm
_____	**8.** ruler in Panama who refused to honor his country's national elections	**h.**	Americans With Disabilities Act
_____	**9.** the first woman to run for Vice President on the ticket of a major political party	**i.**	Geraldine Ferraro
_____	**10.** the name given to the day in October 1987 when the stock market suffered a large drop	**j.**	"Black Monday"
_____	**11.** a law that protected the rights of people with disabilities	**k.**	al Qaeda

B. Write *T* on the line if the statement is true. Write *F* if the statement is false.

_____ **12.** Serbian troops hoped to kill or expel all Muslims and Croats from their villages so that only Serbs would be left.

_____ **13.** During Clinton's presidency, the nation experienced the lowest inflation in 30 years.

_____ **14.** After President Reagan's appointments to the Supreme Court, the Supreme Court developed a strong conservative voice.

_____ **15.** President Bush stopped the sale of military supplies to China after several hundred Chinese protesters were killed in Tiananmen Square.

_____ **16.** Vice President Al Gore won the election of 2000 with the majority of the electoral votes.

_____ **17.** Afghan opponents of the Taliban are known as the Northern Alliance.

_____ **18.** The bombing of the Alfred P. Murrah Federal Building was the first foreign act of terrorism to take place on American soil.

_____ **19.** H. Ross Perot was the third-party presidential candidate in the 1992 election who won more popular votes than any other third-party candidate in history.

C. Choose one of the following essay topics. Write your answer in a paragraph on a separate sheet of paper.

20. a. How did President H. W. Bush's policies sometimes differ from his conservative supporters' policies?

b. In what ways did President Clinton's foreign policy of nation-building lead to problems?

Name ______________________ Date ______________

Chapter 32

Assessment

Chapter Test

A. Choose the answer that best completes each of the following sentences. Circle the letter of the correct answer.

1. The Kyoto Protocol was aimed at slowing

a. water pollution.
b. global warming.
c. landfill use.
d. oil production.

2. By 2000, the number of computer users in the United States had grown to more than

a. 60 million.
b. 100 million.
c. 160 million.
d. 200 million.

3. The second largest group of U.S. immigrants comes from

a. Asia.
b. Russia.
c. Europe.
d. Africa.

4. The growing number of elderly Americans in the United States requires more money in the national budget for

a. defense.
b. transportation.
c. Social Security.
d. education.

5. Healthcare professionals are working hard to find a cure for

a. smallpox.
b. malaria.
c. tuberculosis.
d. AIDS.

6. In 1996, scientists in Scotland cloned a

a. dog.
b. cat.
c. sheep.
d. monkey.

Assessment

Chapter Test *continued*

7. The United States is working with 14 other countries to build
   a. an International Space Station.
   b. the Hubble Space Telescope.
   c. a space shuttle.
   d. a solar-sail spacecraft.

8. One problem with many of the newer prescription medications is that
   a. they are not effective.
   b. they are very dangerous.
   c. they are very expensive.
   d. they are not available in the United States.

B. Match each item with its description. Write the correct letter on the line.

_____	9. thin layer of gas that surrounds Earth and shields it against harmful radiation from the Sun	a. NAFTA
_____	10. trade agreement between the United States, Canada, and Mexico	b. World Health Organization
_____	11. group that works everywhere in the world to help people achieve a decent level of health	c. ENIAC
_____	12. a workable computer that came out in 1946	d. Internet
_____	13. people who use their computer to work from home	e. ozone
_____	14. global network of computers	f. telecommuters

C. Choose one of the following essay topics. Write your answer in a paragraph on a separate sheet of paper.

15. a. How might globalization both help and hurt the U.S. economy?

    b. Discuss one of the global problems humans face. How will this problem affect the world in the future?

Name ______________________ Date ______________

Midterm Exam

Assessment, Chapters 1–18

A. Circle the letter of the correct answer to each question.

1. How did the development of agriculture change the way Native Americans lived?
- **a.** They became more nomadic.
- **b.** They learned to hunt smaller animals.
- **c.** They established communities in one place.
- **d.** They learned to grow squash, beans, and peppers.

2. Which of the following best describes the civilizations in North, Central, and South America before Europeans arrived?
- **a.** undeveloped
- **b.** complex
- **c.** disorganized
- **d.** simple

3. Which Native American groups followed great herds of buffalo?
- **a.** Algonquin and Iroquois
- **b.** Arapaho and Comanche
- **c.** Hopi and Zuni
- **d.** Inuit and Aleuts

4. Who controlled the Trans-Sahara trade route from West Africa to Europe?
- **a.** Muslim merchants
- **b.** Songhai farmers
- **c.** Middle Eastern scholars
- **d.** African kings

5. What did Portugal's Prince Henry attempt to do?
- **a.** defeat the Muslims in the Crusades
- **b.** establish an overland route to Asia
- **c.** find the best ways to travel on the ocean
- **d.** gain power from European nobles

6. Christopher Columbus sailed west across the Atlantic Ocean in order to
- **a.** find a water route to Asia.
- **b.** become the first to sail across the ocean.
- **c.** locate supplies of iron.
- **d.** raise crops in the Americas.

7. Spaniards established missions in New Spain to
- **a.** house Spaniards in search of gold.
- **b.** stop the spread of European diseases.
- **c.** control the conquered Aztecs.
- **d.** spread the Catholic faith to the native people.

Midterm Exam *continued*

Assessment, Chapters 1–18

8. What event allowed the English to colonize North America?
- **a.** the success of the Jamestown settlement
- **b.** the English defeat of the Spanish Armada
- **c.** the establishment of New Amsterdam on Manhattan Island
- **d.** the exploration of Canada by Champlain

9. How were slaves different from indentured servants?
- **a.** Slaves were not given land in the colonies, but indentured servants usually were.
- **b.** Slaves were required to harvest tobacco, but indentured servants were not.
- **c.** Slaves worked for the English, but indentured servants worked for the Portuguese.
- **d.** Slaves worked on plantations, but indentured servants worked on farms.

10. The desire for religious freedom caused
- **a.** Puritans to leave New England.
- **b.** the Catholic Church to gain power.
- **c.** colonists to give back Native American lands.
- **d.** Pilgrims to move away from England.

11. Which of these Middle colonies welcomed people of all religions?
- **a.** Delaware
- **b.** New York
- **c.** Pennsylvania
- **d.** New Jersey

12. The crop most commonly grown in the Southern colonies was
- **a.** corn.
- **b.** tobacco.
- **c.** rice.
- **d.** wheat.

13. The mercantile system was the idea that a nation could become wealthy from trade if the nation
- **a.** sold lumber, iron, and furs.
- **b.** exported more products than it imported.
- **c.** relied heavily on farming.
- **d.** imported more products than it exported.

14. The Great Awakening helped many American colonists become more interested in
- **a.** science.
- **b.** education.
- **c.** religion.
- **d.** wealth.

15. What did all enslaved Africans in the American colonies have in common?
- **a.** All worked in fields as farmhands.
- **b.** All were taught to read and write.
- **c.** All attempted to rebel against their owners.
- **d.** All were prevented from owning property.

16. How were most governments in the American colonies organized?
- **a.** A proprietor was elected to run the assembly.
- **b.** A governor was chosen by Parliament to run the government.
- **c.** A monarch oversaw the ruling proprietor.
- **d.** A council and assembly worked with a governor.

17. Which of the following was the most significant result of the French and Indian War?
- **a.** Great Britain became the dominant power in North America.
- **b.** Native Americans gained new lands.
- **c.** The French took control of North America.
- **d.** The American colonies became trading partners with France.

18. Why were the colonists against British taxation?
- **a.** The colonists believed it was wrong to place a tax on sugar.
- **b.** The British were using the tax money to pay back the French.
- **c.** The revenue brought in by the taxes did not help the British.
- **d.** The colonists had no representation in Parliament.

19. Why did Samuel Adams make sure all colonists heard about the Boston Massacre?
- **a.** to encourage Americans to support the cause of liberty
- **b.** to anger the British
- **c.** to encourage colonists to support the British
- **d.** to stop resolutions from being passed

20. How did American colonists state their loyalty to King George of Britain?
- **a.** the Loyalty Congress
- **b.** the Olive Branch Petition
- **c.** the First Continental Congress
- **d.** the Minuteman Pledge

21. Americans who were against independence from Britain were called
- **a.** Patriots.
- **b.** Colonials.
- **c.** Loyalists.
- **d.** Mercenaries.

Midterm Exam *continued*

22. Why did France support the colonists during the Revolutionary War?
- **a.** France wanted to end its reliance on Great Britain.
- **b.** French merchants were opposed to British rule.
- **c.** France was the long-time enemy of Great Britain.
- **d.** The colonists threatened French settlements.

23. The Revolutionary War ended at the battle of
- **a.** Valley Forge.
- **b.** Yorktown.
- **c.** Lexington.
- **d.** Saratoga.

24. The main goal of the Articles of Confederation was to
- **a.** increase federal power.
- **b.** reserve most powers for the states.
- **c.** reduce the need for a constitution.
- **d.** create a national government.

25. The Northwest Ordinance of 1787
- **a.** created the Northwest Territory.
- **b.** transferred government-owned land to private citizens.
- **c.** legalized slavery in the Northwest Territories.
- **d.** stated that the United States would not own colonies.

26. Which of the following problems was handled successfully by the newly created federal government?
- **a.** the settling of western territory
- **b.** the border dispute with Spain
- **c.** the economic crisis of the 1780s
- **d.** Shays's Rebellion

27. The U.S. Constitution's checks and balances rules were designed to
- **a.** create both state and federal governments.
- **b.** strengthen the Articles of Confederation.
- **c.** keep one part of government from being stronger than any other.
- **d.** allow both Federalists and Antifederalists to serve in government.

28. President George Washington stayed neutral in foreign affairs because he believed
- **a.** getting involved in other nations' disputes would be harmful to the United States.
- **b.** staying neutral would strengthen the economy in the United States.
- **c.** staying neutral would weaken foreign nations.
- **d.** staying neutral would prevent other nations from challenging the United States.

29. In the late 1700s, the United States fought the "undeclared war" with
- **a.** Great Britain.
- **b.** France.
- **c.** the Netherlands.
- **d.** Spain.

30. In the presidential election of 1800, which two men received the same number of votes?
- **a.** John Adams and Thomas Jefferson
- **b.** Thomas Jefferson and Aaron Burr
- **c.** Aaron Burr and John Adams
- **d.** C. C. Pinckney and John Adams

31. Judicial review is the process by which the Supreme Court decides
- **a.** whether or not courts may try certain criminals.
- **b.** which political candidates may run for election.
- **c.** whether or not a law is constitutional.
- **d.** when new judges may be appointed by the government.

32. Which of the following contributed to the start of the War of 1812?
- **a.** Britain supporting Native American raids on U.S. settlements
- **b.** U.S. ships attempting to block supply ships sailing to France
- **c.** the Treaty of Ghent
- **d.** France interfering in the settlement of the Northwest Territories

33. Nationalism refers to
- **a.** disappointment with one's nation.
- **b.** distrust of foreign nations.
- **c.** concern for other nations.
- **d.** pride in one's nation.

34. Henry Clay's American System was designed to
- **a.** boost foreign trade.
- **b.** stop the government from forming a national bank.
- **c.** make the United States more self-sufficient.
- **d.** eliminate tariffs on foreign goods.

35. Why did President Andrew Jackson order the march that became known as the Trail of Tears?
- **a.** to remove the Choctaw people from government-owned land in Florida
- **b.** to help the Chippewa people settle in Minnesota
- **c.** to provide the Chickasaw people with lands west of the Mississippi River
- **d.** to remove the Cherokee people from their lands east of the Mississippi River

Midterm Exam *continued*

Assessment, Chapters 1–18

36. What did Eli Whitney develop?
- **a.** healthier cotton plants
- **b.** interchangeable parts
- **c.** coal and power factories
- **d.** canals

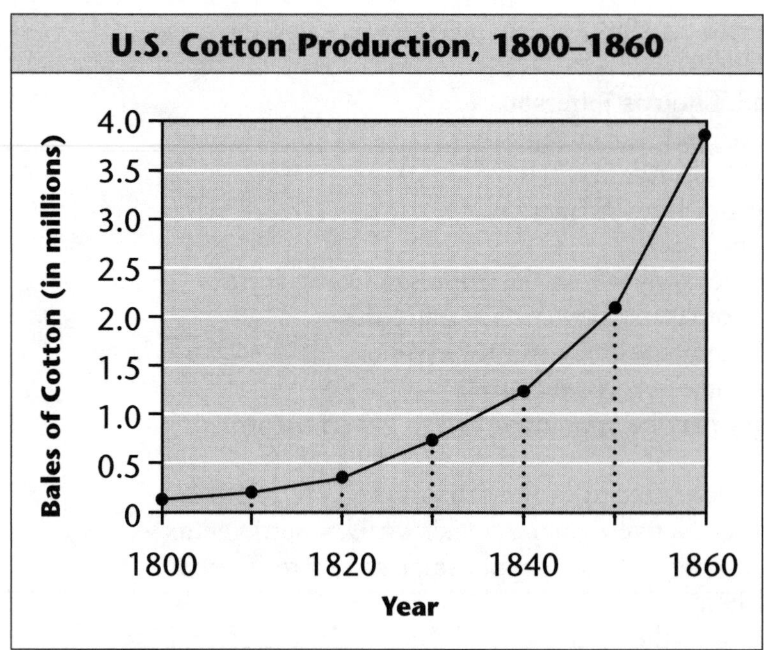

Base your answer to question 37 on the graph above.

37. In which year did cotton production exceed two million bales?
- **a.** 1800
- **b.** 1820
- **c.** 1840
- **d.** 1860

38. The goal of the temperance movement was to
- **a.** provide equal rights to women.
- **b.** improve education.
- **c.** outlaw alcoholic beverages.
- **d.** end slavery.

39. To acquire new territory in the mid-1800s, the United States expanded
- **a.** northward.
- **b.** southward.
- **c.** eastward.
- **d.** westward.

40. Why were gold prospectors in California called "forty-niners"?
- **a.** They sold gold for $49 per ounce.
- **b.** Most of them came to the area in 1849.
- **c.** They found gold on a 49-acre section of land.
- **d.** A permit to search for gold cost $49.

41. The Missouri Compromise
- **a.** allowed the North to ban slavery in Missouri.
- **b.** kept the balance of power in the Senate even between the North and the South.
- **c.** made it legal for slaves to be sold in the North.
- **d.** allowed Californians to buy and sell slaves.

42. Southern states decided to secede from the Union after
- **a.** Abraham Lincoln was elected President.
- **b.** Congress passed the Compromise of 1850.
- **c.** the Dred Scott case ended.
- **d.** John Brown's raid at Harpers Ferry.

43. The South planned to win the Civil War by
- **a.** producing more weapons than the North.
- **b.** having their slaves fight in battles.
- **c.** surviving until the North quit.
- **d.** repeatedly attacking the North.

44. The Emancipation Proclamation
- **a.** allowed slaves to fight for the Confederacy.
- **b.** banned the South from making slaves fight in battles.
- **c.** promised to free all slaves of the Confederacy.
- **d.** made it illegal for France or Great Britain to help the Union.

45. Which battle effectively ended the Civil War?
- **a.** Petersburg
- **b.** Cold Harbor
- **c.** Gettysburg
- **d.** Vicksburg

46. John Wilkes Booth assassinated President Abraham Lincoln to
- **a.** help the Republican Party take control of the South.
- **b.** make Andrew Johnson President.
- **c.** stop Lincoln's Reconstruction plan.
- **d.** get back at the North for their victory in the war.

Name ______________________________ Date ______________

Midterm Exam *continued*

Assessment, Chapters 1–18

B. Analyze the engraving and answer the question that follows in the space provided.

47. Based on this engraving, how was life for white plantation owners different from life for enslaved Africans on plantations?

____

____

C. Write an essay about the topic listed below. Use facts and specific historical details in your answer. Write your essay on a separate sheet of paper.

48. After the Civil War ended, newly freed African Americans had to adjust to a new way of life. Freedom and the end of war brought new opportunities and challenges. Explain how freed African Americans tried to rebuild their lives. Your essay should include the following:

- the ways that African Americans in the South were affected by Reconstruction
- the ways that many white Southerners tried to make life difficult for African Americans
- the freedoms emancipated African Americans gained under Reconstruction

Name ______________________ Date ______________

Final Exam

Assessment, Chapters 19–32

A. Circle the letter of the correct answer to each question.

1. The Pacific Railway Act of 1862
- **a.** banned the building of railroads on Native American lands.
- **b.** provided public land for the building of railroads.
- **c.** helped railroads develop along the East Coast.
- **d.** made it legal for former slaves to travel by rail.

2. The political party formed by farmers was called the
- **a.** Commerce Party.
- **b.** Farmers' Alliance.
- **c.** Grange Party.
- **d.** Populist Party.

3. The U.S. government forced Native Americans onto land called
- **a.** containments.
- **b.** reservations.
- **c.** settlements.
- **d.** assimilations.

4. Which of the following improved communication in the 1800s?
- **a.** the alternating current
- **b.** the Bessemer process
- **c.** the telegraph
- **d.** the patent

5. Most union labor strikes in the late 1800s were
- **a.** dangerous.
- **b.** unsuccessful.
- **c.** effective.
- **d.** overpowering.

6. For most immigrants at the turn of the century, life in the United States was
- **a.** difficult.
- **b.** easy.
- **c.** pointless.
- **d.** pleasurable.

7. Which group was kept separate from the rest of society by the Jim Crow laws?
- **a.** Native Americans
- **b.** African Americans
- **c.** Latin Americans
- **d.** Asian Americans

Name ________________________ Date ____________

Final Exam *continued*

Assessment, Chapters 19–32

8. A goal of the Progressive movement was to
- **a.** help governments increase the power of political bosses.
- **b.** stop the sale and use of alcohol.
- **c.** prevent African Americans from gaining civil rights.
- **d.** deny women suffrage.

9. The President who most supported Progressive ideas was
- **a.** William McKinley.
- **b.** Theodore Roosevelt.
- **c.** William Taft.
- **d.** Woodrow Wilson.

10. Americans who believed the nation should build an overseas empire were called
- **a.** colonists.
- **b.** traitors.
- **c.** isolationists.
- **d.** imperialists.

11. Which colony's bid for independence started the Spanish-American War?
- **a.** Cuba
- **b.** Puerto Rico
- **c.** Philippines
- **d.** Guam

12. President William Taft's approach to foreign policy was to use
- **a.** military force.
- **b.** secret deals.
- **c.** economic power.
- **d.** human rights laws.

13. During World War I, which nations formed the Central Powers?
- **a.** Great Britain, France, Russia
- **b.** France, Austria-Hungary, Italy
- **c.** Russia, Italy, Germany
- **d.** Ottoman Empire, Austria-Hungary, Germany

14. Which of the following prompted the United States to enter World War I?
- **a.** Germany began sinking American ships bound for Europe.
- **b.** Mexico declared war on the United States to reclaim Texas.
- **c.** Great Britain asked the United States for help because it was losing the war.
- **d.** Russia joined forces with Germany.

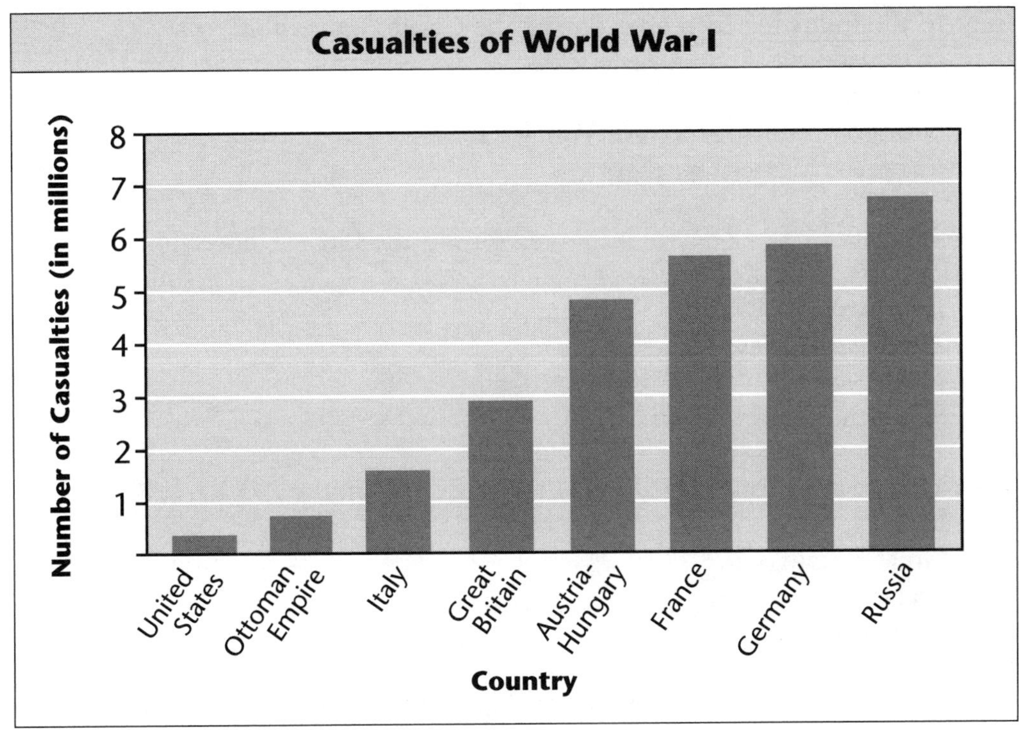

Base your answer to question 15 on the graph above.

15. Which nation suffered about 1.5 million casualties in World War I?

a. Great Britain
b. Austria-Hungary
c. Italy
d. Russia

16. Americans in the 1920s were able to buy expensive items through the use of

a. mass production.
b. assembly lines.
c. installment plans.
d. advertising campaigns.

17. The Dust Bowl of the 1930s was caused by

a. the crash of the stock market.
b. a severe drought in the Great Plains.
c. large Midwestern banks that closed.
d. farmers who refused to tend to their land.

Name ______________________ Date ______________

Final Exam *continued*

Assessment, Chapters 19–32

18. Which of the following increased during the Great Depression?
- **a.** crimes against African Americans
- **b.** jobs for American men
- **c.** bonus payments for World War I veterans
- **d.** wages for Mexican workers

19. The mood in the United States improved during the Great Depression because of President Franklin Roosevelt's
- **a.** Improvement Law.
- **b.** Tennessee Valley Authority.
- **c.** New Deal.
- **d.** Share the Wealth program.

20. Which European nation was led by a Fascist dictator in the 1930s?
- **a.** Italy
- **b.** Great Britain
- **c.** France
- **d.** Czechoslovakia

21. What event prompted the Soviet Union to join the Allies in World War II?
- **a.** Hitler's attack on Great Britain
- **b.** Japan's bombing of Pearl Harbor
- **c.** Germany's attempt to invade Moscow
- **d.** the defeat of Mussolini in Italy

22. On June 6, 1944, the Allies
- **a.** began an attack on the German army in France.
- **b.** launched a siege on the Soviet city of Stalingrad.
- **c.** set up an invasion of Italy.
- **d.** established a port for Axis submarines.

23. Who had to decide whether or not to use the atomic bomb in World War II?
- **a.** Winston Churchill
- **b.** Joseph Stalin
- **c.** Harry Truman
- **d.** Franklin D. Roosevelt

24. The Cold War is best described as
- **a.** an economic battle between the United States and the Soviet Union.
- **b.** military battles between the United States and the Soviet Union.
- **c.** a period of tension and distrust between the United States and the Soviet Union.
- **d.** a bloody war fought over whether the United States or Soviet Union would control Europe.

25. The goal of the Marshall Plan was to
- **a.** free the nations controlled by the Soviet Union.
- **b.** help European nations recover economically.
- **c.** stop the spread of communism in Europe.
- **d.** increase the Soviet Union's control over Eastern Europe.

26. The Korean War resulted in
- **a.** a major military victory for the Soviet Union.
- **b.** the country of Korea being divided into two separate nations.
- **c.** the United States' first loss in a major war.
- **d.** a demilitarized zone between North Korea and South Korea.

27. The so-called "space race" between the United States and the Soviet Union was started by
- **a.** the launch of the satellite named *Sputnik*.
- **b.** an American U-2 spy plane being shot down by the Soviet Union.
- **c.** a summit meeting between Nikita Khrushchev and Dwight Eisenhower.
- **d.** the development of the CIA.

28. The differences between teenagers and their parents in the 1950s was called the
- **a.** hippie movement.
- **b.** counter culture.
- **c.** baby boom.
- **d.** generation gap.

29. The Bay of Pigs invasion was staged in order to
- **a.** prevent guerrilla warfare in Cuba.
- **b.** keep Soviet missiles out of Cuba.
- **c.** topple Fidel Castro's government in Cuba.
- **d.** provide military aid to Cuba.

30. President Kennedy believed that helping developing nations would
- **a.** weaken the power of the United States.
- **b.** slow the spread of communism.
- **c.** improve the American economy.
- **d.** weaken the Soviet Union.

31. What did civil rights protesters in the 1960s demand?
- **a.** the end of desegregation
- **b.** racial equality
- **c.** segregation
- **d.** separate but equal public facilities

32. Lyndon Johnson's Great Society program was an attempt to
- **a.** block laws favored by President Kennedy.
- **b.** prevent the spread of communism.
- **c.** improve life for all Americans.
- **d.** help the American military grow stronger.

33. The Voting Rights Act of 1965 was designed to help
- **a.** African Americans.
- **b.** women.
- **c.** Latinos.
- **d.** Native Americans.

34. The domino theory stated that if
- **a.** one country became democratic, others would too.
- **b.** a Communist nation became democratic, its leaders would too.
- **c.** democratic nations fought communism, people would benefit.
- **d.** one country became Communist, others would too.

35. In general, the Vietnam War
- **a.** was supported by all Americans.
- **b.** divided the American people.
- **c.** was opposed by most Americans.
- **d.** united the American people.

36. President Nixon attempted to end U.S. involvement in Vietnam by
- **a.** evacuating all anti-Communists from South Vietnam.
- **b.** helping South Vietnamese forces fight the war themselves.
- **c.** staging a massive bombing of North Vietnam.
- **d.** immediately withdrawing all American troops.

37. Which of the following actions by the Nixon administration played no part in improving relations between the United States and Communist countries?
- **a.** Nixon visiting China in 1972
- **b.** creating the SALT treaty
- **c.** following the policy of détente
- **d.** Nixon supporting affirmative action

38. Which President failed to end the Iranian hostage crisis?
- **a.** Richard Nixon
- **b.** Gerald Ford
- **c.** Jimmy Carter
- **d.** Ronald Reagan

Name ______________________________ Date ____________________

39. Which group gained power during Ronald Reagan's presidency?
- **a.** conservatives
- **b.** independents
- **c.** liberals
- **d.** environmentalists

40. Which nation was pushed from Kuwait during the Persian Gulf War?
- **a.** Iraq
- **b.** Israel
- **c.** Iran
- **d.** Saudi Arabia

41. Which of the following stayed strong during Bill Clinton's presidency?
- **a.** the Soviet Union
- **b.** the peace agreement between Palestinians and Israelis
- **c.** the economy in the United States
- **d.** American relations with Somalia

42. Who gave a speech to Congress and to all Americans on September 20, 2001?
- **a.** President Clinton
- **b.** Albert Gore Jr.
- **c.** the Director of Homeland Security
- **d.** President George W. Bush

43. The U.S. economy reached low levels in 2001 after
- **a.** the terrorist attacks on September 11.
- **b.** the election of George W. Bush.
- **c.** the price of American goods increased.
- **d.** the unemployment rate fell.

44. Globalization of the U.S. economy means that
- **a.** prices of American-made goods will increase.
- **b.** the U.S. economy has nothing to do with other nations' economies.
- **c.** the U.S. economy is connected to the economies of other countries.
- **d.** fewer American-made products will be sold in other countries.

45. After the September 11, 2001, terrorist attacks on the United States,
- **a.** the people of the United States came together as a nation.
- **b.** the economy in the United States grew.
- **c.** Americans were less committed to freedom and equality.
- **d.** the United States focused less on global security.

Name ______________________________ Date ______________

Final Exam *continued*

Assessment, Chapters 19–32

B. Analyze the photograph and answer the question that follows in the space provided.

46. This photograph shows a family from the Oklahoma Dust Bowl in 1935. What is the most likely reason that they have packed all they own into their car?

____

____

C. Write an essay about the topic listed below. Use facts and specific historical details in your answer. Write your essay on a separate sheet of paper.

47. John F. Kennedy became President at a very important time in American history. The United States was involved in the Cold War and American society was beginning to change. Describe the goals, successes, and failures of Kennedy's presidency. Your essay should include the following:

- some of the goals of the Kennedy administration
- some of the successes of the Kennedy administration
- some of the failures of the Kennedy administration

Contents

Concept Builders

About Concept Builders

The worksheets in this section provide the support needed to develop critical thinking, reading, and writing skills. Students will have an opportunity to develop skills for organizing and interpreting information. The variety of activities is especially helpful for second-language learners working with other limited-English speakers and students proficient in English. You may want to use these worksheets to accommodate the special needs of mainstream students. There is one **Concept Builder** for each of the 32 chapters of the Student Edition.

- **Before You Read** Concept Builders access students' prior knowledge of the subject.
- **While You Read** Concept Builders provide tips on important items for students to look for as they read.
- **After You Read** Concept Builders provide a review of major concepts in the chapter.

Have students read completed assignments aloud whenever possible. Read-aloud activities will help students develop oral language skills and reading comprehension. Encourage students to work in groups of two or three to complete assignments.

Use the worksheets to ensure students' understanding of chapter content.

Name ______________________ Date ____________

Chapter 1

Concept Builder

Organize Facts

While You Read

A. Complete the chart below by filling in facts about the five civilizations from Mexico, Central America, and South America. The first one is done for you.

Civilization	Where they lived	When they lived	Major accomplishments
Olmec	Mexico's Gulf Coast		
Maya			
Toltec			
Inca			
Aztec			

B. Choose one of the civilizations from the chart. Working with a partner, write a paragraph on a separate sheet of paper about that civilization.

Name ______________________ Date ______________

Concept Builder

Chapter 2

Learn Key Facts

After You Read

A. Complete the graphic organizer below. Write key facts about each of the West African trading empires. Some of the graphic organizer has been filled in for you.

West African Trading Empires

Ghana	Songhai	Mali
1. *Earliest known West African trading empire*	1. *Largest and most powerful West African trading empire*	1. *Controlled the gold trade*
2.	2.	2.
3.	3.	3.

B. Choose one of the trading empires from the graphic organizer. Write a paragraph on a separate sheet of paper about that empire. Include key facts from the graphic organizer in your paragraph.

Name ______________________ Date ______________

Chapter 3

Concept Builder

Learn Key Facts

While You Read

A. Complete the chart below to show key facts about some of the European explorers who helped settle the Americas. The first one is done for you.

Who?	What?	Where?	When?	Why?
Hernándo Cortés	Conquered Aztecs	Gulf Coast of Mexico	1519	To take their land and gold

B. Choose one of the explorers from the chart. Working with a partner, write a paragraph on a separate sheet of paper about that explorer. Include facts to explain why this person was important.

Name ______________________ Date ______________________

Concept Builder

Chapter 4

Use Illustrations to Predict Main Ideas

Before You Read

A. Complete the chart below by describing one illustration from each section of Chapter 4. Then, write the caption of the illustration and the main idea you expect to learn. The first one is done for you.

Section	Describe the illustration	Write the caption	What main idea do you expect to learn?
I	A painting of Pilgrims signing a piece of paper.	The Mayflower Compact was the first example of self-rule by colonists in the Americas.	Early settlers in North America created their own laws and societies.
II			
III			

B. Choose one of the illustrations from the chart. Write a creative paragraph on a separate sheet of paper about that illustration. Include information from the chart in your paragraph.

Concept Builders

Name ____________________ Date ____________

Chapter 5

Concept Builder

Learn Key Facts

While You Read

A. Complete the boxes below by filling in key facts about the economy of each of the three regions of the American colonies. The first one is done for you.

New England colonies
System of farming: *small farms*
Land: *hilly and tree-covered*
Soil: *rocky*
Climate: *long, cold winters*
Crops: *corn, wheat, and barley*
Natural resources: *fish and forests*
Industry: *fishing, lumber,*
and shipbuilding

Southern colonies
System of farming:
Land:
Soil:
Climate:
Crops:
Natural resources:
Industry:

Middle colonies
System of farming:
Land:
Soil:
Climate:
Crops:
Natural resources:
Industry:

Concept Builders

B. Choose one of the three regions. Working with a partner, write a paragraph on a separate sheet of paper about that region. Include key facts about the region in your paragraph.

Name ______________________ Date ______________

Concept Builder

Chapter 6

Organize Information

After You Read

A. Complete the chart below to organize information about how the American colonies were governed. Fill in the information about who made up each governing body and what powers each one had. The first one is done for you.

Governing Body	Made Up Of	Powers
Monarch	*king or queen*	*Could approve or disapprove actions of colonial governments*
Governor		
Assembly		
Council		

B. Choose one of the governing bodies from the chart. Write a paragraph on a separate sheet of paper about that governing body. Try to include a detailed description of the duties of the governing body, the methods used for selecting the governing body, and any differences from colony to colony.

Name ______________________ Date ______________

Chapter 7

Concept Builder

Cause and Effect

While You Read

A. Complete the chart below by writing the cause and effect for each event. The first one is done for you.

Cause	Event	Effect
British government wants colonists to pay a share of the war debt	Stamp Act	*Colonists argue that Parliament does not have the right to tax them*
	Boston Massacre	
	Boston Tea Party	
	The Second Continental Congress	
	Signing of the Declaration of Independence	

B. Choose one of the events from the chart. Write a paragraph on a separate sheet of paper about that event. Include additional details from the chapter about the causes and effects of the event.

Concept Builders

Name ______________________ Date ______________

Concept Builder

Chapter 8

Make a Flowchart

After You Read

A. Complete the flowchart to show the major battles of the Revolutionary War. Write the events in the box below in the order in which they occurred. The first one is done for you.

British victory at Brooklyn Heights, New York

British victory at Charleston, South Carolina

British victory at Philadelphia, Pennsylvania

American victory at Yorktown, Virginia

American victory over the British navy

American victory over Hessian troops at Trenton, New Jersey

American victory at Saratoga, New York

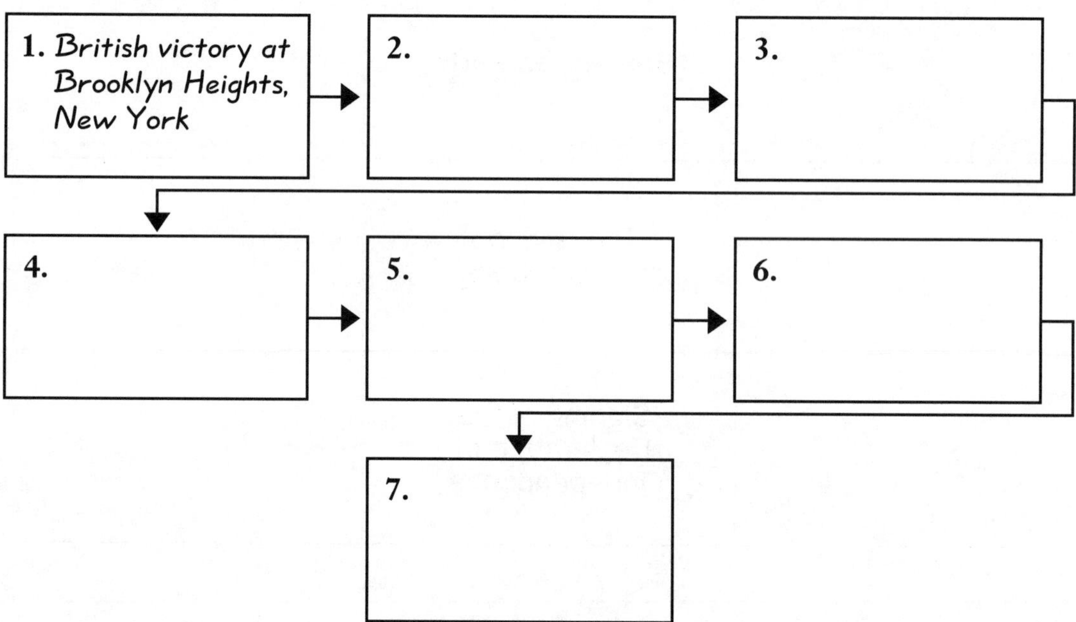

B. Choose one of the battles from the flowchart. Working with a partner, write a paragraph on a separate sheet of paper about that battle. Explain how the outcome of the battle affected both the British and the Americans.

Name ______________________ Date ______________

Chapter 9

Concept Builder

Learn Key Facts

While You Read

A. Place each key fact in the box below where it belongs in the chart that follows. The facts are from each section of Chapter 9. The first one is done for you.

November 1777	to create the Northwest Territory
The Articles of Confederation	Annapolis, Maryland
to discuss problems with the Articles of Confederation	land north of the Ohio River and east of the Mississippi River
13 states	1786
to create a new government to unite the states	Annapolis Convention
1787	Northwest Ordinance

	Section I	Section II	Section III
What?	1. *The Articles of Confederation*	5.	9.
Where?	2.	6.	10.
When?	3.	7.	11.
Why?	4.	8.	12.

B. After you have finished reading Chapter 9, review your completed chart. Write a paragraph on a separate sheet of paper about the Articles of Confederation or the Constitutional Convention. Include reasons and facts to explain why the topic of your paragraph was important.

Concept Builders

Name ______________________ Date ______________

Concept Builder

Chapter 10

Learn Key Facts

While You Read

A. As you read Chapter 10, look for some of George Washington's acts to establish a working government and a stable nation. Write them in the chart below. The first one is done for you.

George Washington's Presidency
1. *created a Cabinet*
2.
3.
4.
5.
6.

B. Review your completed chart. Write a paragraph on a separate sheet of paper explaining the most important act of George Washington as President.

Name ______________________________ Date ______________

Chapter 11

Concept Builder

Sequence Events

After You Read

A. Complete the flowchart below to show some of the events from Chapter 11 of your textbook. Write the events listed in the box below in the order in which they occurred. The first one is done for you.

James Madison is elected President.

The power of judicial review is used in the *Marbury* v. *Madison* case.

The British are defeated at Fort McHenry.

France sells the Louisiana Territory to the United States.

War begins between the United States and Britain.

Lewis and Clark set out on their expedition.

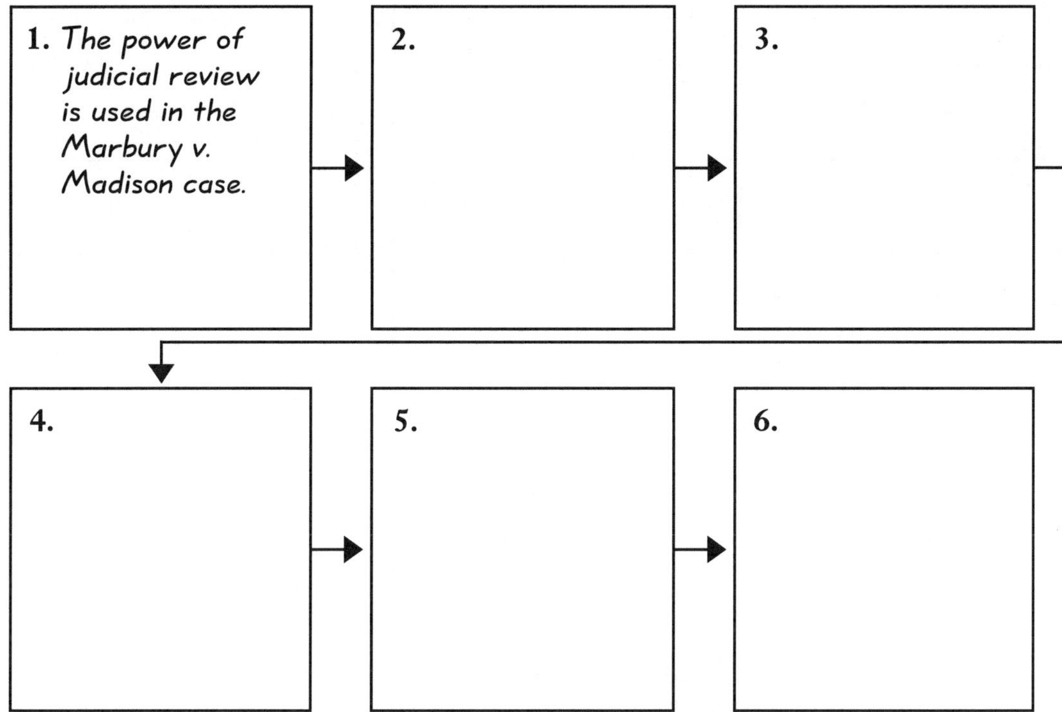

B. Choose one of the events from the flowchart. Working with a partner, write a paragraph on a separate sheet of paper about that event. Try to include causes and effects in your paragraph.

Concept Builders

Name ______________________ Date ______________

Concept Builder

Summarize

After You Read

A. Complete the chart below to summarize the views and actions of Andrew Jackson during his presidency.

Andrew Jackson

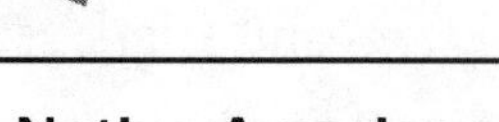

Bank of the United States	Nullification Crisis	Native Americans

B. Choose one of the issues from the chart. Working with a partner, write a paragraph on a separate sheet of paper explaining why you agree with or disagree with Jackson's views and actions on that issue.

Name ______________________ Date ______________

Chapter 13

Concept Builder

Organize Facts

While You Read

A. Complete the chart below to show each person's invention and its important effect.

Inventor	Invention	Effect
Samuel Slater		
Eli Whitney		
Cyrus McCormick		
John Deere		
Samuel Morse		

B. Choose one of the inventions from the chart. Working with a partner, write a paragraph on a separate sheet of paper about that invention. Include the effect of the invention in your paragraph.

Name ______________________ Date ______________

Concept Builder

Assess Prior Knowledge

Before You Read

A. Read each of the following terms. Write what you think each means. Then, use a dictionary to check your definitions.

1. immigration ______________________________

____

2. literature ______________________________

____

3. reform ______________________________

____

4. discrimination ______________________________

____

B. Complete the Venn diagram below to show what you know about life in cities and life in the country. Fill in the top circle with facts about city life. Fill in the bottom circle with facts about country life. Fill in the middle with facts that are the same in both the city and the country.

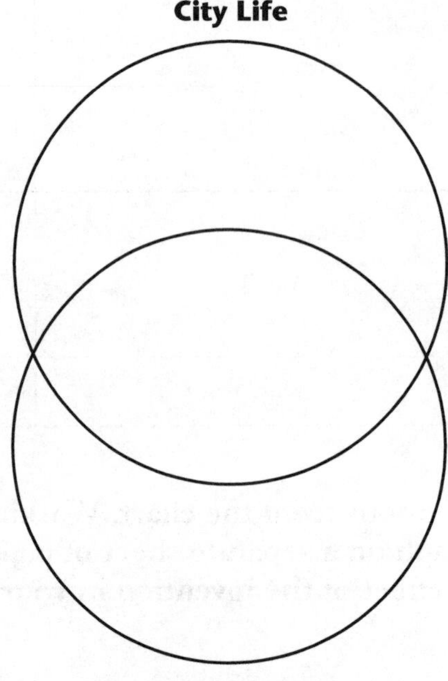

Name ________________________ Date ______________

Chapter 15

Concept Builder

Sequence Events

After You Read

A. Complete the flowchart below. Trace the westward expansion of the United States by summarizing the important event or events that occurred each year.

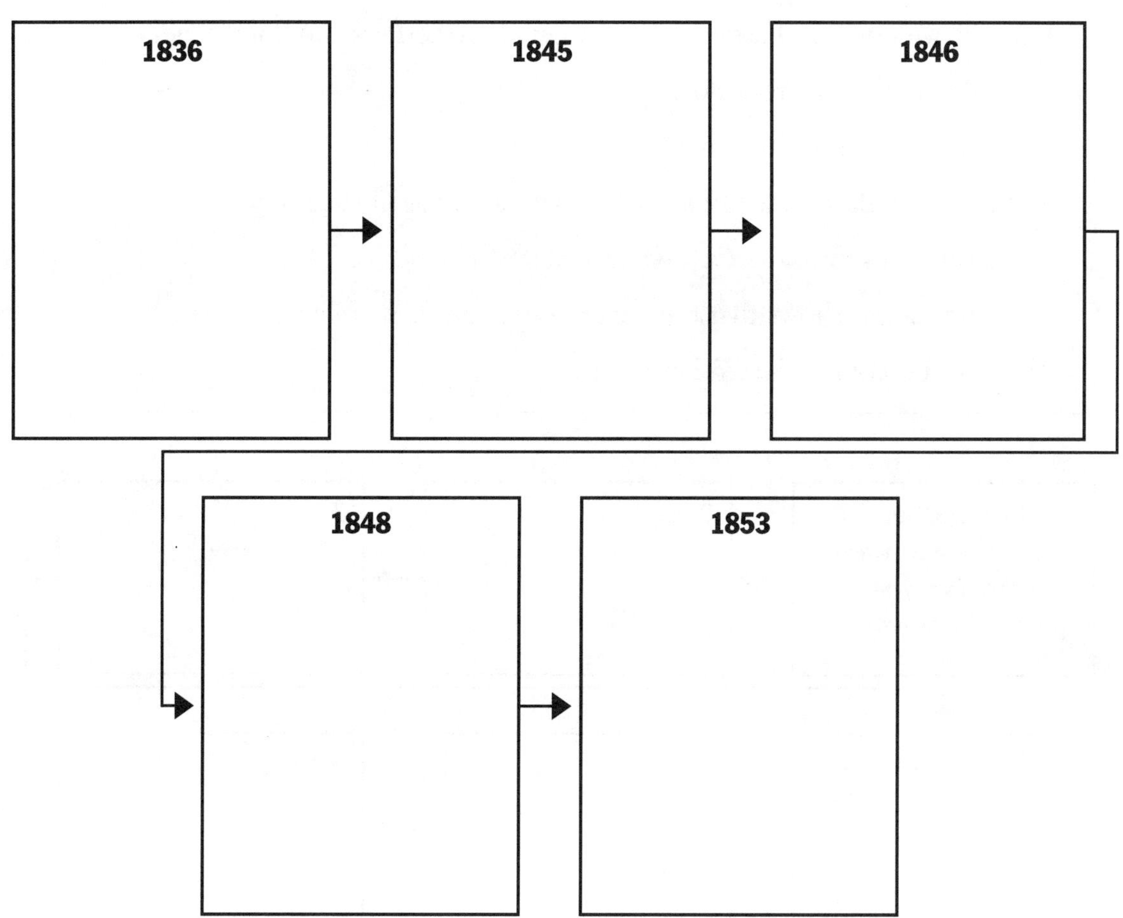

B. Choose the event in the flowchart that you believe was most significant in the nation's westward expansion. Write a paragraph on a separate sheet of paper explaining your opinion.

Concept Builders

Name ______________________ Date ______________

Concept Builder

Sequence Events

Before You Read

A. Complete the flowchart below to show events leading to the start of the Civil War. Write the events listed below in the order in which they occurred. The first one is done for you.

John Brown's raid on Harpers Ferry angers Northerners and Southerners.
Confederate forces attack Fort Sumter.
Southern states begin to leave the Union.
The Fugitive Slave Law turns many Northerners against slavery.
Southern states form the Confederate States of America.
Bleeding Kansas shows that the slavery issue can turn violent.
Abraham Lincoln is elected President.

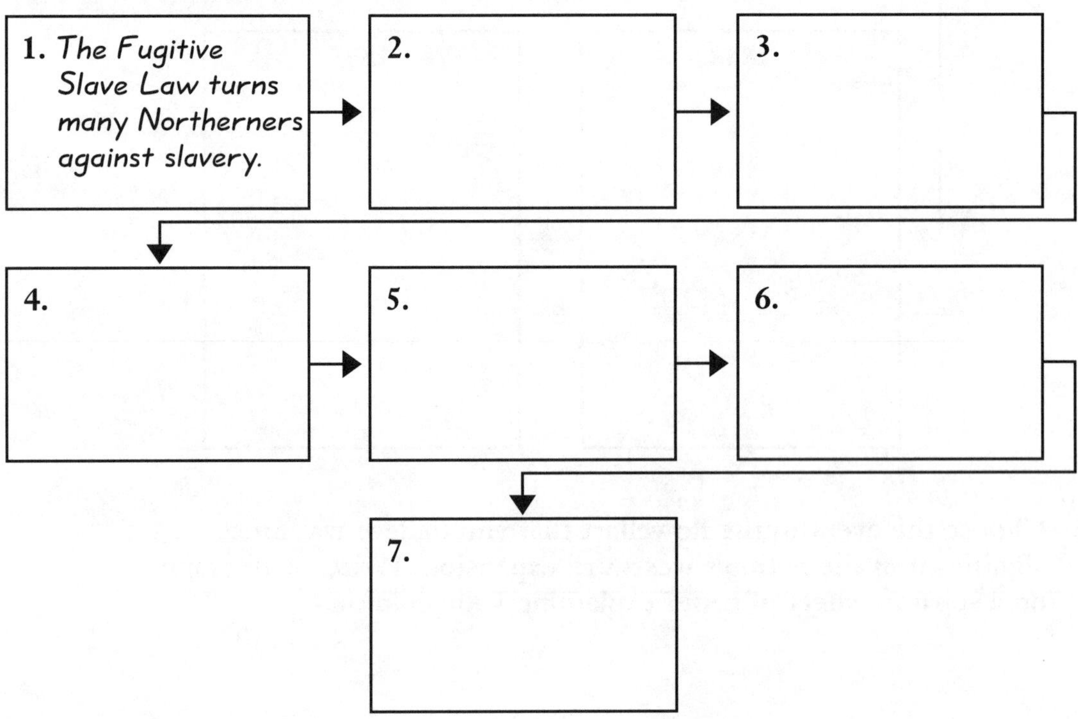

B. Choose one of the events from the flowchart. Working with a partner, write a paragraph on a separate sheet of paper about that event. Try to include causes and effects of the event in your paragraph.

Name ______________________ Date ______________

Chapter 17

Concept Builder

Review Previous Chapters

Before You Read

A. Complete the chart below. Decide which words or phrases in the box were part of life in the North. Write those in the first column. Complete the second column with words or phrases that were part of life in the South. The first one is done for you.

slavery	spirituals
better transportation	banks to make loans
cotton	rebellions
factories	technical schools
plantations	larger population

North	South
better transportation	

B. Choose one fact from the chart. Write a paragraph on a separate sheet of paper about how that fact would help during a war. Explain your reasons.

Concept Builders

Name ________________________ Date ____________

Concept Builder

Chapter 18

Sequence Events

After You Read

A. Complete the flowchart below to show some of the events that took place during Reconstruction. Write the events listed in the box below in the order in which they occurred. The first one is done for you.

Abraham Lincoln is assassinated.

Reconstruction ends.

Congress passes the Civil Rights Act of 1866.

Congress passes the Military Reconstruction Act.

Congress passes the Thirteenth Amendment to the Constitution.

Rutherford B. Hayes becomes President.

The Fifteenth Amendment to the Constitution is adopted.

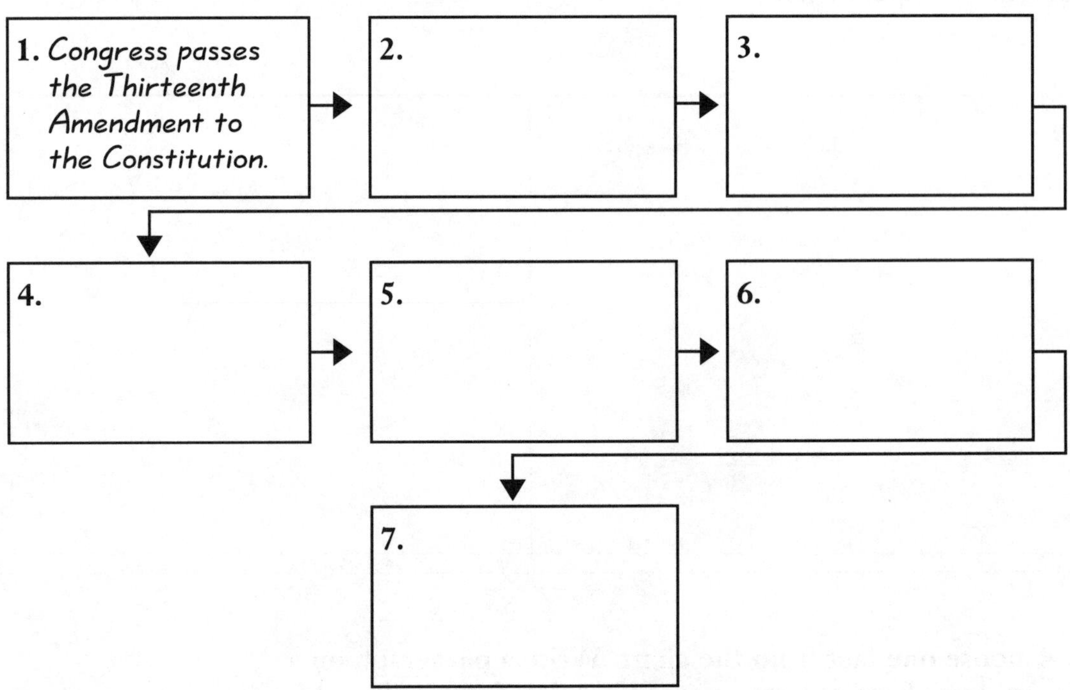

B. Choose one of the events from the flowchart. Working with a partner, write a paragraph on a separate sheet of paper about that event. Try to include causes and effects in your paragraph.

Name ______________________ Date ____________

Chapter 19

Concept Builder

Assess Prior Knowledge

Before You Read

A. Before you read Chapter 19, answer the questions below. Your answers will show what you already know about the settlement of the Great Plains of the West.

Farming

1. What was the main crop grown by the farmers who settled in the Great Plains?

____

2. What were some of the problems the farmers in the Great Plains faced?

____

Hunting

3. Which animal did the Native Americans of the Great Plains depend on the most for food, shelter, and clothing?

____

Ranching

4. How were beef cattle moved from the open range to markets in East Coast cities?

____

5. What was life like for a cowhand who rode the open range in the West?

____

Mining

6. What valuable materials were the miners who came to the West looking for?

____

B. Compare your answers with information from Chapter 19. Fill in any additional information from the text on the lines above and on a separate sheet of paper if you need more space.

Name ______________________ Date ______________

Concept Builder

Chapter 20

Make a Venn Diagram

After You Read

A. Complete the Venn diagram below to identify similarities and differences between Andrew Carnegie and John D. Rockefeller. In the top circle, write two characteristics of Carnegie. In the bottom circle, write two characteristics of Rockefeller. In the center section, write two characteristics that they share.

Andrew Carnegie

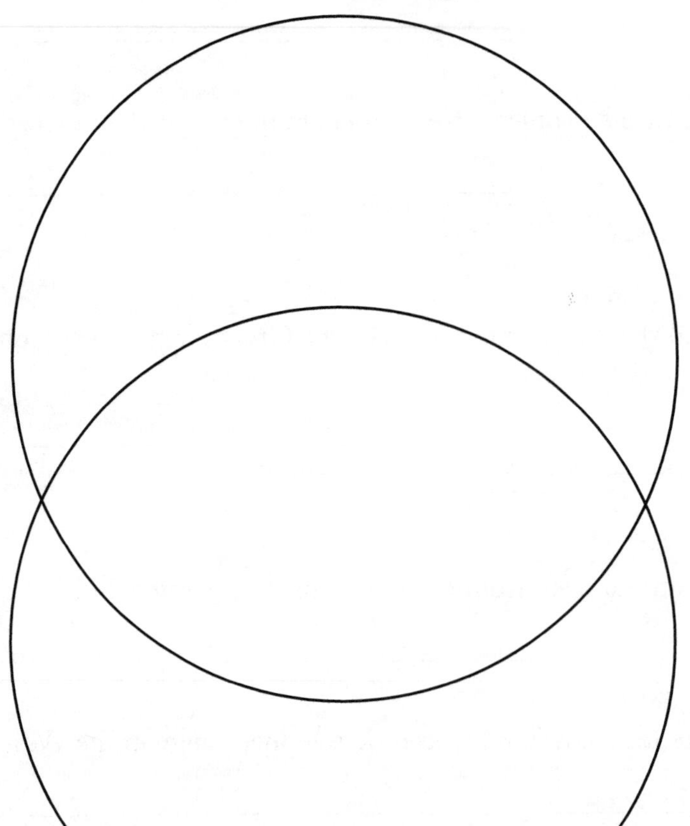

John D. Rockefeller

B. Working with a partner, write a paragraph on a separate sheet of paper comparing and contrasting Andrew Carnegie and John D. Rockefeller.

Concept Builders

Name ______________________ Date ______________

Chapter 21

Concept Builder

Learn Key Facts

While You Read

A. As you read each section of Chapter 21, write two social problems the nation faced in the chart below. The first one is done for you. Then, write the solutions to these problems.

Section	Problem	Solution
I	1. *Corrupt politicians gave jobs to people who would help them even if they were not qualified for the jobs.*	
	2.	
II	3.	
	4.	
III	5.	
	6.	

B. After you have filled in your chart, choose one problem and its solution. Write a paragraph on a separate sheet of paper about that problem and solution. Include reasons why this problem needed to be solved. Explain how the solution helped solve the problem.

Name ______________________ Date ______________

Concept Builder

Chapter 22

Cause and Effect

While You Read

A. As you read Chapter 22, look for the causes and effects of U.S. imperialism. Complete the graphic organizer below by writing three causes and three effects of U.S. imperialism.

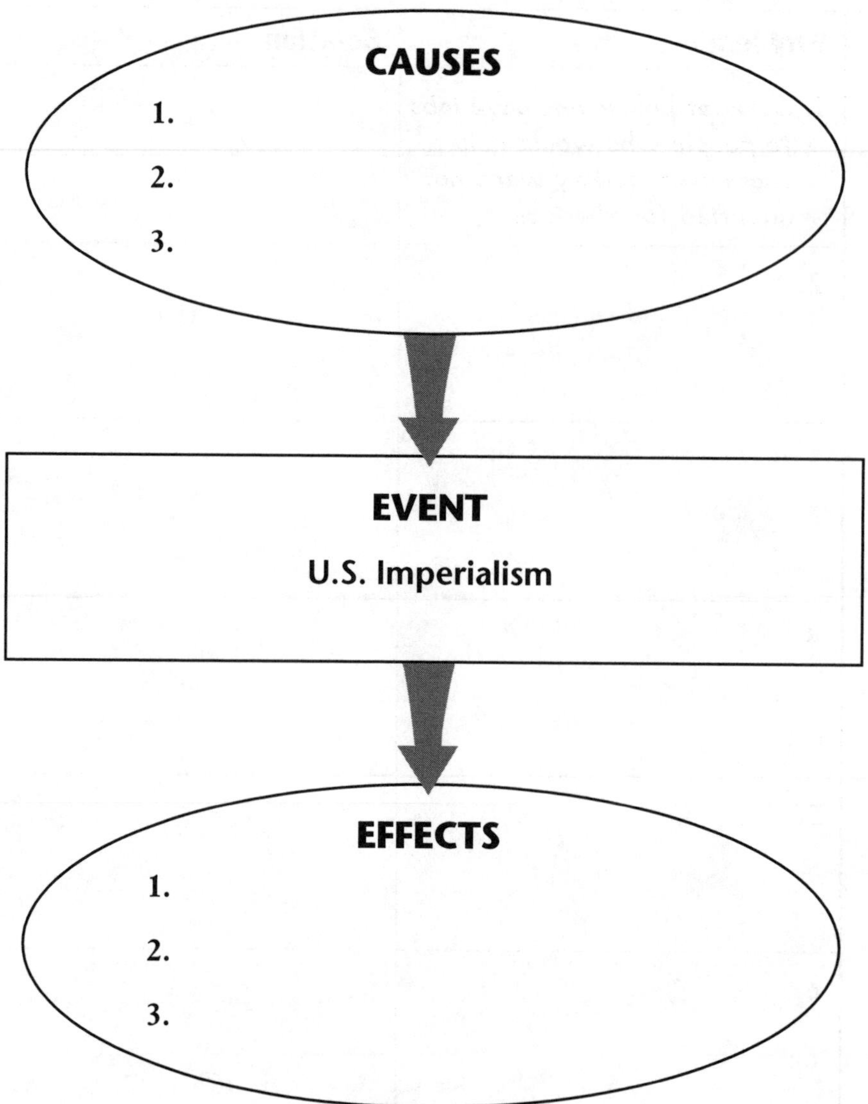

B. Review your completed graphic organizer. On a separate sheet of paper, write a paragraph explaining which effect of imperialism either benefited or harmed the United States the most. Try to include details from Chapter 22 in your paragraph.

Name ______________________ Date ______________

Chapter 23

Concept Builder

Cause and Effect

While You Read

A. As you read Chapter 23, complete the chart below. Write the causes and effects of World War I. Some of the chart is done for you.

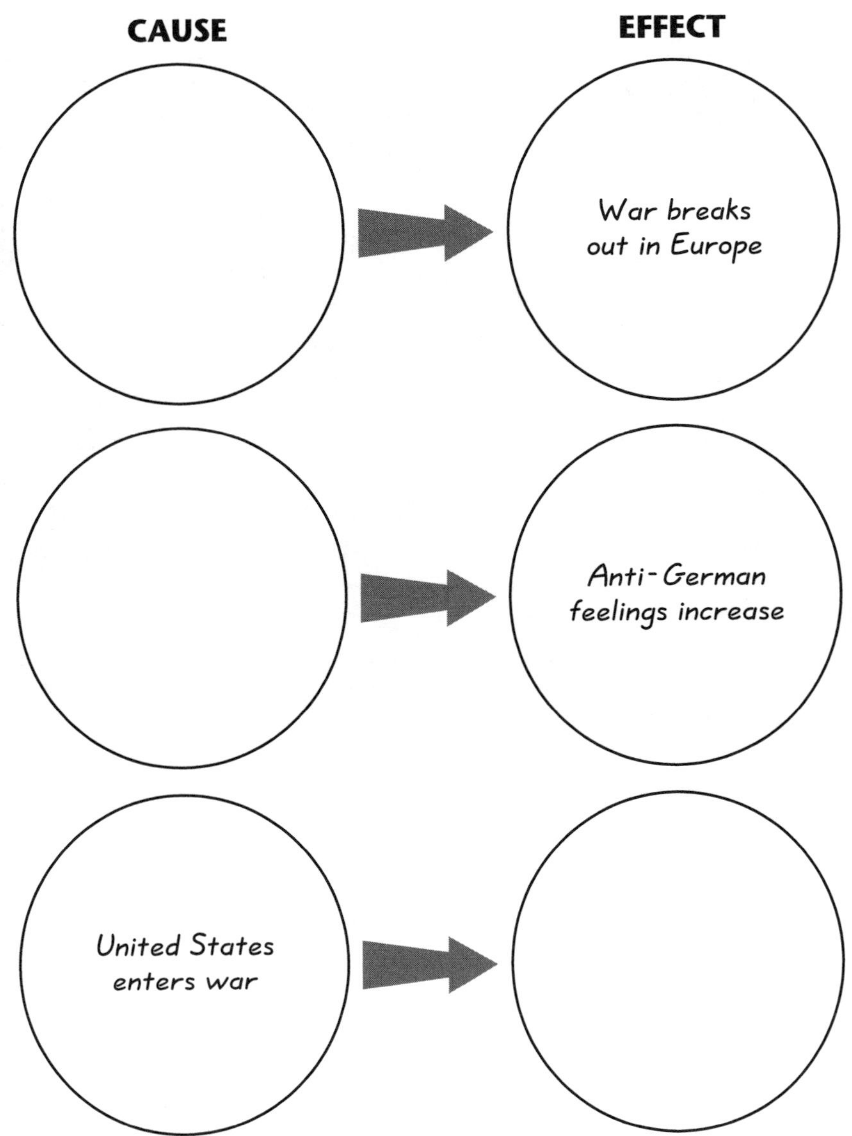

B. Choose one of the events from the chart. Working with a partner, write a paragraph on a separate sheet of paper about that event. Try to include key details describing the cause and effects.

Concept Builders

Name ______________________ Date ______________

Concept Builder

Chapter 24

Use Graphics to Predict

Before You Read

A. Reading graphics and charts in a chapter can help you predict what you will learn. Read the charts on pages 578 and 581 in your textbook. Write two facts that you learned from each chart in the boxes below.

Chart	Fact 1	Fact 2
U.S. Rural and Urban Populations, 1890–1920		
Movie Facts		

B. Choose one of the charts. On a separate sheet of paper, write a paragraph about the chart. Explain what the chart means. What does this chart say about how life was changing in the 1920s?

Name ______________________ Date ______________

Chapter 25

Concept Builder

Use Headings to Predict

Before You Read

A. Complete the chart below to show how chapter headings help you predict what you will be reading. Choose one heading from each section of Chapter 25. Write each heading in a box on the left. The chapter title is filled in for you. Then, write what you expect to learn from the headings in the boxes on the right.

Heading		What I Expect to Learn
The Great Depression and the New Deal	→	
	→	
	→	
	→	

B. After you have completed the chart, scan all the headings in Chapter 25. Working with a partner, write a paragraph on a separate sheet of paper describing what you expect to learn from the chapter.

Concept Builders

Name ______________________ Date ______________

Concept Builder

Chapter 26

Cause and Effect

After You Read

A. Complete the chart below to show the causes and effects of World War II. Write the missing cause or effect for each main idea.

Cause	Effect
Hitler takes control of the Sudetenland.	1.
2.	Japan invades China.
The Japanese bomb Pearl Harbor.	3.
4.	The Allies force German forces out of France.
The United States drops the atomic bomb on Hiroshima and Nagasaki.	5.
6.	More than six million Jewish people are put to death.

B. After you have completed the chart, work with a partner to think of three more cause and effect events from Chapter 26. Write the events on a separate sheet of paper.

Name ______________________________ Date ________________

Chapter 27

Concept Builder

Identify Key Events

After You Read

A. Complete the chart below to show the important political and social events of the Cold War era. The first two are done for you.

Significant Political Events	Significant Social Events
• *NATO is formed.*	• *Montgomery bus boycott*
•	•
•	•
•	•

B. Choose one political event and one social event from the chart. On a separate sheet of paper, write a paragraph about the significance of each event.

Name ______________________ Date ______________

Concept Builder

Chapter 28

Learn Key Facts

Before You Read

A. Complete the chart below to show facts about civil rights and the Cold War. Use information that you remember from Chapter 27 of your textbook. The first fact is done for you.

Topic	Facts
Civil Rights	1. *Brown v. Board of Education of Topeka ended school segregation.* 2. 3. 4. 5.
Cold War	1. 2. 3. 4. 5.

B. Choose a topic from the chart. Working with a partner, write a paragraph about that topic on a separate sheet of paper. Include details from the chart in your paragraph.

Concept Builders

Name ______________________ Date ______________

Chapter 29

Concept Builder

Identify Key Events

While You Read

A. Work with a partner. Identify some problems during the Johnson administration. Then, identify some achievements of the Johnson administration. Include events that took place in the United States and abroad. One achievement is identified for you.

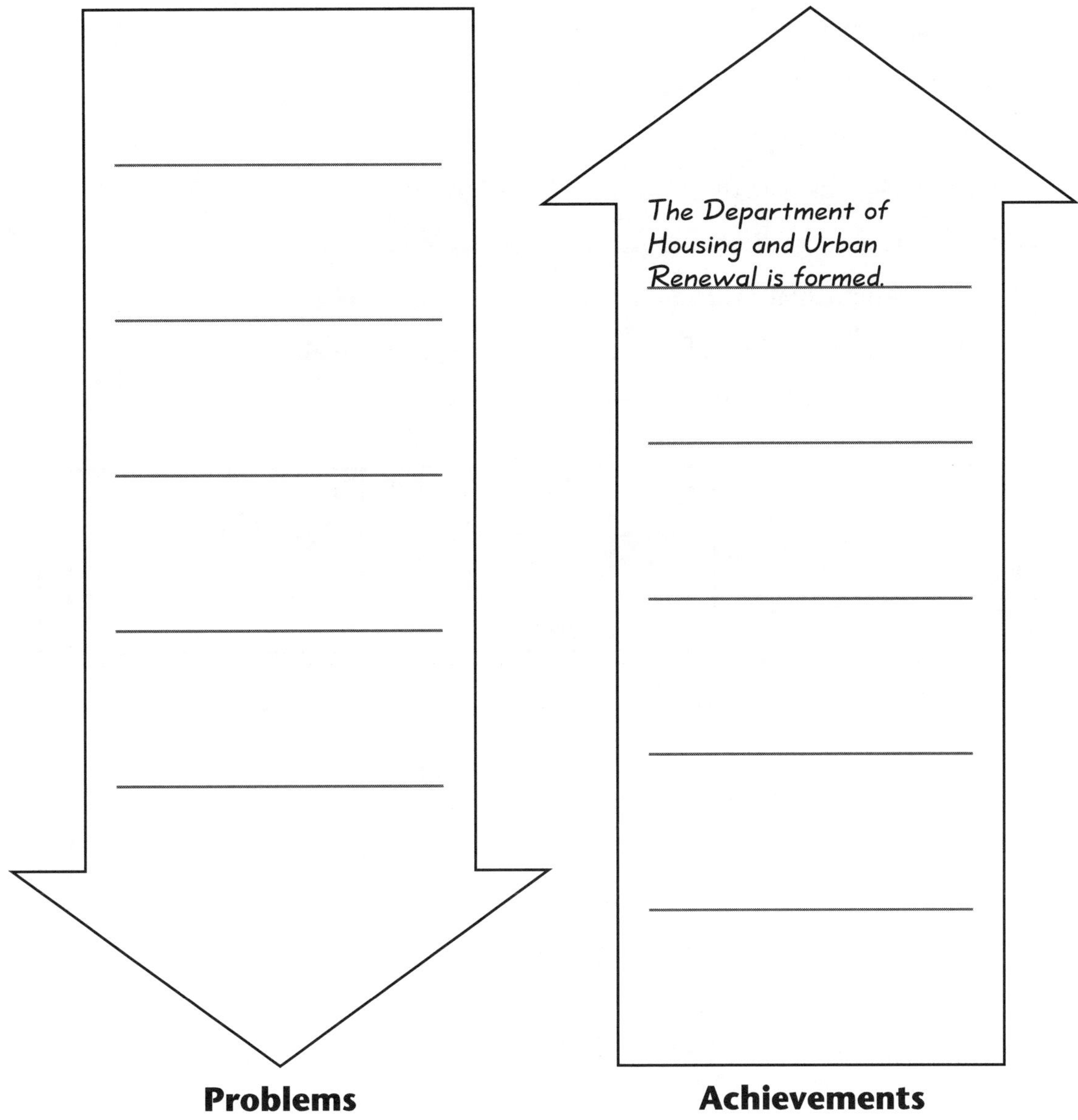

B. Choose one of the achievements from the chart. On a separate sheet of paper, write a paragraph about that achievement.

Concept Builders

Name ______________________ Date ______________

Concept Builder

Chapter 30

Sequence Events

After You Read

A. Complete the flowchart below to show events that took place before and during Richard Nixon's presidency. Write the events below in the order in which they occurred. One is done for you.

Robert Kennedy is assassinated during his presidential campaign.
President Nixon visits China and the Soviet Union.
North Vietnam and the United States agree to a truce.
Congress passes the War Powers Act.
Nixon resigns as a result of the Watergate scandal.
Antiwar protesters disrupt the Democratic National Convention.
The Environmental Protection Agency is created.
OPEC stops the sale of oil to countries that support Israel.

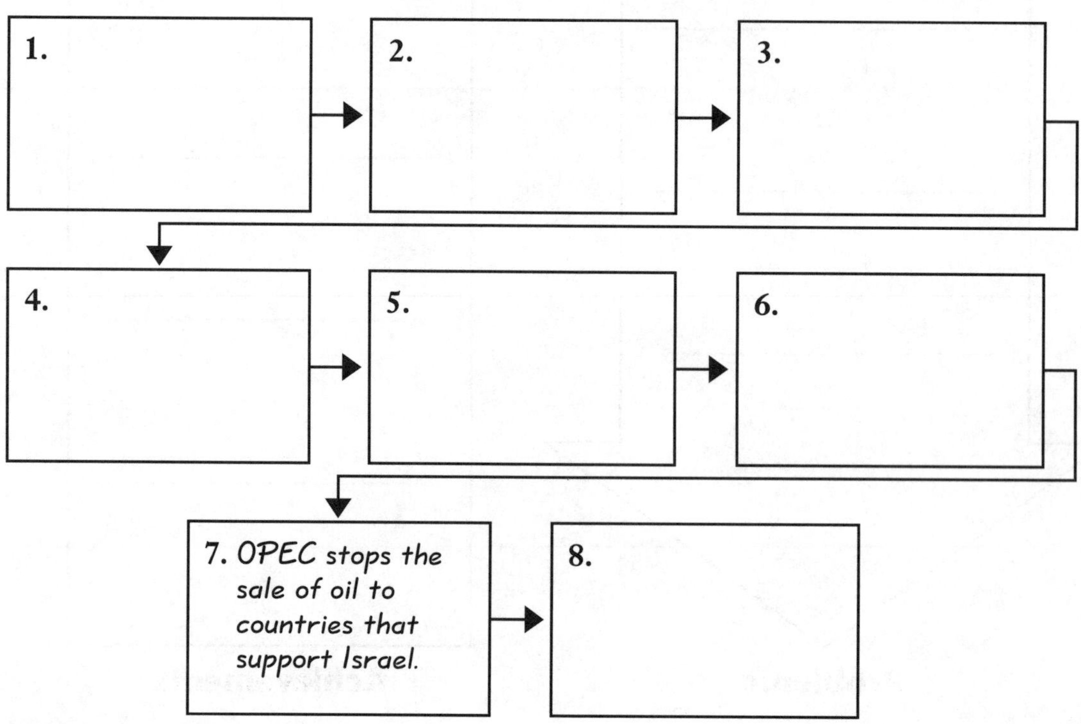

B. Choose one event from the flowchart. On a separate sheet of paper, write a paragraph about that event, including causes and effects.

Concept Builders

Name ______________________ Date ______________

Chapter 31

Concept Builder

Identify Key Events

After You Read

A. Complete the chart with events from the presidencies of Ronald Reagan, George H. W. Bush, and Bill Clinton. Use the events listed in the box below.

Amendments to the Clean Air Act of 1970 are signed.

U.S. troops launch air raids on the Serbs to end ethnic cleansing in Bosnia.

The first truly democratic election is held in South Africa.

Money earned from the arms sale to Iran is used to fund Contras in Nicaragua.

The Berlin Wall separating East and West Berlin is opened.

Sandra Day O'Connor is appointed justice to the Supreme Court.

President Reagan	President Bush	President Clinton
1.	3.	5.
2.	4.	6.

B. Review your completed chart. Write a paragraph on a separate sheet of paper about one foreign policy event listed in your chart. Include reasons and facts to explain why this event was important.

Concept Builders

Name ______________________ Date ______________

Concept Builder

Chapter 32

Organize Information

After You Read

A. Complete the chart below to show some of the problems and goals of the United States in the twenty-first century. In the top row, write sentences describing problems that the United States faces. In the bottom row, write sentences describing goals for the United States. The first one is done for you. You may read a newspaper, watch the news, or talk with others to help you fill in your chart.

Problems	• *Too many people are living in poverty.*	•	•
Goals	• *We should explore other planets.*	•	•

B. Choose one of the problems or goals from the chart. Working with a partner, write a paragraph on a separate sheet of paper explaining how the world could be improved by focusing on this problem or goal.

Concept Builders

Contents

They Made History

Name ______________________ Date ______________

They Made History

Montezuma

Montezuma 1466?–1520

Montezuma became ruler of the Aztec Empire of Mexico in 1502. As emperor, Montezuma expanded the empire to include much of south-central Mexico. Many people living in the empire did not like Montezuma because he made them pay for the buildings he constructed.

In 1519, Hernándo Cortés led a Spanish expedition into Mexico. Many Aztec groups that disliked Montezuma supported Cortés. At first, Montezuma welcomed Cortés and presented him with gifts, including artifacts made of gold. Montezuma may have believed that Cortés was Quetzalcóatl, a legendary god-king.

Later, Cortés held Montezuma prisoner and tried to control the empire. In 1520, the Aztecs rebelled and attacked the palace. They drove the Spanish soldiers out of Tenochtitlán, the capital city. Montezuma then tried to speak to the people, but they hurled stones at him. He died three days later.

Answer each question on the lines below.

1. Who was Montezuma?

____

2. Why did many people in the Aztec Empire dislike Montezuma?

____

____

3. Why did Montezuma welcome Cortés at first?

____

____

4. **Critical Thinking** In what way was Montezuma tricked by Cortés?

____

____

Name ______________________ Date ______________

Chapter 5

They Made History

Jonathan Edwards

Jonathan Edwards 1703–1758

Jonathan Edwards was a central figure in the religious movement known as the Great Awakening. Religious leadership came early to Edwards. He is said to have led a group of children in prayer when he was only seven or eight years old.

Edwards graduated from Yale College and took a job as a minister. In 1726, Edwards moved to Northampton, Massachusetts, to help his grandfather. When his grandfather died in 1729, Edwards became pastor of the church.

Edwards's first revival took place in 1734–1735. The revivals soon spread to other towns and his reputation as a preacher grew. His revivals opened the way for the Great Awakening that spread throughout New England in the early 1740s.

Answer each question on the lines below.

1. What did Jonathan Edwards do in 1734–1735?

____

____

2. What college did Edwards graduate from?

____

3. What did Edwards do after his grandfather died in 1729?

____

____

4. **Critical Thinking** What experiences prepared Edwards to become a central figure in a religious movement?

____

____

Name ______________________ Date ______________

They Made History

Margaret Cochran Corbin

Margaret Cochran Corbin 1751–1800

Margaret Cochran Corbin, an American soldier in the Revolutionary War, was the first woman in U.S. history to receive a soldier's pension, or retirement pay.

After being raised by her uncle, she married John Corbin, a Virginia settler, in 1772. When John joined the Pennsylvania artillery unit at the start of the Revolutionary War, she went with him to the front lines. It was common for soldiers' wives to support troops by cooking, washing, laundering, and nursing the wounded.

Margaret Corbin went beyond cooking and cleaning for the soldiers. During a battle in 1776, she helped her husband fire a cannon. When he was killed, she loaded and fired the cannon herself until she was badly wounded. Although the fort was captured by the British, wounded soldiers were allowed to go free. Corbin eventually made her way to Philadelphia. Her wounds left her permanently disabled.

In 1779, the Continental Congress gave her a lifetime soldier's half-pay pension for bravely serving her country.

Answer each question on the lines below.

1. What is Margaret Cochran Corbin known for?

____

____

2. Why was Corbin present at the battle in 1776?

____

3. Why was Corbin not captured by the British after the battle at Fort Washington?

____

4. **Critical Thinking** How were Margaret Corbin's experiences unusual for a woman in the 1700s?

____

____

Name ______________________ Date ______________

Chapter 10

They Made History

John Jay

John Jay 1745–1829

A close look at John Jay's life reveals many great achievements. He was the first chief justice of the United States Supreme Court, a diplomat, Secretary of Foreign Affairs, and governor of New York.

Jay worked as a diplomat during the Revolutionary War. He traveled to Spain to ask that country to support American independence. Later, Jay helped negotiate the Treaty of Paris, which formally ended the Revolutionary War.

Jay returned from Europe in 1784 and learned that Congress had appointed him Secretary of Foreign Affairs. He held this position until the establishment of the Constitution. Jay believed that the Articles of Confederation could not help the government improve the nation. Instead, Jay favored the Constitution and a strong central government.

After the Constitution was approved, Jay was appointed the first chief justice of the Supreme Court. He was later elected governor of New York and served two terms before retiring.

Answer each question on the lines below.

1. What were some of John Jay's achievements?

____

____

2. Why did Jay travel to Spain?

____

3. Why did Jay urge the states to create a Constitution?

____

4. **Critical Thinking** In your opinion, which achievement was Jay's most important contribution to this country? Explain.

____

____

Name ______________________ Date ______________

They Made History

John C. Calhoun

John C. Calhoun 1782–1850

John Caldwell Calhoun graduated from Yale College in 1804. After college, he studied law and became a lawyer. He moved from law to politics and was elected to the House of Representatives. Several years later, he became Secretary of War. He then became Vice President of the United States in 1825, under John Quincy Adams, and again in 1829, under Andrew Jackson.

Calhoun resigned as Vice President to serve as a senator for South Carolina. This action put him in a better position to protect South Carolina's rights during the Nullification Crisis. Calhoun was successful in helping to end the crisis and served as senator until 1843.

The following year he was called back to politics as Secretary of State. He then served again as senator for South Carolina between 1845 and 1850. He continued to promote states' rights and worked to protect slavery in the South. His career and his life ended in 1850.

Answer each question on the lines below.

1. Why did John Calhoun resign from the office of Vice President?

____

____

2. What crisis did Calhoun help to successfully end?

____

3. What did Calhoun do before he became a politician?

____

____

4. **Critical Thinking** What qualities do you think Calhoun needed to serve his country for so many years?

____

____

Name ______________________ Date ______________

Chapter 16

They Made History

Henry Clay

Henry Clay **1777–1852**

Henry Clay devoted his life to service to his country. He served in the U.S. Congress, as a senator and a diplomat, and as Secretary of State. He once said, "If any man wants the key to my heart, let him take the key of the Union, and that is the key to my heart."

Born in Virginia, Clay moved to Kentucky as a young man. There he was a successful lawyer. In 1811, he was elected to the House of Representatives. He was Speaker of the House for many years.

However, Clay is remembered best for his talents as a problem solver. At three crucial times in U.S. history, Henry Clay kept the Union together. In 1820, he sponsored the Missouri Compromise. In 1833, he wrote the compromise tariff that resolved the Nullification Crisis. In 1850, an elderly Henry Clay proposed the Compromise of 1850 to avoid civil war.

Answer each question on the lines below.

1. Why is Henry Clay called the Great Compromiser?

____

2. In what offices did Henry Clay serve his country?

____

3. What did Henry Clay do in 1850?

____

4. **Critical Thinking** Reread the quotation by Clay in the first paragraph. How does it explain his life?

____

____

____

Name ______________________ Date ______________

They Made History

Sally Louisa Tompkins

Sally Louisa Tompkins 1833–1916

Sally Louisa Tompkins's lifelong wish was to help others. She got her chance while living in Richmond, Virginia, at the beginning of the Civil War.

After the Battle of Bull Run, the Confederate government asked people to bring wounded soldiers into their homes. Using her own money, Tompkins turned Judge John Robertson's home into a hospital.

Tompkins's hospital soon became one of the busiest and best in the Confederacy. Her hospital was such a success that injured soldiers were soon begging to be taken there. Out of more than 1,000 sick and injured soldiers she cared for, only 73 died.

To thank her for her work, Confederate president Jefferson Davis made her a captain. She accepted the rank because it helped her to get more supplies. However, she refused to be paid. Tompkins was the only woman to be named an officer in the Confederate army. For the rest of her life, she was nicknamed Captain Sally.

Answer each question on the lines below.

1. What did Sally Louisa Tompkins do with Judge John Robertson's home?

____

2. Why did soldiers beg to be taken to Tompkins's hospital?

____

____

3. Why did Tompkins accept the rank of captain?

____

____

4. **Critical Thinking** In what ways did Sally Tompkins show her bravery during the Civil War?

____

____

Name ______________________ Date ______________

Chapter 20

They Made History

Nikola Tesla

Nikola Tesla 1856–1943

Nikola Tesla received hundreds of patents during his career as an electrical engineer. He established alternating current (AC) electricity, made discoveries about wireless communication, and invented many electrical devices. Much of modern technology is based on Tesla's ideas.

Tesla was born in a village in Croatia. After college, Tesla worked on developing and selling his ideas on AC electricity, but his work was not appreciated. Tesla immigrated to the United States in 1884 to work with Thomas Edison. From the start, he and Edison disagreed over the importance of AC electricity. Edison worked on his own invention, direct current (DC) electricity. Tesla and Edison soon parted ways.

Tesla was involved with the Niagara Falls Project in 1893. This project created the world's first hydroelectric power plant.

Answer each question on the lines below.

1. What is Nikola Tesla known for?

____

____

2. Why did Tesla immigrate to the United States?

____

____

3. What was the Niagara Falls Project?

____

____

4. **Critical Thinking** How might Tesla's career have been different if he did not immigrate to the United States?

____

____

Name ______________________ Date ______________

They Made History

Chapter 22

William Randolph Hearst

William Randolph Hearst 1863–1951

William Randolph Hearst was born in San Francisco. As a young man, he was thrown out of Harvard University for playing too many pranks and breaking too many rules.

He then decided to start a career in journalism. His father was the publisher of the *San Francisco Examiner*. At just 24 years old, he convinced his father to let him run the newspaper. Hearst increased the paper's circulation by adding huge headlines, sensational stories, cartoons, and comic strips. He had the same success with other newspapers across the United States.

During the late 1890s, Hearst and rival publisher Joseph Pulitzer attempted to gain support for a war with Spain. They published exaggerated and often untrue stories about Spanish forces in Cuba.

After the Spanish-American War, Hearst tried to become a politician. In 1904, he lost the Democratic nomination for President. He also lost the election for mayor of New York City and governor of New York State.

Answer each question on the lines below.

1. Why was William Randolph Hearst thrown out of Harvard?

____

2. How did Hearst boost circulation at his newspapers?

____

3. How was Hearst's effort to become a political leader a failure?

____

4. **Critical Thinking** Do you think, Hearst's actions regarding the Spanish-American War led to his downfall as a politician? Explain.

____

____

They Made History

Name ______________________ Date ______________

Chapter 23

They Made History

James Reese Europe

James Reese Europe 1880–1919

James Reese Europe is best remembered as a jazz pioneer for African American musicians. He was also the first African American to lead troops into battle.

Europe was born in Mobile, Alabama. He studied violin and piano for many years. He moved to New York City to begin a career in music. Europe helped establish the Clef Club. The Clef Club was a union for African American musicians. By 1912, Europe's Clef Club Orchestra became the first African American band to play in New York City's Carnegie Hall.

In 1916, Europe enlisted in the military as a private and later became a lieutenant in the segregated U.S. Army's 369th Infantry. Europe reported to the front lines in France. He received the French Croix de Guerre with Silver Star for his bravery.

Answer each question on the lines below.

1. What role did James Reese Europe play in World War I?

____

____

2. What was the Clef Club?

____

____

3. What award did Europe receive for his bravery?

____

____

4. **Critical Thinking** In your opinion, which achievement is the best example of James Reese Europe's leadership?

____

____

Name ______________________ Date ______________

They Made History

Elie Wiesel

Elie Wiesel **Born 1930**

In 1944, 14-year-old Elie Wiesel was taken from the safety of his Jewish home in Sighet, Romania. Wiesel and about 15,000 other Jewish people in this area were imprisoned in Auschwitz, a Nazi concentration camp in Poland. His parents and youngest sister were killed.

Wiesel's experiences during World War II shaped his career as a Holocaust and human rights writer, speaker, and educator. After he was freed from the concentration camp in 1945, Wiesel became a writer. His most famous novel, *Night*, describes what he went through and how he felt about the war. He has written dozens of novels, plays, articles, and speeches about how human rights are important for everyone.

Wiesel is known around the world for his human rights work. In 1979, he led the President's Commission on the Holocaust. This group helped to create the U.S. Holocaust Museum in Washington, D.C. He was awarded the Nobel Peace Prize in 1986.

Answer each question on the lines below.

1. What is Elie Wiesel known for around the world?

____

2. What shaped Wiesel's career?

____

3. What is Wiesel's most famous novel about?

____

4. **Critical Thinking** Why do you think Elie Wiesel wrote about his experiences?

____

____

Name ______________________ Date ______________

Chapter 28

They Made History

James H. Meredith

James H. Meredith Born 1933

James H. Meredith is an African American civil rights activist. He is best known for his work to end segregation in higher education.

Meredith was born in Mississippi in 1933. He has said that one specific event led him to work toward ending segregation. He and his brother were riding a train from Chicago to New Orleans. As the train entered the South, they were forced to move into a car that was specifically for black riders.

After graduation from high school, he joined the Air Force. After the Air Force, he moved back to Mississippi. He decided to work for the civil rights movement by applying to the University of Mississippi.

Meredith went through many court battles before he was finally allowed to attend the school. At one point, the governor of Mississippi said that he would try to prevent Meredith from attending. Finally, President Kennedy forced the school to accept Meredith. However, he was continually harassed. Federal marshals escorted him to class every day. He became the first African American to attend and graduate from the University of Mississippi.

Answer each question on the lines below.

1. What caused Meredith to decide to work toward ending segregation?

____

2. What did Meredith do after he graduated from high school?

____

3. How did Meredith help the civil rights movement by attending the University of Mississippi?

____

4. **Critical Thinking** Why do you think President Kennedy helped James Meredith?

____

____

Name ______________________ Date ______________

They Made History

Laura Welch Bush

Laura Welch Bush **Born 1946**

Laura Welch Bush always knew she wanted to be a teacher. She was born in Midland, Texas, in 1946, and spent her childhood developing a love for reading and learning.

Bush graduated from Southern Methodist University in 1968. She fulfilled her childhood dream and worked as a teacher until 1972. Then, she worked as a librarian at the Houston Public Library.

Bush worked in the Texas public school system until 1977, when she married George Walker Bush. She was actively involved in many groups that supported local libraries and protected children. After her husband became governor of Texas in 1994, she promoted public library funding and early childhood development.

As First Lady of the United States, Bush continued to focus on literacy and education. However, she was faced with a new challenge. After the September 11, 2001, terrorist attacks on the United States, she helped people, especially children, cope with the tragedy.

Answer each question on the lines below.

1. As a child, what did Laura Bush hope to do when she became an adult?

____

2. In what two ways was Bush involved in the public school system?

____

____

3. How did the terrorist attacks on the United States change Bush's duties as First Lady?

____

____

4. **Critical Thinking** In your opinion, what has been Laura Bush's most significant contribution as First Lady?

____

____

Contents

Document-Based Questions

Name ______________________ Date ______________

Document-Based Questions

Chapter 1

Analyze a Legend

A. Below is a selection from a Native American legend about the beginning of the world. Read the selection carefully and answer the questions that follow.

The Sky Tree

Earth was once completely covered with water. The people lived in Sky Land and ate fruit from the Sky Tree. The Chief of Sky Land fell ill and learned through a dream that he could be cured if he ate fruit from the very top of the Sky Tree. He sent his wife Aataentsic, whose name means "Ancient Woman," to cut the tree down. When she did, a huge hole opened and the Sky Tree fell into it. Aataentsic said,

'Without the tree, there can be no life. I must follow it.'. . . Then. . . she. . . threw herself after the great tree. . . . As Aataentsic fell, Turtle looked up and saw her. Immediately Turtle called together all the water animals. . . . 'All of you must dive down,' Turtle said. 'Bring up soil from the bottom and place it on my back.' . . . Beaver, Mink, Muskrat, and Otter each brought up pawfuls of wet soil and placed the soil on Turtle's back until they had made an island of great size. When they were through, Aataentsic settled down gently on the new Earth, and the pieces of the great tree fell beside her and took root.

1. Why did Aataentsic follow the tree into the hole?

____

2. What did the water animals and Turtle do to help Aataentsic?

____

3. What does the legend suggest happened after Aataentsic and the Sky Tree settled on the island on Turtle's back?

____

B. In your own words, describe the purpose of this legend. Write your answer in a paragraph on a separate sheet of paper.

Name ______________________ Date ______________

Chapter 6

Document-Based Questions

Magna Carta

A. Use the Magna Carta on page 771 of your textbook to answer the following questions. Circle the letter of the correct answer.

1. Which phrase means that no one should be put in jail without a legal process to decide if they are guilty or innocent?

a. "that the English Church shall be free"
b. "To no one will we sell . . . right or justice."
c. "All merchants may enter or leave England . . . for purposes of trade"
d. "No free man shall be seized or imprisoned . . . except by the lawful judgment of his equals"

2. Which phrase means that England will let its citizens trade freely with other countries except in times of war?

a. "that the English Church shall be free"
b. "To no one will we sell . . . right or justice."
c. "All merchants may enter or leave England . . . for purpose of trade"
d. "No free man shall be seized or imprisoned . . . except by the lawful judgment of his equals"

B. Answer the following questions on the lines below.

3. What were some of the important rights that were granted in the Magna Carta?

____

____

____

4. What rights from the Magna Carta are still rights in America today?

____

____

____

Name ______________________ Date ______________

Document-Based Questions

Declaration of Independence

A. Use the Declaration of Independence on pages 157–161 of your textbook to answer the following questions. Circle the letter of the correct answer.

1. The main purpose of the Declaration of Independence is to

a. ask for financial support from Great Britain.
b. announce and defend the colonies' independence from Great Britain.
c. state the colonies' allegiance to the king of Great Britain.
d. establish voting rights for Native Americans in the U.S. colonies.

2. The authors' feelings toward Great Britain are best described as

a. loyal and respectful.
b. forgiving and friendly.
c. frightened and intimidated.
d. angry and resistant.

3. According to the authors, a government should

a. protect people's rights to life, liberty, and the pursuit of happiness.
b. give people more land to build on and farm.
c. increase taxes to pay for exploration and trade.
d. reward those people who agree with all of the government's decisions.

4. The authors back up their introductory statement by

a. describing in detail the settlement of the colonies.
b. listing charges against the king.
c. focusing on how the king has supported the colonies' trade with other countries.
d. showing how the people of Great Britain have been sympathetic to the colonists.

5. The colonists gave themselves the right to

a. be led by a king, pay taxes to Great Britain, and be citizens of Great Britain.
b. establish their own king and demand taxes from Great Britain.
c. make war and peace, form political alliances, and trade with other countries.
d. discriminate against certain religions and settle on Native American land.

Name ______________________ Date ______________

Document-Based Questions

Declaration of Independence *continued*

B. Identify and summarize each section of the Declaration of Independence. The first one is done for you. Write your answers on a separate sheet of paper.

1. **Section:** Preamble

   Summary: *The Preamble briefly states the colonists want to be free from Great Britain.*

2. **Section:** A New Theory of Government
3. **Section:** Abuses by King George III
4. **Section:** Acts of War Against the Colonies
5. **Section:** Taking Action
6. **Section:** A Proclamation of Independence

C. Critical Thinking

What do you think the authors of the Declaration of Independence meant when they wrote that people have the right to life, liberty, and the pursuit of happiness? Explain. Give an example of each right in your explanation. Write your answer on a separate sheet of paper.

D. Link Past to Present

The authors of the Declaration of Independence wrote that the king did not consider the colonists to be equal. To achieve equal rights, the colonists fought to establish a government that would support its citizens. Today, people use the court system to decide whether or not an individual's or group's rights are being respected.

Read a newspaper. Choose an article about a court case in which it was found that a person's or a group's rights were not respected. On a separate sheet of paper, write whether you agree or disagree with the court's decision. Explain your answer.

Name ________________________________ Date ____________________

Document-Based Questions

Analyze a Poster

A. Below is a poster advertising a slave auction in the 1760s. Read the poster carefully and answer the questions that follow.

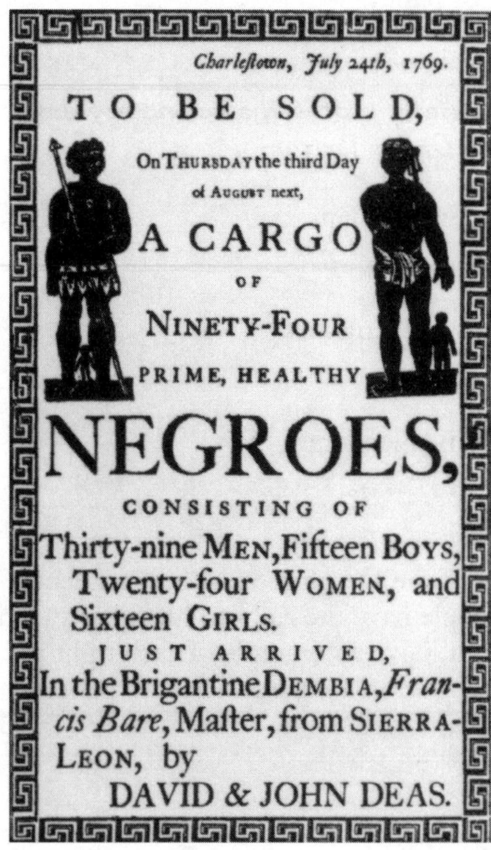
Charleſtown, July 24th, 1769.
TO BE SOLD,
On THURSDAY the third Day of AUGUST next,
A CARGO
OF
NINETY-FOUR
PRIME, HEALTHY
NEGROES,
CONSISTING OF
Thirty-nine MEN, Fifteen BOYS, Twenty-four WOMEN, and Sixteen GIRLS.
JUST ARRIVED,
In the Brigantine DEMBIA, *Francis Bare*, Maſter, from SIERRA-LEON, by
DAVID & JOHN DEAS.

1. When was the auction to take place?

   ____

2. How does the poster describe the people who are going to be auctioned?

   ____

3. What do the illustrations on the poster show?

   ____

B. In your own words, describe the purpose of this poster. Write your answer in a paragraph on a separate sheet of paper.

Name ______________________ Date ______________

Chapter 8

Document-Based Questions

Analyze a Letter

A. Below is part of a letter written by Dr. Benjamin Rush, Surgeon General of the Continental Army, to General George Washington. The letter is dated December 26, 1777. In the letter Dr. Rush describes the conditions of the army hospitals. Read the letter carefully and answer the questions that follow.

> I need not inform Your Excellency that we now have upward of 5,000 sick in our hospitals. This number would cease to be alarming if our hospitals could afford such accommodations to the poor fellows as would ensure them a speedy recovery. But this is far from being the case. . . . Old disorders are prolonged, and new ones contracted among us. This last is so much the case that I am safe when I assert that a great majority of those who die under our hands perish with diseases caught in our hospitals. . . .

1. What is the general mood of the letter?

____

____

2. Who is Dr. Benjamin Rush most worried about?

____

____

3. What happens to many of the patients in this hospital?

____

____

4. Why is the number of patients in hospitals alarming?

____

____

B. In your own words, describe the purpose of this letter. Write your answer in a paragraph on a separate sheet of paper.

Name ______________________ Date ______________

Document-Based Questions

Chapter 9

U.S. Constitution

A. Use the U.S. Constitution on pages 214–239 of your textbook to answer the following questions. Circle the letter of the correct answer.

1. The preamble to the Constitution states

a. the purpose of the Constitution.

b. that all men are created equal.

c. the names of all the Founding Fathers.

d. that the states have agreed to the Constitution.

2. All of the following are branches of government under the Constitution except

a. the legislative branch.

b. the vice-presidential branch.

c. the executive branch.

d. the judicial branch.

3. The first ten amendments were written to

a. declare independence from the king of England.

b. protect the rights of the people.

c. establish tax laws for the federal government.

d. separate the government into three branches.

4. According to the Constitution, Congress has the power to

a. issue warrants with probable cause.

b. try cases concerning disputes between states.

c. veto bills.

d. make new laws needed to carry out the Constitution.

5. The Fifteenth Amendment and the Nineteenth Amendment are similar in that they

a. establish a clearer explanation of the election process.

b. state the circumstances under which the federal government can raise taxes.

c. extend the right to vote to a broader range of people than was originally allowed.

d. explain the process by which a President can be impeached.

Document-Based Questions

B. Answer the following questions on the lines below.

6. Many sections of the Constitution have been changed or no longer apply. Identify one section and explain why it is no longer appropriate.

____

____

____

7. If you were invited to write a section to the Constitution either adding or taking away one of the President's powers or responsibilities, what would that section say?

____

____

____

C. Critical Thinking

The Founding Fathers of the Constitution divided the government into three separate branches: executive, judicial, and legislative. Do you think the separation of powers is necessary? Explain your answer on a separate sheet of paper.

D. Link Past to Present

The Founding Fathers wrote the First Amendment to protect the five basic freedoms of American citizens: freedom of religion, speech, press, assembly, and petition. Throughout history, citizens have referred to the First Amendment to defend these rights. However, sometimes people disagree over how these rights should be used.

Choose one of the five freedoms in the First Amendment. Find a story from a newspaper, a magazine, the Internet, or a TV news broadcast in which a person uses the First Amendment to defend his or her actions. Do you agree with the person? Explain your answer on a separate sheet of paper.

Name ______________________ Date ______________

Document-Based Questions

Analyze a Personal Account

A. Below is a selection from a U.S. soldier's account of the battle between Chief Tecumseh's warriors and U.S. troops at Tippecanoe Creek. The battle took place on a September morning in 1811 in Indiana. Read the account carefully and answer the questions that follow.

> I heard the crack of another rifle, followed by an awful Indian yell all around the encampment. In less than a minute I saw the Indians charging our line most furiously and shooting a great many rifle balls into our camp fires, throwing live coals into the air three or four feet high. . . . Our lines were broken and a few Indians were found on the inside of the encampment. In a few moments they were all killed. Our lines closed up and our men [were again] in their proper places. . . . The Indians made four or five most fierce charges on our lines, yelling and screaming as they advanced, shooting balls and arrows into our ranks. At each charge they were driven back in confusion, carrying off their dead and wounded as they retreated.

1. How did the battle begin?

____

2. What does the soldier mean when he uses the word *encampment*?

____

3. Why do you think the Native Americans fired into the soldiers' camp fires?

____

____

4. What does the soldier mean when he says "our lines were broken"?

____

____

B. In your own words, describe the purpose of this personal account. Write your answer in a paragraph on a separate sheet of paper.

Name ______________________ Date ______________

Chapter 15

Document-Based Questions

Analyze a Letter

A. Below is part of a letter written by a Mexican citizen, José Fernando Ramírez. It was written during the American war with Mexico in the late 1840s. In the letter, Ramírez describes how hard the Mexican army fought against the better-equipped Americans. Read the letter carefully and answer the questions that follow.

> The Government has at last put all its hopes in a plan that is supposed to save the country. . . . This is the one calling for guerrilla warfare, the last hope of peoples overwhelmed by superior forces. . . .
>
> The Yankees . . . have 2,000,000 pesos in their coffers and pay cash for their subsistence and transport. . . . In contrast with this situation is the one our troops are facing. They have nothing and use force in obtaining what they need. . . .
>
> Groups of soldiers like those of Cortés inflict terrible punishment for the death of any Yankee. . . . Our guerrilla troops have been denied the benefit of human rights. . . .

1. According to the letter, what was one advantage that the American army had over the Mexican army?

____

2. What plan did the Mexican government come up with as a last effort against the American army?

____

3. Based on his letter, which adjectives would Ramírez most likely use to describe the Mexican army?

____

4. The writer of this letter compares the American troops to the army of what historic figure?

____

B. In your own words, describe the purpose of this letter. Write your answer in a paragraph on a separate sheet of paper.

Document-Based Questions

Name ______________________ Date __________

Document-Based Questions

Chapter 16

Analyze a Poster

Below is a recruiting poster printed during the Civil War. Posters such as this one appeared throughout the North and the South during the war.

$300-Bounty-$300

$200 Dollars Cash in advance,

BEFORE LEAVING THE CITY.

The men will be mounted upon splendid Chargers, and armed with fine Sabres, Sharps Rifles, and Colt's Revolvers.

☞$100 will be paid to each man when honorably discharged.

Saddlers, Horse Shoers & Buglers, wanted.

Major H. C. SPALDING,

is to command this splendid Battalion, which, in equipment, will be equal to any in the service.

Principal Recruiting Office,

43 LIBERTY STREET, N. Y.

OPPOSITE THE POST OFFICE.

Come on Brave Boys! Now is the time to avoid the DRAFT, and secure a small fortune by enlisting.

A. Read the poster carefully and answer the questions that follow.

1. What is this poster asking for?

____

2. What is the general tone of the poster?

____

3. According to the poster, where is the recruiting office located?

____

B. In your own words, describe the purpose of this poster. Write your answer in a paragraph on a separate sheet of paper.

Document-Based Questions

Name ______________________ Date ______________

Chapter 17

Document-Based Questions

Emancipation Proclamation

A. Use the Emancipation Proclamation on page 775 of your textbook to answer the following questions. Circle the letter of the correct answer.

1. What is meant by the phrase "the United States, including the military and naval authorities thereof, will recognize and maintain the freedom of said persons"?

a. The army and navy will do nothing to help free the slaves.

b. The Supreme Court will free the slaves.

c. The armed forces of the United States will defend the freed slaves.

d. Congress will consider new laws against slavery.

2. What did Abraham Lincoln want to accomplish when he signed the Emancipation Proclamation?

a. to free the slaves in the states that were rebelling against the U.S. government

b. to free slaves in the states that were loyal to the U.S. government

c. to defend the freedom of the emancipated slaves

d. all of the above

3. Which adjective best describes the overall tone of the Emancipation Proclamation?

a. official

b. humorous

c. defeated

d. cheerful

B. Answer the following questions on the lines below.

4. Which regions were affected by the Emancipation Proclamation?

____

____

5. What future actions did the Emancipation Proclamation urge?

____

____

Name ______________________ Date ______________

Document-Based Questions

Chapter 17

Gettysburg Address

A. Use the Gettysburg Address on pages 775–776 of your textbook to answer the following questions. Circle the letter of the correct answer.

1. Why was Abraham Lincoln invited to give this speech?
   - **a.** to dedicate a cemetery for soldiers who had died at the Battle of Gettysburg
   - **b.** to keep the Union army from surrendering to Confederate forces
   - **c.** to recruit troops to fight in the war
   - **d.** to ask Congress to declare war on the Confederate states

2. Which of the following ideas was not included in Lincoln's address?
   - **a.** The dead could best be honored if the living dedicated themselves to the cause of freedom.
   - **b.** The outcome of the Civil War would determine whether a nation based on liberty could survive.
   - **c.** Soldiers who die in battle should always be laid to rest in a national cemetery.
   - **d.** The cemetery was on a part of the battlefield where these men had died.

B. Answer the following questions on the lines below.

3. What did Lincoln mean when he said the nation should have "a new birth of freedom"?

   ____

   ____

4. What beliefs about the United States did Lincoln address in the Gettysburg Address?

   ____

   ____

Document-Based Questions

Name ______________________________ Date ______________

Chapter 17

Document-Based Questions

Analyze a Diary

A. Below is an entry from the diary of Mary Boykin Chestnut. She was the wife of James Chestnut, a former senator and an aide to Confederate President Jefferson Davis. This entry is from September 21, 1864, and describes the effect of the Civil War on the South. Read the diary entry carefully and answer the questions that follow.

> September 21 – Went with Mrs. Rhett to hear Dr. Palmer. I did not know before how utterly hopeless was our situation. . . . He is not for slavery, he says; he is for freedom, and the freedom to govern our own country as we see fit. He is against foreign interference in our State matters. That is what Mr. Palmer went to war for, it appears. Every day shows that slavery is doomed the world over; for that he thanked God.

1. What adjective best describes Chestnut's mood?

____

2. What reason does Dr. Palmer give for favoring the war?

____

____

3. When Dr. Palmer speaks of "foreign interference," what is he referring to?

____

____

4. What event might have happened around the time of this entry?

____

____

B. In your own words, describe the purpose of this diary entry. Write our answer on a separate sheet of paper.

Document-Based Questions

Name ______________________ Date ______________

Document-Based Questions

Chapter 19

Chief Joseph's Speech

A. Use Chief Joseph's speech on page 776 of your textbook to answer the following questions. Circle the letter of the correct answer.

1. For whom is Chief Joseph speaking?

a. the U.S. government
b. the white people
c. his people, the Nez Percé
d. the government of Oklahoma

2. What is Chief Joseph's tone in this speech?

a. angry and disappointed
b. excited and enthusiastic
c. accepting and contented
d. friendly and welcoming

3. What is the main message of Chief Joseph's speech?

a. that his people have reached Canada and are now free
b. that his people were treated badly by the U.S. government
c. that his people will no longer fight against U.S. troops
d. that his people don't want to live with white men

4. What has happened to some of Chief Joseph's people?

____

____

5. What does Chief Joseph feel like?

____

____

B. In your own words, describe the purpose of this speech. Write your answer in a paragraph on a separate sheet of paper.

Name ______________________ Date ______________

Chapter 21

Document-Based Questions

Analyze a Photograph

A. Below is a photograph that shows young boys working in a factory in the early 1900s. The boys are fixing broken threads and replacing empty bobbins used for making clothes. Look at the photo carefully and answer the questions that follow.

1. What social issue does this photograph most closely relate to?

____

2. Where might these children be if they lived in today's society?

____

3. Based on what you can see from the photograph, what is making this work more dangerous?

____

4. Why are these children most likely working in a factory?

____

B. In your own words, describe the purpose of this photograph. Write your answer in a paragraph on a separate sheet of paper.

Name ______________________ Date ______________

Document-Based Questions

Fourteen Points

A. Use the Fourteen Points on page 777 of your textbook to answer the following questions. Circle the letter of the correct answer.

1. When did Woodrow Wilson deliver this address to Congress?

a. as World War I was beginning
b. on his election day
c. as World War I was ending
d. when the League of Nations was established

2. What did Wilson state was demanded in the war?

a. that the world be made fit and safe to live in
b. that the most powerful countries win the war
c. that the least powerful countries win the war
d. none of the above

3. Which phrase describes Wilson's ideas about preventing attacks by one country on another?

a. "Open covenants of peace, openly arrived at"
b. "Absolute freedom of navigation upon the seas"
c. "national armaments will be reduced to the lowest point consistent with domestic safety"
d. all of the above

B. Answer the following questions on the lines below.

4. What was the purpose of Woodrow Wilson's Fourteen Points?

____

____

____

5. Why did Woodrow Wilson believe in his Fourteen Points?

____

____

____

Name ______________________ Date ______________

Chapter 24

Document-Based Questions

Analyze a Poem

A. Below is a poem by Langston Hughes titled "Mother to Son." This poem expresses Hughes's views on the struggle of African Americans in the United States in the early 1900s. Read the poem carefully and answer the questions that follow.

Mother to Son

Well, son, I'll tell you:
Life for me ain't been no crystal stair.
It's had tacks in it,
And splinters,
And boards torn up,
And places with no carpet on the floor—
Bare.
But all the time
I'se been a-climbin' on,
And reachin' landin's,
And turnin' corners,
And sometimes goin' in the dark
Where there ain't been no light.
So, boy, don't you turn back.
Don't you set down on the steps.
'Cause you finds it kinder hard.
Don't you fall now—
For I'se still goin', honey,
I'se still climbin',
And life for me ain't been no crystal stair.

1. What image is a symbol of problems in the speaker's life?

____

2. What does the speaker mean when she says "Life for me ain't been no crystal stair"?

____

3. Why is the speaker describing her life to her son?

____

B. In your own words, describe the purpose of this poem. Write your answer in a paragraph on a separate sheet of paper.

Name ______________________ Date ______________

Document-Based Questions

Chapter 24

Analyze an Advertisement

A. Below is an advertisement from the 1920s. Read the advertisement carefully and answer the questions that follow.

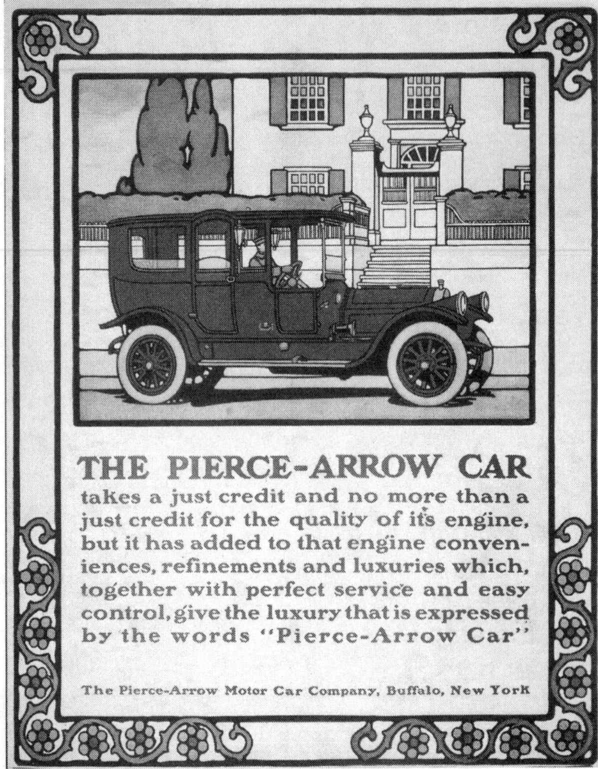

1. What does the advertisement say about a Pierce-Arrow car?

____

2. What does the phrase "together with perfect service and easy control" mean?

____

____

3. What does the advertisement tell you about life in the 1920s?

____

____

B. In your own words, describe the purpose of this advertisement. Write your answer in a paragraph on a separate sheet of paper.

Document-Based Questions

Name ______________________ Date ______________

Chapter 28

Document-Based Questions

"I Have a Dream"

A. Use Martin Luther King Jr.'s "I Have a Dream" speech on page 778 of your textbook to answer the following questions. Circle the letter of the correct answer.

1. What is the main point of the first paragraph of Martin Luther King Jr.'s speech?

a. Abraham Lincoln signed the Emancipation Proclamation.
b. One hundred years ago, many African Americans were slaves.
c. The end of slavery brought freedom to African Americans.
d. Although slavery had ended one hundred years ago, African Americans still were not free.

2. What did King mean by the phrase "all of God's children"?

a. minorities all over the world
b. all human beings everywhere
c. minorities in the United States
d. Protestants, Catholics, and Jews

3. What did King mean when he said "they will not be judged by the color of their skin but the content of their character"?

a. People should be judged by who they are, not by what they look like.
b. You can tell whether a person is bad or good by the color of their skin.
c. People should not judge each other.
d. The nation should not be judged by the color of its people.

B. Answer each question on the lines below.

4. What was the purpose of the civil rights march on Washington, D.C., in 1963?

____

____

5. What is the main reason why King quoted the song "My Country 'Tis of Thee" in his speech?

____

____

Name ______________________ Date ______________

Document-Based Questions

Chapter 29

Analyze a Personal Essay

A. Below is a selection from an essay written by Richard Rodriguez, the son of Hispanic immigrants. Rodriguez was born in the United States. He writes about what it was like to learn English when he began going to school. Read the essay carefully and answer the questions that follow.

> One Saturday morning I entered the kitchen where my parents were talking in Spanish. I did not realize that they were talking in Spanish however until, at the moment they saw me, I heard their voices change to speak English. Those gringo sounds they uttered startled me. Pushed me away. In that moment of trivial misunderstanding and profound insight, I felt my throat twisted by unsounded grief. . . . Only then did I determine to learn classroom English. Weeks after, it happened: One day in school I raised my hand to volunteer an answer. I spoke out in a loud voice. And I did not think it remarkable when the entire class understood.

1. Why do you think Richard Rodriguez's parents spoke to him in English instead of Spanish?

____

2. When did Rodriguez begin using English confidently in front of others?

____

3. Why was Rodriguez upset when he heard his parents change from Spanish to English when they spoke to him in the kitchen?

____

4. What did Rodriguez mean when he felt his throat "twisted by unsounded grief"?

____

B. In your own words, describe the purpose of this essay. Write your answer in a paragraph on a separate sheet of paper.

Contents

Reading, Writing, and Test Taking

Name ______________________________ Date ______________

Reading, Writing, and Test Taking

Key Words for a Writing Assignment

A. Learn the Skill

When you begin a writing assignment, the way in which you approach the topic and what you say about it will depend on a few key words. These key words are also known as writing prompts. Become familiar with the following list of key words, or writing prompts, and their definitions.

KEY WORDS

compare: show how things are similar

contrast: show how things are different

explain: give facts about

tell why: give reasons

review: summarize

describe: create a picture of

identify: place the person or event in a time period and relate it to other people or events

discuss: give ideas about

define: give the meaning of

illustrate: give examples of

evaluate: give good and bad points about and come to a conclusion

B. Practice the Skill

Use the list of key words and their definitions to answer each of the following questions.

1. Which key word means "to give ideas"? ____________________

2. Which key word asks you to give facts about something?

   ____

3. Which key word asks you to give examples? ____________________

4. Which key word asks you to give a summary? ____________________

Name ________________________________ Date ____________________

Reading, Writing, and Test Taking

Key Words to Answer Essay Questions

A. Learn the Skill

Identifying key words in an essay question helps you concentrate on what the question is asking. Now that you can define key words, or writing prompts, practice recognizing them in actual writing assignments.

Read each of the following essay topics. For each topic, identify the key word or writing prompt used. Write the key word on the line below each essay topic.

1. After World War II, the economies of many European countries were in shambles. The Marshall Plan was developed to help rebuild some European economies. Describe how the Marshall Plan helped strengthen these countries' economies.

   ____

2. The Constitution of 1787 established a new government. Explain the provisions of the Constitution.

   ____

3. The Industrial Revolution brought many changes to the United States. Evaluate these changes and their effects on people and businesses throughout the nation.

   ____

4. Discuss the ways in which the lives of African Americans, Native Americans, and women were affected by the New Deal.

   ____

B. Practice the Skill

Choose one of the topics above. Write a short essay showing that you understand the writing prompt. Write your essay on the lines below and on a separate sheet of paper. Use your textbook if you need help.

____

____

____

Name ____________________ Date ____________

Reading, Writing, and Test Taking

Writing an Effective Sentence

A. Learn the Skill

Writing an effective sentence is an important part of communicating. Every sentence should express a complete thought. An effective sentence presents an idea in a clear and direct way.

Read the four sentences below. Place a check on the line beside the best, or most effective, sentence. Then, rewrite the other three sentences to make them better. Write your three sentences on the lines that follow.

_____ **1.** What a main issue was during Reconstruction was African American rights.

_____ **2.** John Wilkes Booth assassinated President Abraham Lincoln on April 14, 1865.

_____ **3.** It was Andrew Johnson after President Lincoln's death who took over the White House.

_____ **4.** Defined by the Fourteenth Amendment was who was a citizen.

____

____

____

____

____

____

____

____

____

B. Practice the Skill

On a separate sheet of paper, write four sentences about four events from your textbook. Each sentence should focus on a single idea. Then, work with a partner and read each other's sentences. Decide which sentences are the most effective. Write down reasons to support your answers.

Name ______________________ Date ______________

Reading, Writing, and Test Taking

Writing an Effective Paragraph

A. Learn the Skill

An effective paragraph focuses on one main idea. This idea is presented in a topic sentence. All the other sentences in the paragraph should relate to the topic sentence.

Develop the main idea with enough supporting details to write an effective paragraph. Your supporting details should answer the questions *who? what? where? when? why?* and *how?*

B. Practice the Skill

The following paragraph contains sentences that are not related to the topic sentence. Write the topic sentence on the lines below. Then, write the sentences that you think should be removed from the paragraph.

Clara Barton's work as a nurse during the Civil War did not end with the last battle in 1865. She was such a good nurse that she was often referred to as the "Angel of the Battlefield." Instead, she took on the difficult tasks of locating soldiers who were missing in action and of contacting their families. By the time she closed the Missing Soldiers Office in 1868, she had tracked down information about 22,000 soldiers. Clara Barton was also a teacher, one of the first women clerks in the U.S. Patent Office, and the founder of the American Red Cross. Women from around the country were grateful for the efforts of Clara Barton in helping to locate their sons, husbands, and brothers.

____

____

____

____

____

____

____

____

____

____

Name ______________________ Date ______________

Reading, Writing, and Test Taking

Writing an Effective Conclusion

A. Learn the Skill

An effective conclusion closes an essay in a meaningful way. It completes the development of the idea presented in the introduction. It also helps readers recall and understand the point of the essay.

Read the two paragraphs below. Place a check on the line beside the paragraph with the better conclusion. Then, rewrite the conclusion sentence for the paragraph that you did not check. Write your answer on the lines that follow.

_____ **1.** African Americans faced hardships during the Great Depression. Many African Americans who had moved to northern cities for employment began returning to the South when they were laid off. They faced increases in segregation and discrimination. It was a difficult time for African Americans.

_____ **2.** Mexican immigrants struggled during the Great Depression. Many had immigrated to the United States between 1910 and 1920 for jobs. During the Great Depression, many of these immigrants lost their jobs and were forced to return to Mexico. Mexican immigrants were happy during the Great Depression.

____

____

____

____

____

____

____

____

B. Practice the Skill

Read a paragraph from your textbook. On a separate sheet of paper, write a conclusion to that paragraph. Work with a partner and read each other's conclusions. Decide if each conclusion is effective. If it is not, rewrite it to make it more effective.

Name ______________________________ Date ______________

Reading, Writing, and Test Taking

Writing to Describe

A. Learn the Skill

In a descriptive essay, the writer uses language that helps readers see, hear, smell, and feel what is being described. The writer wants readers to have feelings about an event.

Read the two paragraphs below. Place a check on the line beside the paragraph that is the most descriptive. Then, complete the exercises that follow using the paragraph you checked.

_____ **1.** The Jamestown settlers built their homes on damp, swampy land. They were not prepared when the bitterly cold winter struck. The wealthy gentlemen settlers refused to risk their reputations by searching for food. Those who survived scavenged for plant roots, red berries, and wild herbs.

_____ **2.** The Jamestown settlers built their houses on the land. They were unprepared when winter came. Some settlers refused to search for food. Those who survived scavenged for plants to eat.

- Circle the words that describe the land on which the settlers built their homes.
- Draw boxes around the words used to describe the season.
- Underline the descriptive words in the last sentence.

B. Practice the Skill

Write a descriptive paragraph about an event in your textbook. Be sure to use details to give your reader a clear understanding of what you are describing. Write your paragraph on the lines below and on a separate sheet of paper if you need more space.

____

____

____

____

____

____

____

____

Name ________________________ Date ____________

Reading, Writing, and Test Taking

Writing to Persuade

A. Learn the Skill

A persuasive essay gives the writer's point of view. It tries to convince readers to agree with the writer. The writer uses facts and strong reasons to support the position that is taken.

Read the left side of the chart. These are opinions of an Antifederalist who does not want to ratify the Constitution. Complete the right side of the chart. Write what a Federalist might think. You can use Chapter 9 of your textbook if you need help.

Ratify the Constitution	
Notes from an Antifederalist	**Notes from a Federalist**
Take a stand: We should not ratify the Constitution.	**Take a stand:**
My audience: fellow neighbors	**My audience:**
Reasons to support my position: • A strong government would take away power from the states. • A president is no different from a King who will take away our rights. • Under the Constitution, the federal government will become like the British monarchy.	**Reasons to support my position:** • • •
Conclusion: We should keep the Articles of Confederation.	**Conclusion:**

B. Practice the Skill

Read the chart above. Decide which opinions to support. On a separate sheet of paper, write a paragraph about the side you have chosen. Your essay should take a clear stand. Include facts from the chart to support your statement.

Name ______________________ Date ______________

Reading, Writing, and Test Taking

A. Learn the Skill

A summary presents the main ideas of a passage. When writing a summary, you present the main ideas in your own words. A summary is always shorter than the original passage since it is not necessary to restate every point or idea.

Read the paragraph below. Then, read the main idea and the key supporting details. Combine the main idea and key details to write a summary on the lines that follow.

The Maya developed one of the most powerful Native American civilizations in Mexico and Central America because of their superior knowledge of farming and science. They mapped and used the movement of the stars to keep track of when to plant and harvest their crops. This helped them produce many types of fruits and vegetables. It also helped them come up with an accurate calendar.

Main Idea: The Maya developed one of the most powerful Native American civilizations because of their knowledge of farming and science.

Key Details:

1. They mapped and used star movement for planting and harvesting.
2. They produced many types of fruits and vegetables.
3. They came up with an accurate calendar.

____

____

____

____

____

____

____

B. Practice the Skill

Read a paragraph from your textbook. On a separate sheet of paper, write the main idea and the key supporting details of the paragraph. Then, write a summary.

Name ______________________ Date ______________

Reading, Writing, and Test Taking

Comparing and Contrasting

A. Learn the Skill

Comparing is looking for similarities between two or more things. Contrasting shows how two or more things are different. A diagram like the one below is a good way to compare and contrast things.

Read the two paragraphs below. Decide what the similarities and differences are between President Roosevelt and President Wilson. Then, complete the diagram that follows.

Theodore Roosevelt was a Republican who served less than two full terms as President of the United States. He believed that the government should play a big role in making people's lives better. Roosevelt helped break up many business trusts and monopolies.

Woodrow Wilson was a Democrat who worked to break up business trusts and monopolies. He served two full terms as President of the United States. While he was President, he helped pass many bills that brought about social reform.

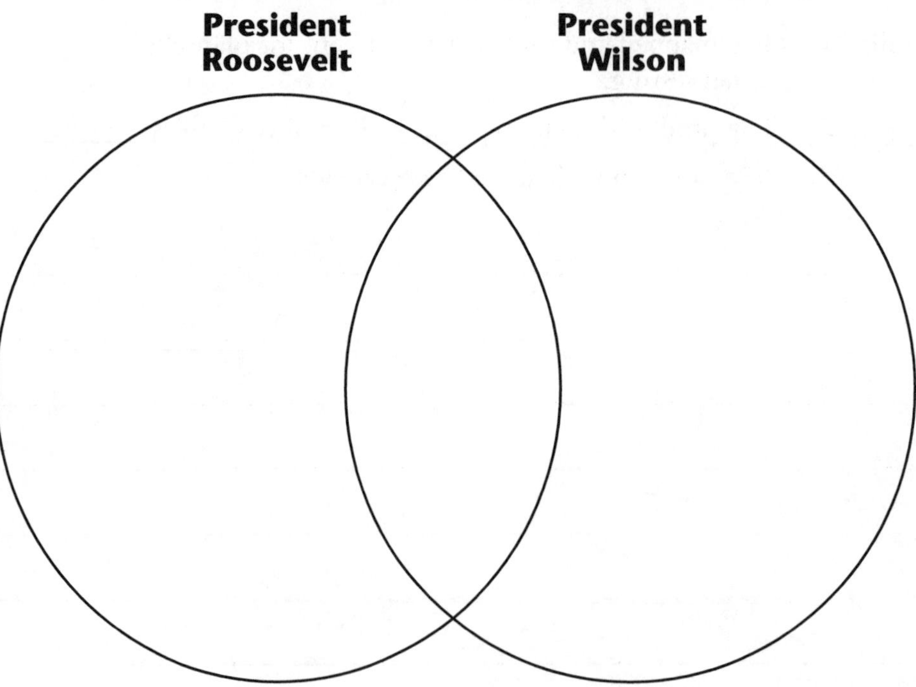

B. Practice the Skill

Choose two people from your textbook. On a separate sheet of paper, write a paragraph comparing and contrasting the people. Be sure to include reasons why they are different and reasons why they are similar.

Name ______________________ Date ______________

Reading, Writing, and Test Taking

Fact and Opinion

A. Learn the Skill

Understanding the differences between facts and opinions is helpful for reading. Facts are statements that can be proven. Opinions are personal feelings or beliefs. Reading facts and opinions helps you make conclusions about a topic.

Read the statements below. Then, complete the exercises on the lines that follow.

1. **Fact:** In the late 1800s, about 15 percent of all cowhands in the United States were African American.

   Why is this statement a fact? Explain your answer.

   ____

   ____

2. **Opinion:** I feel that the transcontinental railroad did more harm than good for this country.

   Why is this statement an opinion? Explain your answer.

   ____

   ____

B. Practice the Skill

Read the two statements below. On the lines provided, write *F* if the statement is a fact. Write *O* if the statement is an opinion. Then, write why the statement is a fact or opinion on the lines that follow.

_____ 3. Homesteaders had to be at least 21 years of age.

____

____

_____ 4. The most exciting thing about life on the prairies was the freedom.

____

____

Name ______________________ Date ______________

Reading, Writing, and Test Taking

Organizing Information in Chronological Order

A. Learn the Skill

Chronological, or time, order is a way of organizing events in the order in which they occur. Chronological order begins with what occurs first and ends with what occurs last. This method of organization is useful for relating historical events, explaining a process, or telling a story. Look for terms such as *again*, *as soon as*, *before*, *then*, *during*, *early*, *first*, *later*, *after*, *since*, and *soon*.

Read the paragraph below. The sentences are arranged in chronological order. Then, answer the questions that follow.

World War I started in Europe in 1914. At first, President Woodrow Wilson avoided entering the war. However, after three years, he realized neutrality was no longer possible. In 1917, President Wilson declared war, and U.S. troops were sent to Europe. Eventually, Germany surrendered in 1918.

1. What three terms show chronological order?

____

2. What event happened first in the paragraph?

____

B. Practice the Skill

Read the following topic sentence and list of events. On a separate sheet of paper, write a paragraph in which this list of events is organized in chronological order.

Topic Sentence: It took almost two hundred years for every citizen in the United States to be able to vote.

List of Events:

1770 Adult white men who own property can vote.

1828 Property qualifications for voting no longer exist in most states.

1870 Adult African American men can vote.

1920 Women gain the right to vote.

1924 Native Americans are able to vote.

1971 Eighteen-year-olds are able to vote.

Name ______________________ Date ______________

Reading, Writing, and Test Taking

Organizing Information by Cause and Effect

A. Learn the Skill

You can organize information in an essay by cause and effect to explain why something happened or how it happened. A cause is something that brings about a result. An effect is what happens as a result. Look for key words such as *because*, *if*, *since*, and *as a result*.

The paragraph below is organized by cause and effect. Read the paragraph and answer the questions that follow.

The British blocked the U.S. Navy ship, the USS *Chesapeake*. As a result of this, the United States banned British warships from American waters. Then, Congress passed the Embargo Act of 1807. This act banned U.S. ship owners from trading with European countries.

1. What was the effect of the British blocking the U.S. Navy ship?

____

2. What key word told you that an effect would follow?

____

B. Practice the Skill

Choose one of the topics below. Write a paragraph about that topic. Organize the information by cause and effect. Write your paragraph on the lines below and on a separate sheet of paper if you need more space.

1. The United States fought bravely in the War of 1812.
(Use information from Chapter 11 of your textbook to help with this topic.)

2. Television has had a strong influence on family life.
(Use information from Chapter 27 of your textbook to help with this topic.)

____

____

____

____

____

Name ______________________________ Date ______________

Reading, Writing, and Test Taking

Ruling Out Incorrect Answer Choices

A. Learn the Skill

Ruling out incorrect answer choices is an important test-taking strategy. This strategy can help you focus on what the questions are asking and help you select the right answer. First, read the question. Then, read the answer choices. Decide which answer choices *must* be incorrect. Be sure you are able to explain why these answer choices are wrong.

Read the paragraph below. Then, read the question and answer choices that follow. An *X* has been placed next to each incorrect answer choice. Explain how you know these answer choices are incorrect on the lines that follow.

President Ronald Reagan wished to strengthen a weak American economy. He attempted to do this by cutting taxes for businesses and the wealthy. He felt that these tax breaks would give companies and individuals more money to spend. This spent money would eventually make its way to middle- and lower-income households, who would then also have more money to spend. This idea became known as Reaganomics, or Reagan's economic plan.

Reaganomics is

__X__ **a.** a plan to limit military spending.

____

____

__X__ **b.** a plan to cut taxes for middle-class people.

____

____

__X__ **c.** the term for President Jimmy Carter's tax-cut plan.

____

____

_____ **d.** a way to increase economic growth.

Reading, Writing, and Test Taking

Name ____________________ Date ____________

Reading, Writing, and Test Taking

Answering Completion Questions

A. Learn the Skill

A completion question is a sentence with a word or phrase missing. A completion question usually has key words. These key words help the reader complete the question.

Read the two completion questions below. The missing word or phrase is filled in for you. On the lines that follow, write the key words of each completion question. These key words give clues to what the missing word or phrase is.

1. Abraham Lincoln was assassinated at Ford's Theater by John Wilkes Booth, an opponent of the Union.

____

2. The first southern state to secede from the Union was South Carolina.

____

B. Practice the Skill

Read the completion questions below. Use the terms from the box to complete the questions. Then, underline the key words that helped you complete the question. Use your textbook if you need help.

Confederacy	slaves	Missouri Compromise	Abraham Lincoln

3. The President who spoke out against slavery was ____________________.

4. The ____________________ maintained a balance between free and slaveholding states and was named after a state.

5. The southern states that seceded from the Union were called the ____________________.

6. Southern plantation owners relied on ____________________ and often treated them unfairly.

Name ____________________ Date ____________

Reading, Writing, and Test Taking

Writing and Editing Checklist

A. Learn the Skill

Editing is an important step in the writing process. Writing that is smooth and free of errors will help your readers understand your work.

Use these editing steps when writing.

- Read through your work and try to improve your choice of words and sentences.
- When you are taking a test, try to allow enough time to read over your answers.
- Always read your work before you hand it in. Ask yourself if it is complete, correct, and makes sense.

B. Practice the Skill

Read the editing checklist. Use it with an essay you have written. It can be an old essay that was returned to you. Put a check in each box as you complete the task.

☐ **1.** I located key words and responded to their directions.

☐ **2.** I included details to support the main idea of my essay.

☐ **3.** I checked for unnecessary words and sentences. I drew a straight line through them.

☐ **4.** I checked to see if important ideas or events were missing. I added important details using arrows to show where they belonged.

☐ **5.** I checked for sentence fragments or run-on sentences.

☐ **6.** I used the correct verb tense throughout my essay.

☐ **7.** I checked punctuation.

☐ **8.** I checked for correct spelling.

Contents

Graphic Organizers/Outline Maps

Graphic Organizers

Outline Maps

Name ______________________ Date ______________

Graphic Organizer

Outline

____

I.

A.

B.

C.

II.

A.

B.

C.

III.

A.

B.

C.

IV.

A.

B.

C.

Name ______________________ Date ______________

Graphic Organizer

Venn Diagram

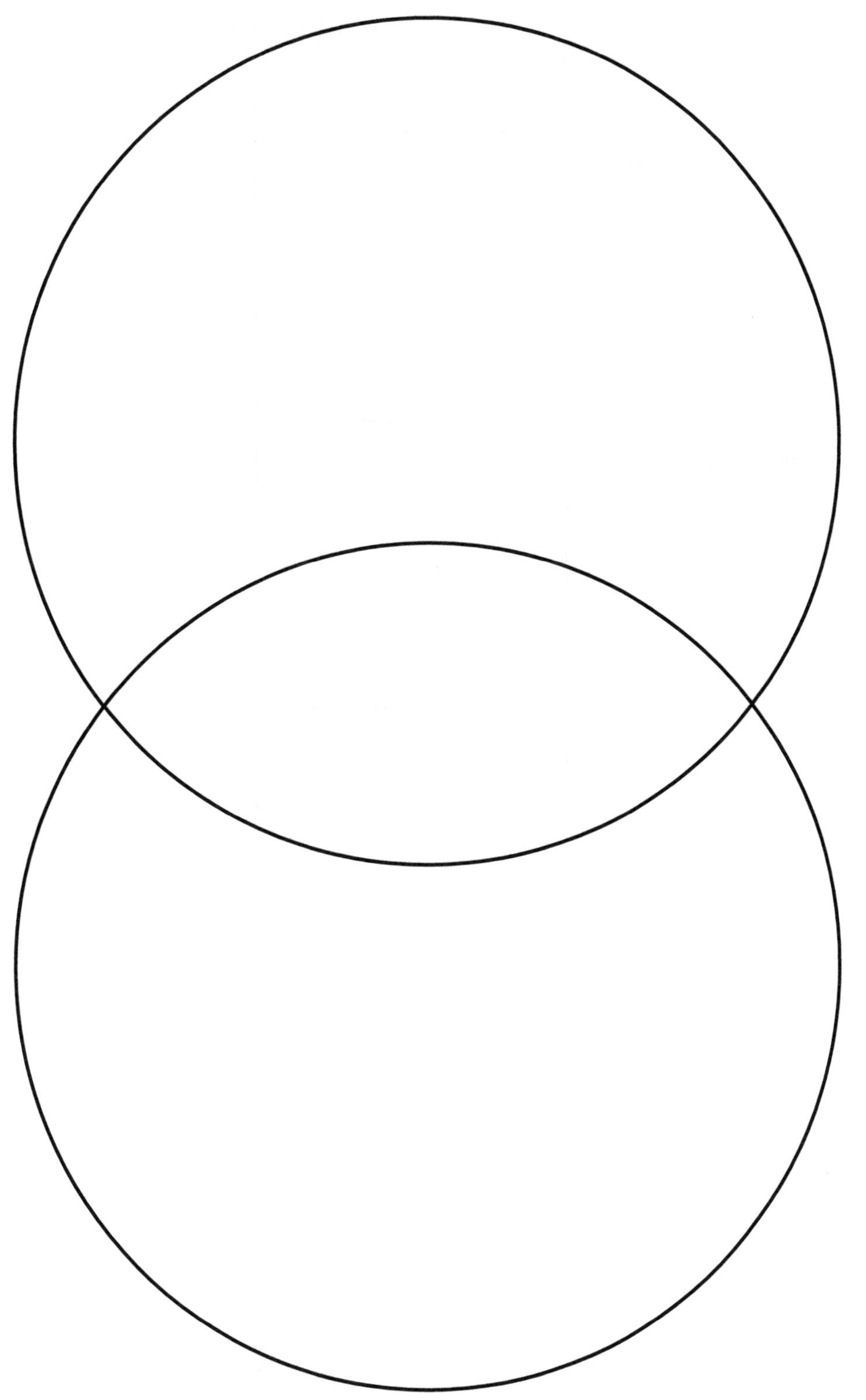

Graphic Organizers

Name ______________________ Date ______________

Graphic Organizer

Timeline

Name ______________________ Date ______________

Graphic Organizer

KWL Chart

Know
Want to Know
Learned

Graphic Organizers

Name ______________________ Date ______________

Graphic Organizer

Main Idea/Supporting Details Chart

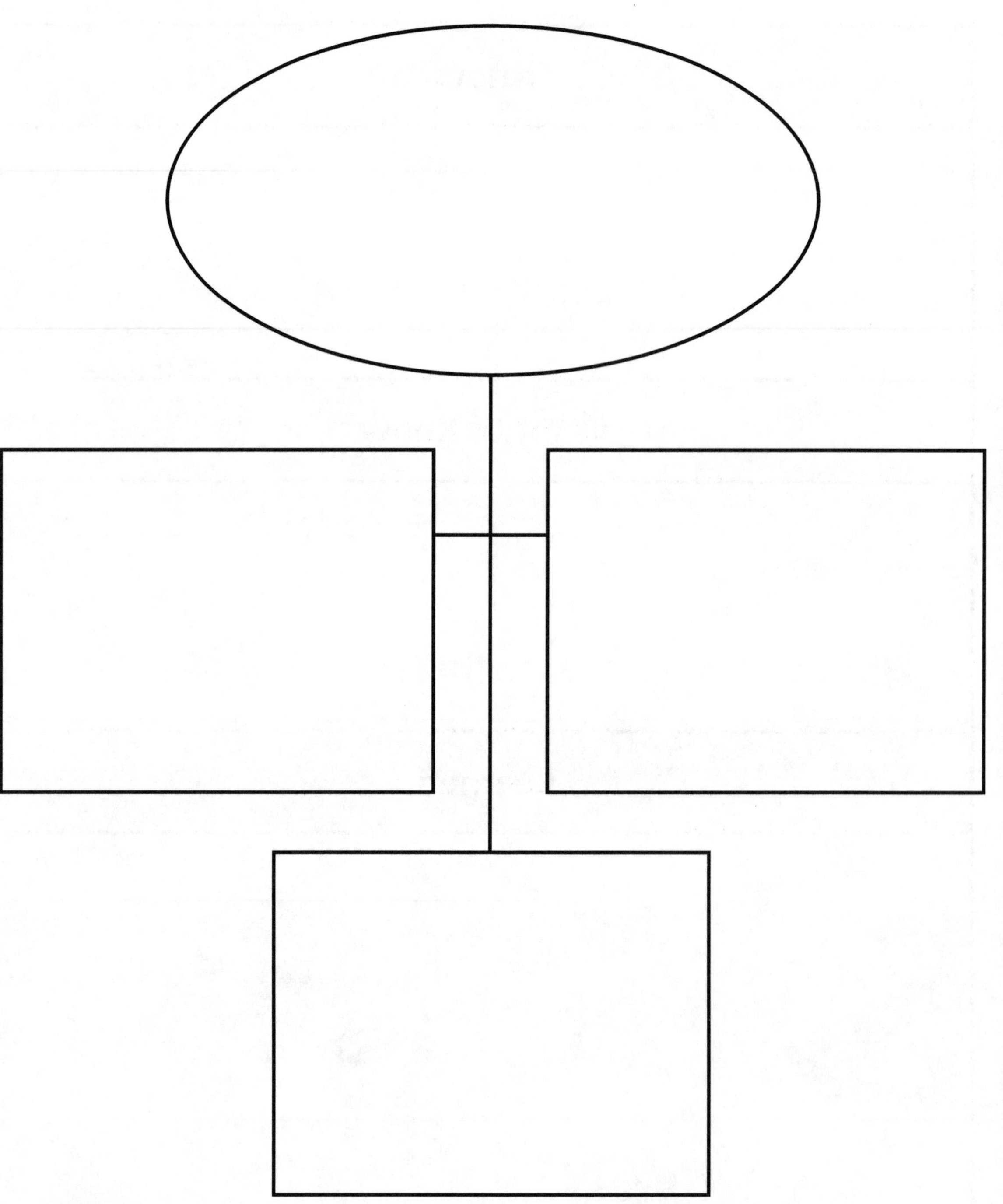

Graphic Organizers

Name ______________________________ Date ____________________

Graphic Organizer

Five *W*s Chart

Who?	
What?	
Where?	
When?	
Why?	

Name ______________________ Date ______________

Graphic Organizer

Cause/Effect Chart

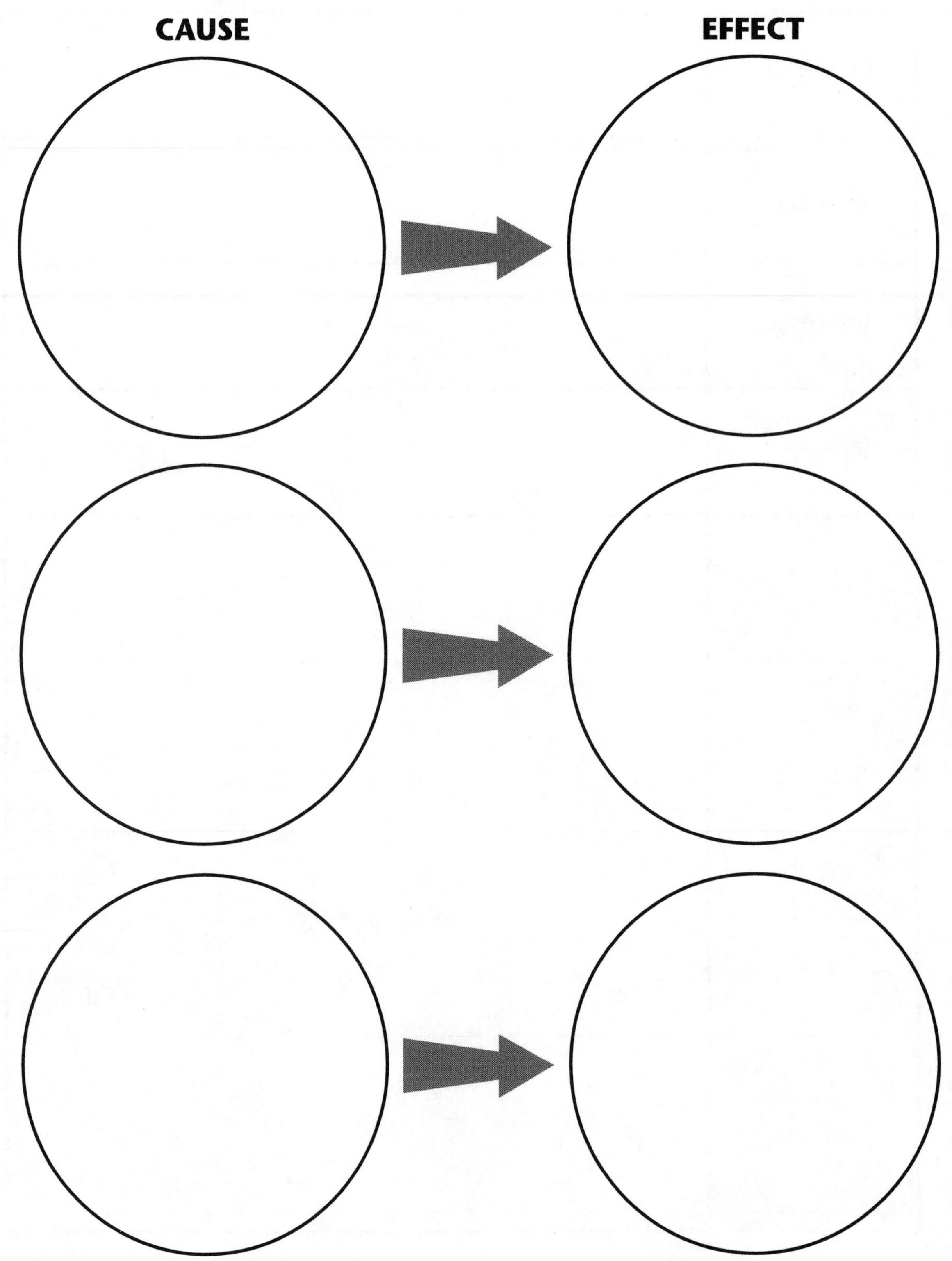

Graphic Organizers

Name ______________________ Date ______________

Graphic Organizer

Two-Column Chart

Graphic Organizers

Name ______________________ Date ______________

Graphic Organizer

Flowchart

1

2

3

4

Name ______________________________ Date ____________________

Graphic Organizer

Idea Web

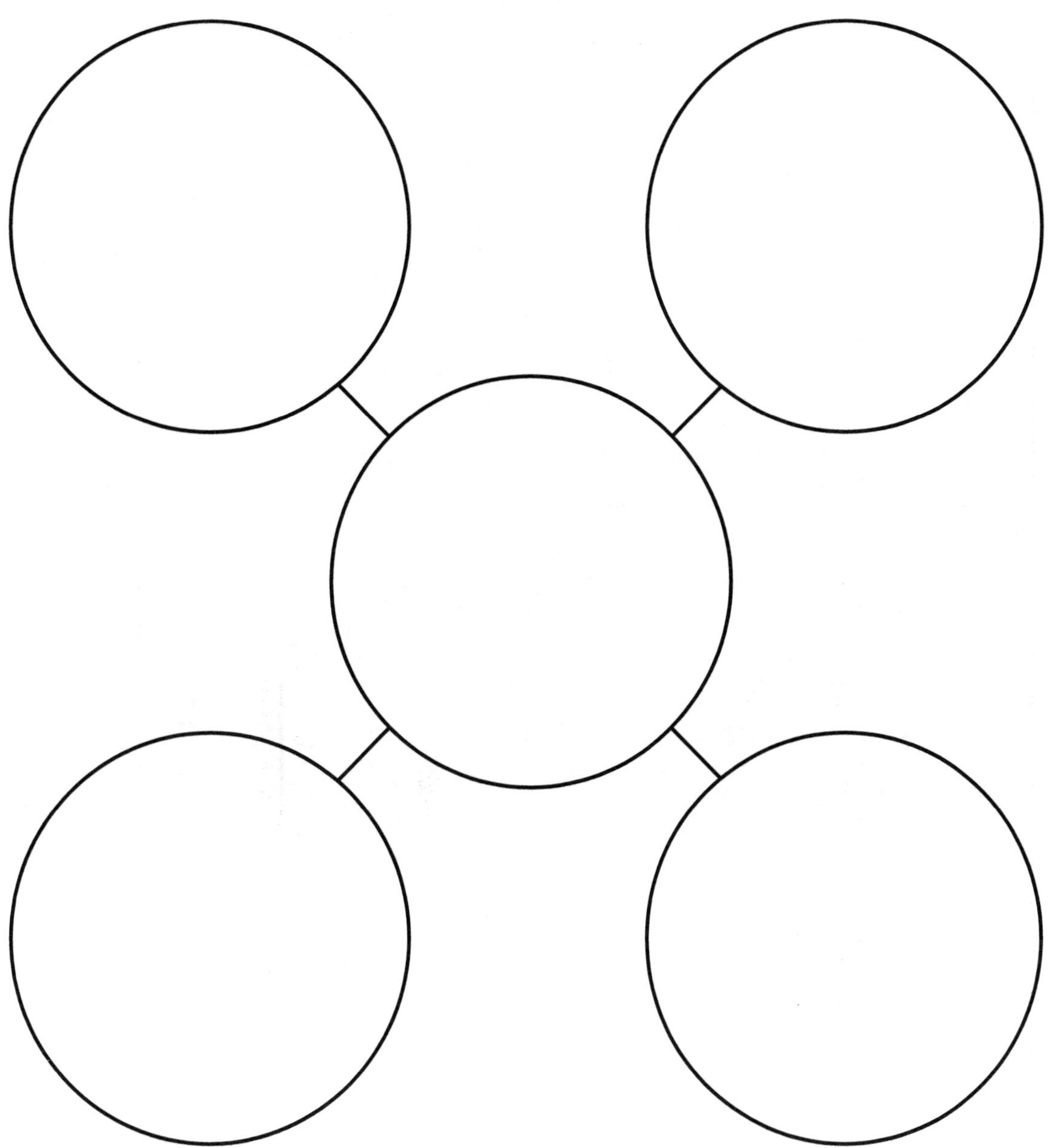

Graphic Organizers

Name ______________________________ Date ______________

Outline Map

The World

Outline Maps

Name ______________________ Date ______________

Outline Map

The United States

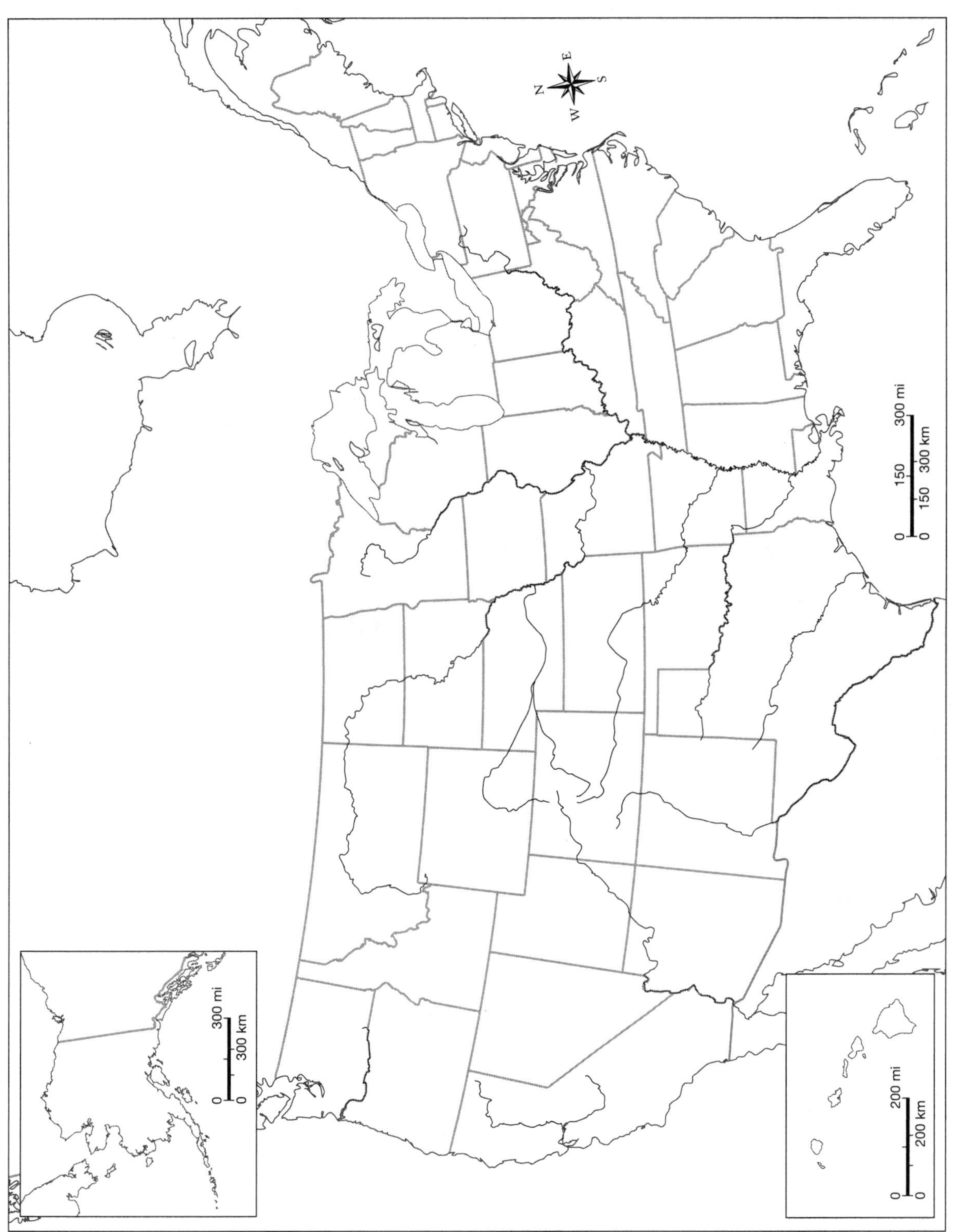

Outline Maps

Name ______________________ Date ______________

Outline Map

North America

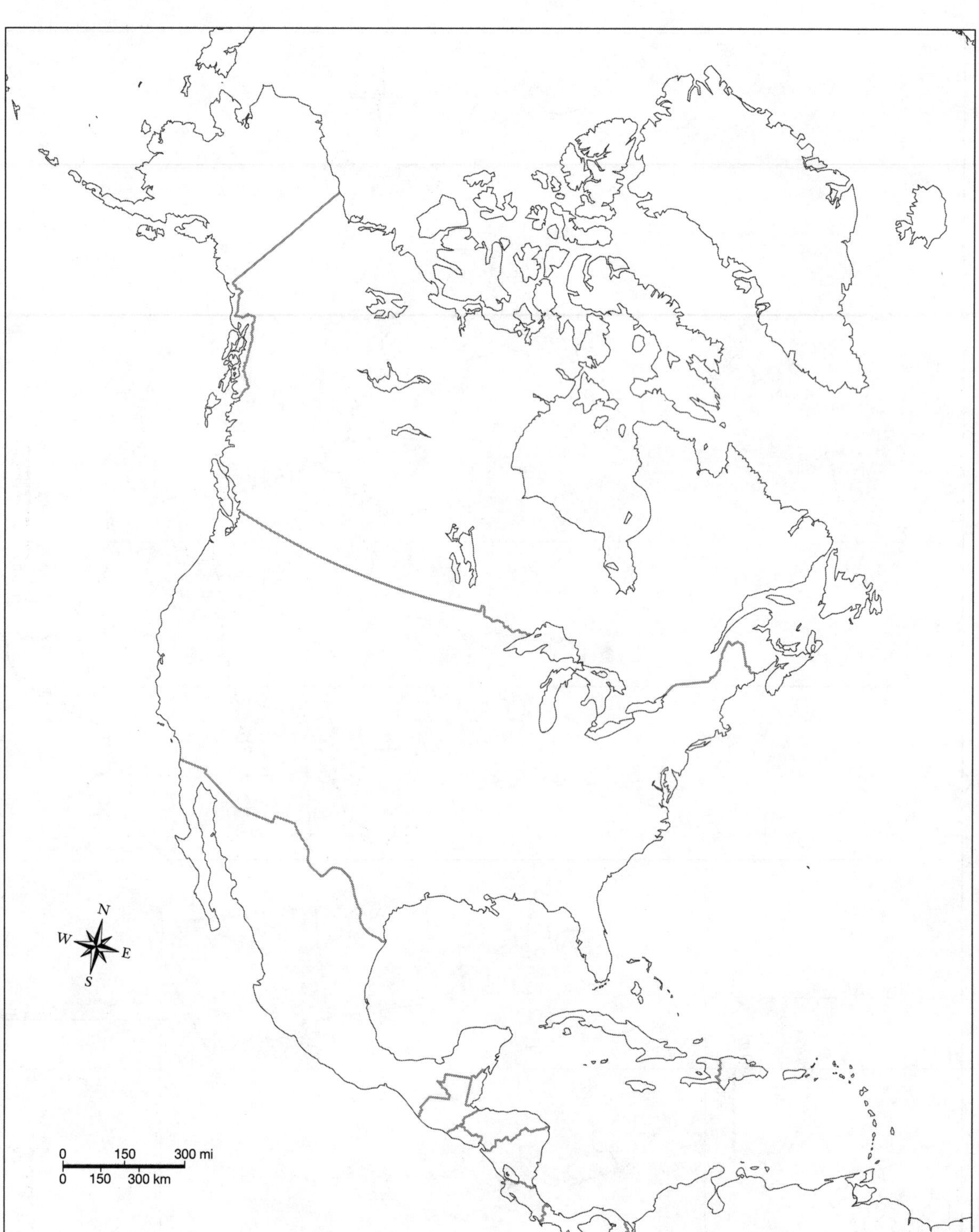

Name ______________________ Date ______________

Outline Map

South America

Name ______________________ Date ______________________

Outline Map

Europe

Name ______________________________ Date ________________

Outline Map

Asia and The Middle East

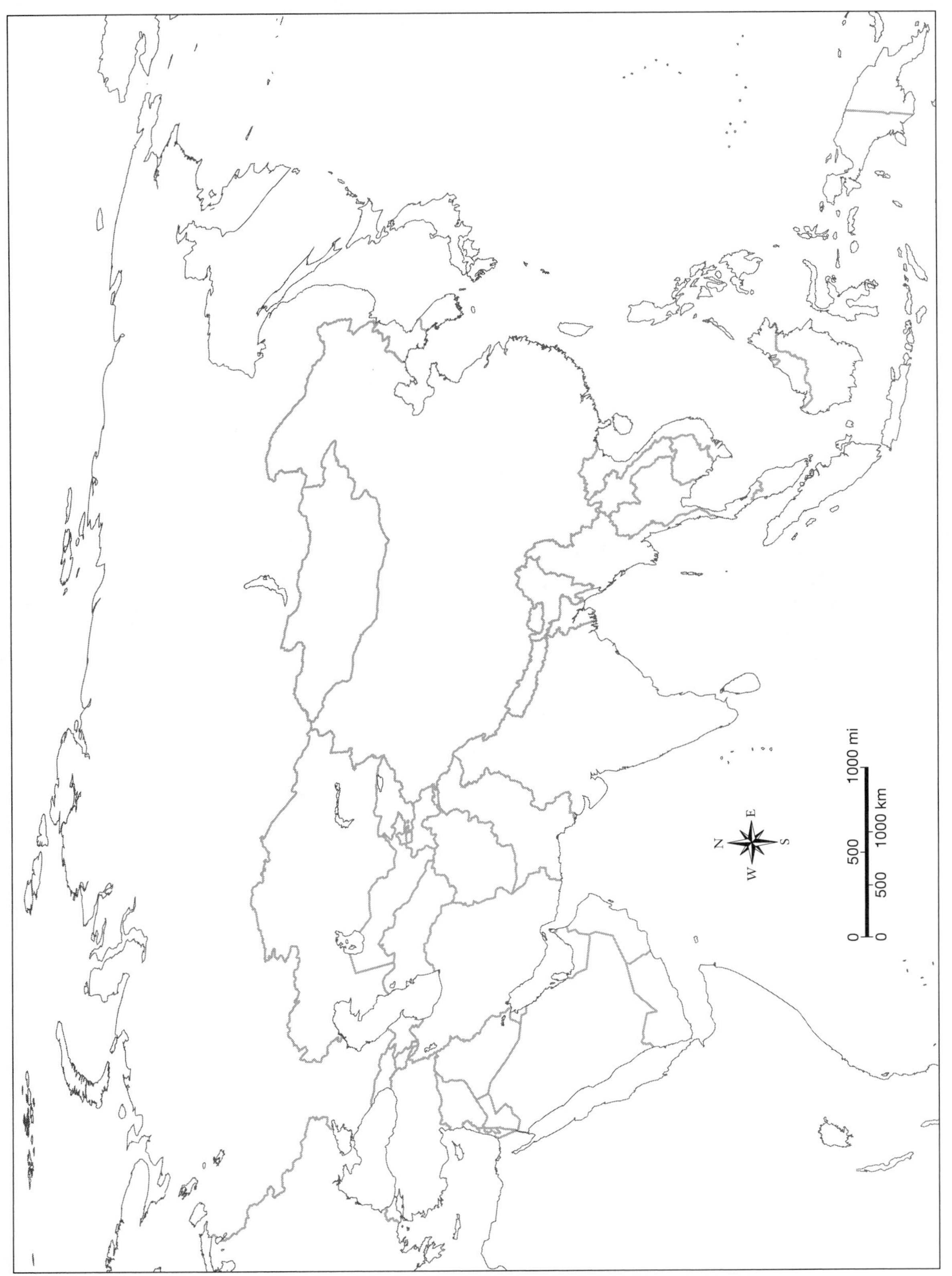

Outline Maps

Name ______________________ Date ______________

Outline Map

Africa

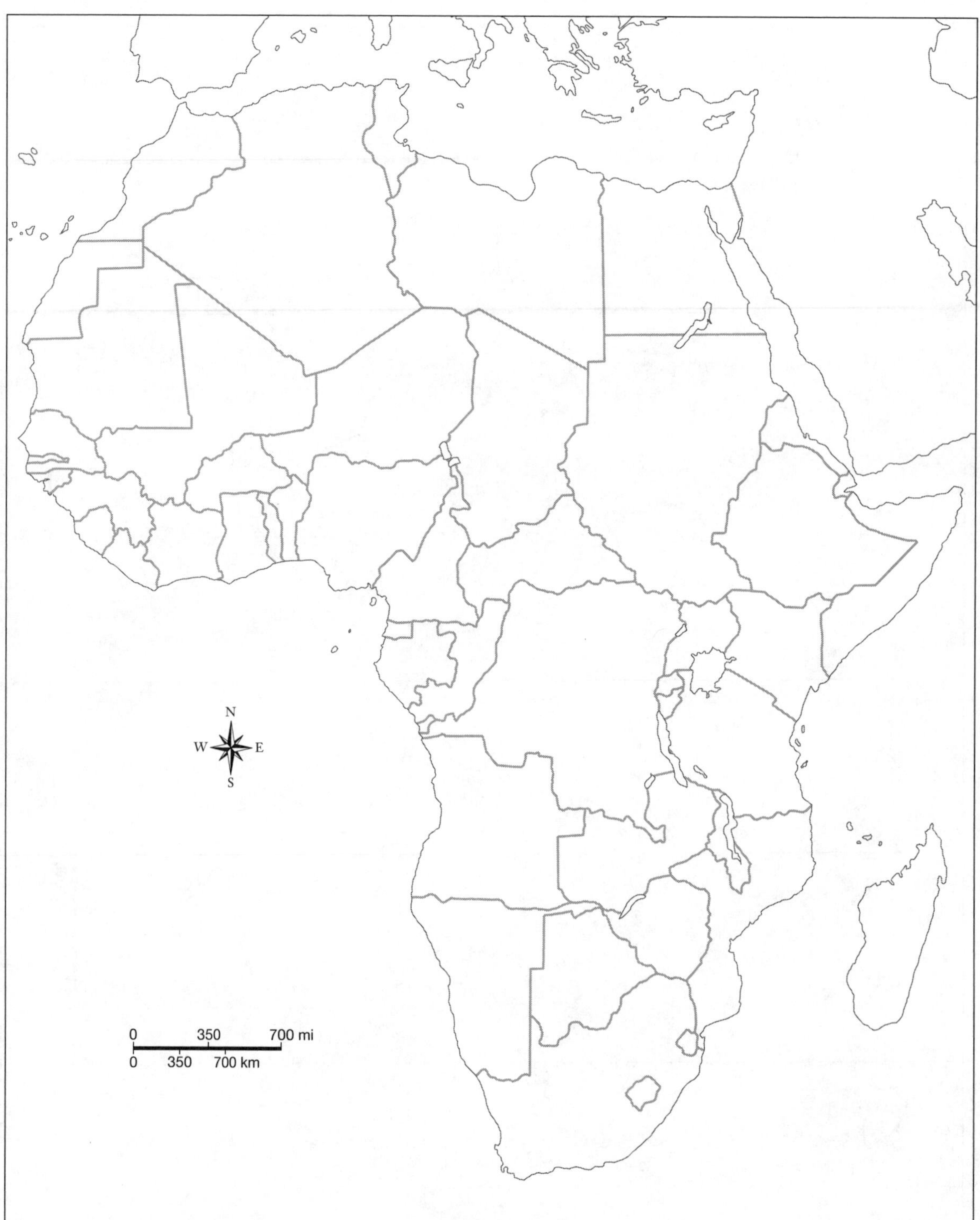

Name ______________________________ Date ________________

Outline Map

Australia and Oceania

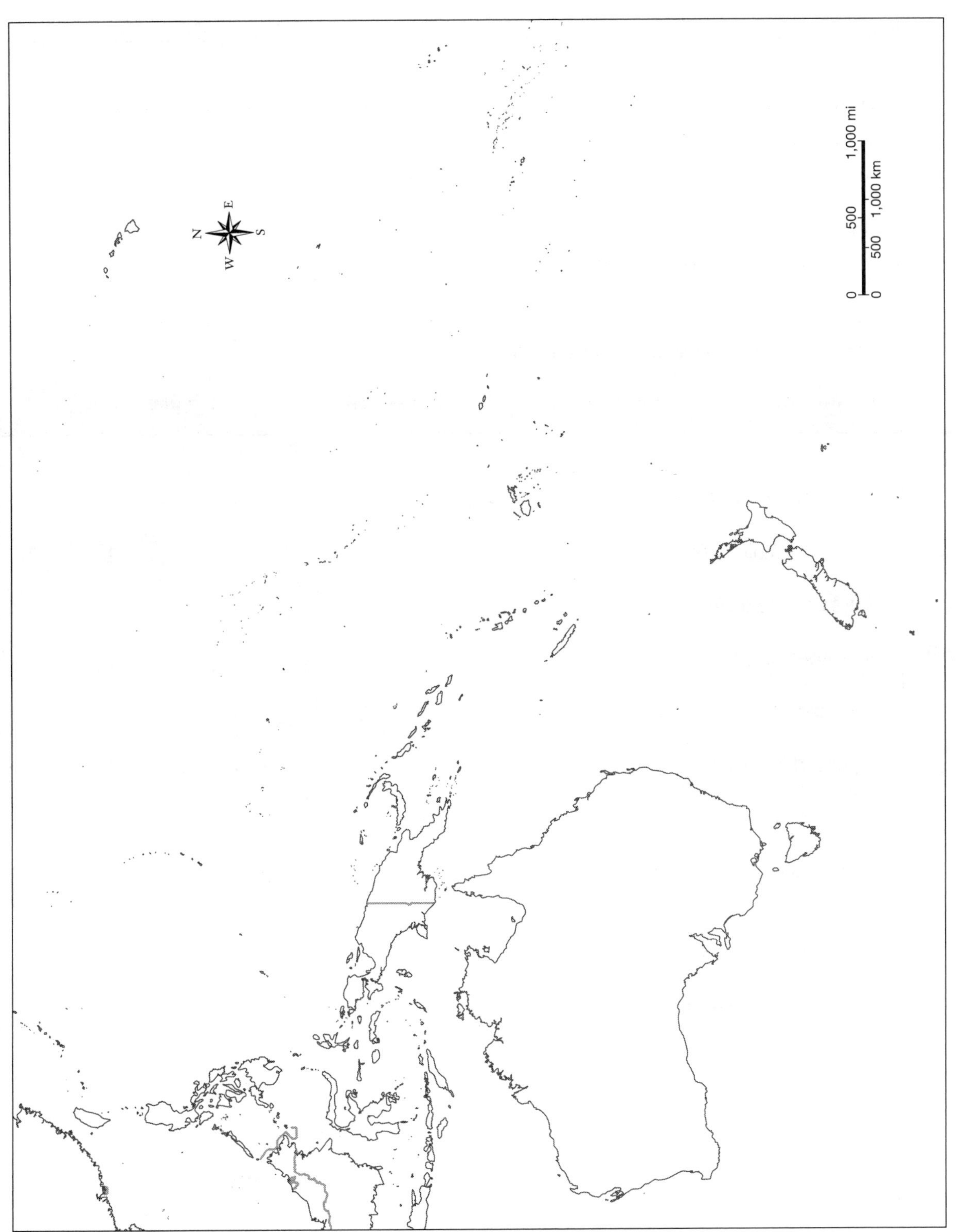

Rubric

Chapter Summary

Name ______________________________ Date ______________

Chapter Number ______________ Activity ______________

Directions

Score each item by circling a number from 1 to 4.
Add all of the circled numbers.
Divide by 10.
Round the number to the nearest whole number.

Use the following scale to score each item.

4 = excellent **3 = good** **2 = average** **1 = poor**

Answered the assignment	4	3	2	1
Stated the main idea	4	3	2	1
Stayed on the topic	4	3	2	1
Developed ideas fully	4	3	2	1
Gave specific details or examples	4	3	2	1
Organized ideas well	4	3	2	1
Ideas flow smoothly	4	3	2	1
Used correct capitalization and punctuation	4	3	2	1
Used complete sentences	4	3	2	1
Spelled words correctly	4	3	2	1

Total = __________

Divided by 10 = __________

Score = __________

Rubric

Alternative Assessment

Name ______________________________ Date ________________

Chapter Number ________________ Activity ________________

Directions
Check (✓) one box in each row to finish each item.
Give each check (✓) the assigned number of points.
Add the points in each column. Write the sum. Then add across to find the total score.

POINTS	10	9	8	7	6	
For this activity, Student's name ______	**all of the time**	**most of the time**	**half of the time**	**less than half of the time**	**none of the time**	
Followed directions						
Participated in group discussions						
Listened carefully to others						
Used appropriate resources and materials						
Completed assigned tasks						
Showed an understanding of the content						
Presented materials without errors						
Explained thinking with support						
Asked questions when help was needed						
Worked independently when required						
POINTS	+	+	+	+	=	
						TOTAL SCORE

Rubrics

Name ______________________ Date ______________

Rubric

Scantron® Sheet

PLEASE NOTE
• Use only a no. 2 pencil.
• Example: (A) ● (C) (D)
• Erase changes COMPLETELY.

Mark one answer for each question.

1. (A) (B) (C) (D)
2. (A) (B) (C) (D)
3. (A) (B) (C) (D)
4. (A) (B) (C) (D)
5. (A) (B) (C) (D)
6. (A) (B) (C) (D)
7. (A) (B) (C) (D)
8. (A) (B) (C) (D)
9. (A) (B) (C) (D)
10. (A) (B) (C) (D)
11. (A) (B) (C) (D)
12. (A) (B) (C) (D)
13. (A) (B) (C) (D)
14. (A) (B) (C) (D)
15. (A) (B) (C) (D)
16. (A) (B) (C) (D)
17. (A) (B) (C) (D)
18. (A) (B) (C) (D)
19. (A) (B) (C) (D)
20. (A) (B) (C) (D)
21. (A) (B) (C) (D)
22. (A) (B) (C) (D)
23. (A) (B) (C) (D)
24. (A) (B) (C) (D)
25. (A) (B) (C) (D)
26. (A) (B) (C) (D)
27. (A) (B) (C) (D)
28. (A) (B) (C) (D)
29. (A) (B) (C) (D)
30. (A) (B) (C) (D)
31. (A) (B) (C) (D)
32. (A) (B) (C) (D)
33. (A) (B) (C) (D)
34. (A) (B) (C) (D)
35. (A) (B) (C) (D)
36. (A) (B) (C) (D)
37. (A) (B) (C) (D)
38. (A) (B) (C) (D)
39. (A) (B) (C) (D)
40. (A) (B) (C) (D)
41. (A) (B) (C) (D)
42. (A) (B) (C) (D)
43. (A) (B) (C) (D)
44. (A) (B) (C) (D)
45. (A) (B) (C) (D)
46. (A) (B) (C) (D)
47. (A) (B) (C) (D)
48. (A) (B) (C) (D)
49. (A) (B) (C) (D)
50. (A) (B) (C) (D)

UNIT 1 EARLY AMERICA

Chapter 1 The First Americans

Terms to Know (p. 14) **A. 1.** d **2.** e **3.** f **4.** c **5.** a **6.** b **B. 7.** F **8.** T **9.** T **10.** F **11.** T **12.** T

Review History (p. 47) **A. 1.** a **2.** b **3.** d **4.** c **B. 5.** Anasazi **6.** buffalo **7.** maize (corn) **8.** glaciers **9.** Olmec

Build Your Skills (p. 80) **1.** 1,500 years **2.** 500 years **3.** before **4.** 625 years **5.** before **6.** 1570

Chapter Test (pp. 115–116) **A. 1.** k **2.** f **3.** b **4.** m **5.** a **6.** c **7.** l **8.** j **9.** d **10.** g **11.** e **12.** h **13.** i **B. 14.** T **15.** T **16.** T **17.** F **18.** F **19.** T **C. 20. a. Possible answer:** People did not have to travel as much in search of food. They could establish communities. Having a steady supply of food enabled some people to devote time to other things. **b. Possible answer:** Animals provided a source of food, clothing, utensils, and other items. For example, Plains people used buffaloes for clothing, shelter, and tools, while the Inuit and Aleuts made clothes from the skins of seals and otters.

Chapter 2 Early Exploration

Terms to Know (p. 15) **A. 1.** d **2.** b **3.** e **4.** a **5.** c **B. 6.** a **7.** b **8.** d **9.** b

Review History (p. 48) **A. 1.** T **2.** T **3.** F **4.** T **5.** F **6.** T **7.** F **B. 8.** Ghana, Mali, Songhai **9.** Cape of Good Hope **10.** Asia **11.** eastern Asia **12.** Pedro Cabral

Build Your Skills (p. 81) **1.** Portuguese exploration in the late 1400s **2.** dotted line signifies Dias's voyage; solid line signifies da Gama's voyage **3.** Both explorers sailed down the west coast of Africa. Dias reached the tip of the continent. Da Gama sailed around Africa to India—he traveled farther. **4.** the Atlantic Ocean

Chapter Test (pp. 117–118) **A. 1.** m **2.** j **3.** l **4.** h **5.** e **6.** c **7.** f **8.** k **9.** b **10.** a **11.** d **12.** g **13.** i **B. 14.** F **15.** O **16.** F **17.** O **18.** F **19.** F **C. 20. a. Possible answer:** Farming varied, depending on the particular land and climate. In wet and warm coastal areas, farmers grew yams, bananas, and beans. In the drier savannas, farmers grew grains, such as sorghum and millet. **b. Possible answer:** Portuguese sailors designed the caravel ship, which was able to sail long distances. The Portuguese also made use of the compass and the astrolabe, two navigational tools.

Chapter 3 New Settlements in the Americas

Terms to Know (p. 16) **A. 1.** cash crop **2.** mission **3.** indentured servant **4.** sanitation **B. 5.** c **6.** b **7.** d **8.** c

Review History (p. 49) **A. 1.** b **2.** a **3.** d **4.** c **B. 5.** O **6.** O **7.** F **8.** F **9.** F **10.** O

Build Your Skills (p. 82) Answers will vary.

Chapter Test (pp. 119–120) **A. 1.** c **2.** f **3.** l **4.** i **5.** g **6.** h **7.** a **8.** b **9.** d **10.** k **11.** j **12.** e **B. 13.** F **14.** T **15.** F **16.** T **17.** T **18.** F **19.** F **C. 20. a. Possible answer:** West Africans and Native Americans were forced to work for the settlers. They had no rights, lived in harsh conditions, and suffered from overwork and disease. **b. Possible answer:** The first settlers of Jamestown suffered from hunger and cold. The land was harsh. They frequently had conflicts with the Native Americans.

UNIT 2 THE AMERICAN COLONIES

Chapter 4 Founding Colonial America

Terms to Know (p. 17) **A. 1.** d **2.** c **3.** b **4.** f **5.** e **6.** a **7.** g **B. 8.** freedom **9.** slavery **10.** war **11.** religion **12.** shipbuilding

Review History (p. 50) **A. 1. a.** C **b.** E **2. a.** C **b.** E **3. a.** E **b.** C **4. a.** C **b.** E **B. 5.** T **6.** F **7.** F **8.** T **9.** T **10.** T **11.** F

Build Your Skills (p. 83) **1.** Boston **2.** Charleston **3. Possible answers:** Baltimore may have been a very new city and few people lived there. Baltimore's population in 1730 may not be known. **4.** about 4,800 people

Chapter Test (pp. 121–122) **A. 1.** a **2.** a **3.** d **4.** a **5.** c **6.** b **7.** b **B. 8.** F **9.** T **10.** F **11.** T **12.** T **13.** F **14.** T **15.** F **16.** T **C. 17. a. Possible answer:** Because of poor soil and a short growing season, the economy of the

New England colonies was based mainly on fishing, whaling, shipbuilding, shipping, and lumbering. The economy of the Southern colonies was based on farming. The Southern colonies had better soil and a longer growing season. **b. Possible answer:** Tobacco farming was both good and bad for Virginia and Maryland. It was good because tobacco was easy to grow and made these colonies very wealthy. However, tobacco brought more settlers to these colonies, and people fought over land and resources.

Chapter 5 The Thirteen Colonies

Terms to Know (p. 18) **A. 1.** overseer **2.** slave code **3.** apprentice **4.** libel **B. 5.** c **6.** a **7.** d **8.** b

Review History (p. 51) **A. 1.** newspapers **2.** New England **3.** Middle Passage **4.** John Peter Zenger **5.** Stono Rebellion **6.** Pennsylvania and New York **B. 7.** T **8.** T **9.** F **10.** T **11.** F

Build Your Skills (p. 84) **I.** Colonial Education **A.** Schools in New England **1.** high priority from the earliest time **2.** Primary and secondary schools were started by Puritans. **3.** Only boys were allowed to go to school. **B.** Schools in Southern colonies **1.** harder to establish **2.** both public and private schools **3.** Boys spent more time working on farms and less time at school. **II.** Slave Codes **A.** Laws took rights away from enslaved Africans **1.** were not allowed to serve as witnesses in trials **2.** could not run businesses, own property, or gather publicly **3.** were not allowed to learn to read and write **B.** People born into slavery **1.** Children of enslaved Africans were enslaved from birth. **2.** Slavery from birth made slavery in colonies different from slavery in Africa. **C.** Slave codes reinforced **1.** Most colonists believed that Africans were inferior. **2.** Enslaved Africans were thought of as property.

Chapter Test (pp. 123–124) **A. 1.** Navigation Acts **2.** University of Pennsylvania **3.** tar **4.** religion **5.** Puritans **6.** Southern colonies **7.** trade **8.** Great Awakening **9.** slavery **10.** Enlightenment movement **B. 11.** F **12.** F **13.** F **14.** T **15.** T **16.** F **17.** T **18.** F **19.** T **C. 20. a. Possible answer:** Slave codes took rights away from enslaved people. The laws made it possible for children to be born as slaves. The codes were established and reinforced based on the colonial slaveholding belief that Africans were inferior. **b. Possible answer:** Colonial women had very limited rights under the law but contributed greatly to life in the colonies. They took care of their homes and families and cared for and educated their children. Women contributed to the economy by making products in their homes, and some even worked outside of their homes.

Chapter 6 Roots of Rebellion

Terms to Know (p. 19) **A. 1.** d **2.** c **3.** b **4.** e **5.** a **B. 6.** monarch **7.** Parliament **8.** militia **9.** assembly

Review History (p. 52) **A. 1.** Parliament worried that the king wanted absolute power. Also, the king wanted an all-Catholic government, but most members of Parliament were Protestant. **2.** Only white male landowners were allowed to vote. Women, nonwhite people, and people who were not wealthy enough to own land were not allowed to vote. **3.** These laws required the colonists to pay taxes on goods imported from other countries. British customs officials could search a ship if they thought a merchant was smuggling goods. People suspected of breaking trade laws were put on trial in British naval courts, rather than in colonial courts. **4.** They were battling each other for territory, resources, and power. **5.** They wanted to send a strong message to the British that the French claimed possession of the Ohio River valley. **B.** Answers will vary.

Build Your Skills (p. 85) **Possible answers: Cause:** Both France and Great Britain claim control of the Ohio River valley. France builds Fort LeBoeuf to assert its claim to the Ohio River valley. **Effect:** The British take control of Quebec and begin to win the war. **Cause:** The Treaty of Paris is signed.

Chapter Test (pp. 125–126) **A. 1.** council **2.** assembly **3.** England **4.** governor **5.** Iroquois **6.** "power of the purse" **7.** self-government **8.** English Bill of Rights **9.** Parliament **B. 10.** F **11.** F **12.** T **13.** T **14.** T **15.** T **16.** T **17.** T **C. 18. a. Possible answer:** The French allowed only Catholics to emigrate to America. Most French Catholics already owned land in their own country, so they weren't very interested in leaving. British people were more likely to want to leave their country to seek religious freedom and better economic opportunities. **b. Possible answer:** Native American power declined because the British colonists now did not have the French blocking them from western expansion. Diseases and warfare over the fur trade further reduced Native American power.

UNIT 3 FOUNDING A NATION

Chapter 7 Road to Independence

Terms to Know (p. 20) **A. 1.** b **2.** c **3.** d **4.** f **5.** a **6.** e **B. 7.** revenue **8.** repeal **9.** minuteman **10.** boycott **11.** petition **12.** traitor

Review History (p. 53) **A. 1.** F **2.** T **3.** F **4.** T **B. 5.** d **6.** g **7.** a **8.** f **9.** b **10.** h **11.** e **12.** c

Build Your Skills (p. 86) **1.** taxes were placed on all printed documents **2.** Stamp Act **3.** 1774 **3.** Intolerable Acts **4.** The acts are listed in the order they were passed.

Chapter Test (pp. 127–128) **A. 1. a.** 5 **b.** 1 **c.** 3 **d.** 2 **e.** 4 **2. a.** 1 **b.** 2 **c.** 4 **d.** 3 **e.** 5 **B. 3.** Great Britain tried to control the colonists by taxing them, by trying to force them to buy only British products, and by limiting the areas in which they could live. **4.** The colonists claimed that they could not legally be taxed by Parliament unless they had their own representatives who could vote in Parliament. **5.** Colonists protested the Tea Act by throwing British tea into Boston's harbor. **6.** The Tea Act made tea sold by British merchants much cheaper than tea sold by colonial merchants. **7.** The colonists came together and held the First Continental Congress. **8.** The courts interfered with the colonists' right to govern themselves. **9.** He argued that King George, like other kings throughout history, had become a tyrant. **C. 10. a. Possible answer:** Colonists printed angry statements in newspapers. People served homegrown tea instead of British tea. The Daughters of Liberty made homespun clothing to replace fabric bought from Britain. **b. Possible answer:** The delegates put together the colonies' militias into a single colonial army led by George Washington. They sent King George the Olive Branch Petition. The king ignored the petition, and the delegates finally decided to declare independence from Great Britain.

Chapter 8 The Revolutionary War

Terms to Know (p. 21) **A. 1.** mercenary **2.** Loyalist **3.** inflation **4.** casualty **B. 5.** b **6.** a **7.** d **8.** c

Review History (p. 54) **A. 1.** France **2.** Treaty of Paris **3.** Yorktown, VA **4.** British **B. 5.** c **6.** g **7.** e **8.** d **9.** f **10.** a **11.** h **12.** b

Build Your Skills (p. 87) **1.** Peekskill, NY; Fort Lee, NJ; New Brunswick, NJ; Morristown, NJ **2.** Morristown, NJ **3.** battles fought at Trenton and Princeton **4.** battles fought at Brooklyn Heights and White Plains **5.** December 26, 1776

Chapter Test (pp. 129–130) **A. 1.** British troops in the frontier, outlaws and other troublemakers in Spanish Florida, and inflation **2.** Most trade had stopped because of the fighting, so fewer people were earning money. **3.** freedom and equality for all people **4.** France sent badly needed troops and supplies and made it possible for the colonists to defeat the British. **5.** George Washington and Count de Rochambeau led American and French troops to victory over British General Cornwallis, bringing the Revolutionary War to an end. **6.** The Continental army was outnumbered and defeated by the British army. The Americans were chased by the British as they retreated. **7.** The Americans prevented reinforcements from reaching the British, forcing the British to surrender. **8.** They went to Paris to decide the terms of the peace treaty between the United States and Great Britain. **B. 9. a.** 4 **b.** 5 **c.** 2 **d.** 1 **e.** 3 **10. a.** 3 **b.** 5 **c.** 4 **d.** 2 **e.** 1 **C. 11. a. Possible answer:** The Continental army was poorly trained, poorly equipped, and smaller than the British army. Hispanic and African American troops fought in the Continental army. The British troops were well equipped and well trained. They included mercenary soldiers from Germany and Native Americans. **b. Possible answer:** No. At the time the new government began, real freedom belonged only to white men who were allowed to vote. Others, including women, free African

Americans, and enslaved people, did not have the same rights to participate in government as those who could vote.

Chapter 9 Forming a Government

Terms to Know (p. 22) **A. 1.** d **2.** f **3.** i **4.** m **5.** b **6.** c **7.** g **8.** h **9.** e **10.** k **11.** l **12.** n **13.** a **14.** j

Review History (p. 55) **A. 1.** a **2.** c **3.** b **4.** c **B. 5.** the Great Compromise **6.** Articles of Confederation **7.** Federalists **8.** Shays's rebellion

Build Your Skills (p. 88) **1.** The Articles of Confederation are approved by the Second Continental Congress. **2.** The Ordinance of 1784 is created by Congress. **3.** Daniel Shays leads farmers in a rebellion against the government. **4.** Delegates meet at the State House in Philadelphia. **5.** The delegates agree to the Great Compromise. **6.** The Constitution is signed by the delegates.

Chapter Test (pp. 131–132) **A. 1.** a **2.** m **3.** j **4.** k **5.** e **6.** h **7.** c **8.** b **9.** i **10.** f **11.** d **12.** l **13.** g **B. 14.** F **15.** T **16.** T **17.** F **18.** T **19.** T **C. 20. a. Possible answer:** Federalists supported a strong federal government and ratifying the Constitution. Antifederalists opposed the Constitution and supported stronger state powers. **b. Possible answer:** The Articles of Confederation encouraged state control and a weak federal government with no President, no court system, and no federal taxes. The Constitution divided the federal government into three branches and allowed the government to tax the states.

UNIT 4 BUILDING THE REPUBLIC

Chapter 10 A Government for a New Nation

Terms to Know (p. 23) **A. 1.** Cabinet **2.** inauguration **3.** impressment **4.** alliance **B. 5.** h **6.** i **7.** b **8.** a **9.** f **10.** d **11.** e **12.** c **13.** g

Review History (p. 56) **A. 1.** a **2.** c **3.** b **4.** b **B. 5.** F **6.** T **7.** F **8.** T **9.** T **10.** T

Build Your Skills (p. 89) **A. Type of Source:** primary source **Why:** The best way to determine how Jefferson and Hamilton felt about each other's views would be to find quotes from each man regarding this subject. **Type of Source:** secondary source **Why:** Only after Washington's presidency ended would historians be able to reflect on the importance of the precedents set during his tenure. **B.** Answers will vary.

Chapter Test (pp. 133–134) **A. 1.** f **2.** b **3.** h **4.** a **5.** d **6.** g **7.** j **8.** c **9.** e **10.** i **B. 11. a.** 3 **b.** 2 **c.** 4 **d.** 1 **12. a.** 2 **b.** 1 **c.** 4 **d.** 3 **C. 13. a. Possible answer:** Hamilton believed in a loose interpretation of the Constitution. He felt that Congress could expand its power beyond what was stated in the Constitution. Jefferson favored a strict interpretation of the Constitution. He felt that Congress could not extend its powers beyond what was stated explicitly in the Constitution. **b. Possible answer:** Washington did not support the formation of political parties. He believed political parties would destroy American unity and would have a harmful influence on the government. Washington also felt the United States should not get involved in other countries' disputes.

Chapter 11 An Era of Expansion

Terms to Know (p. 24) **A. 1.** radical **2.** anthem **3.** embargo **B. 4.** a **5.** b **6.** d

Review History (p. 57) **A. 1.** Louisiana Purchase **2.** Canada **3.** Embargo Act of 1807 **4.** Lewis and Clark Expedition **5.** War of 1812 **6.** Battle of Tippecanoe Creek **7.** Twelfth Amendment **8.** Alexander Hamilton **B. 9. Possible answer:** Jefferson refused to pay the pirates more money. The ruler of Tripoli declared war. Pirates captured the USS *Philadelphia* and held its crew hostage. After the USS *Constitution* bombarded Tripoli, the United States negotiated a peace treaty. It agreed to pay the ruler of Tripoli $60,000 to rescue the hostages.

Build Your Skills (p. 90) **1.** He is shown as a large man and is holding a stick. **2.** He is shown as a short man and is pulling money out of Thomas Jefferson's pockets. **3.** He is standing in the middle of the two men and is holding his hands in the air. **4.** It shows Jefferson as a victim caught up in a conflict he does not wish to be a part of.

Chapter Test (pp. 135–136) **A. 1.** true **2.** false: Zebulon Pike **3.** true **4.** true **5.** false: British warships **6.** true **7.** true **8.** false: Thomas Jefferson **9.** false: except Great Britain or France **10.** true **11.** true **B. 12.** F **13.** O **14.** F **15.** O **16.** F **17.** O **18.** O **C. 19. a. Possible answer:** When Jefferson was elected President, it was the first time in U.S. history that the political party in power changed. Jefferson placed Democratic-Republicans in government jobs formerly held by Federalists. These actions began a trend that continues today when the political party in power changes. **b. Possible answer:** The War Hawks were a group in Congress who were angry because British ships continued seizing cargo and sailors from American ships. They hoped that winning a war against Great Britain would allow the United States to gain more territory in Canada and Florida for its settlers.

Chapter 12 The Nation Grows

Terms to Know (p. 25) **A. 1.** b **2.** d **3.** c **4.** a **B. 5.** a **6.** c **7.** a

Review History (p. 58) **A. 1.** T **2.** F **3.** F **4.** T **B. 5.** states' rights **6.** two-party system **7.** American System **8.** Whig Party **9.** Five Tribes **10.** Bank of the United States

A. Build Your Skills (p. 91) **A. Details: Possible answers:** Napoleon needed money to help pay for the war. Napoleon wanted to avoid a conflict with the United States. Napoleon wanted to concentrate on defeating the British. Napoleon was worried he would not be able to defend Louisiana if the British or Americans attacked it. **Conclusion: Possible answers:** Napoleon sold the Louisiana Territory to raise money for the war and to avoid any chance of going to war with the United States. The French might not have sold the Louisiana Territory if they had not been at war with Great Britain. **B.** Answers will vary.

Chapter Test (pp. 137–138) **A. 1.** d **2.** e **3.** f **4.** g **5.** b **6.** a **7.** h **8.** i **9.** c **10.** j **B. 11. a.** 4 **b.** 2 **c.** 1 **d.** 3 **12. a.** 4 **b.** 1 **c.** 3 **d.** 2 **C. 13. a. Possible answer:** He began the spoils system, which allowed more people to work in government. He also opened the nomination process to more people by developing the convention system. **b. Possible answer:** The supporters of Andrew Jackson accused John Quincy Adams and Henry Clay of entering into a dishonest bargain to give Adams the presidency.

UNIT 5 THE NATION EXPANDS

Chapter 13 Life in the North and the South

Terms to Know (p. 26) **A. 1.** c **2.** e **3.** a **4.** b **5.** d **B. 6.** c **7.** b **8.** a

Review History (p. 59) **A. 1.** b **2.** a **3.** c **4.** d **B. 5.** T **6.** T **7.** T **8.** F **9.** T **10.** F **11.** T

Build Your Skills (p. 92) **1.** the total number of immigrants to the United States between 1820 and 1840 **2.** the percentage of immigrants from various countries **3.** 70 percent **4.** that most of the immigrants to the United States between 1820 and 1840 came from Germany and Ireland; very few people outside Northern Europe immigrated to the United States between 1820 and 1840

Chapter Test (pp. 139–140) **A. 1.** f **2.** a **3.** i **4.** k **5.** b **6.** d **7.** h **8.** e **9.** c **10.** j **11.** l **12.** g **B. 13.** 3 **14.** 4 **15.** 5 **16.** 1 **17.** 2 **C. 18. a. Possible answer:** Industrialization brought about the need to transport products and raw materials more quickly and easily, which led to improvements in transportation systems. **b. Possible answer:** Slavery supported the southern economy and maintained the social order desired by many living in the South.

Chapter 14 The Spirit of Change

Terms to Know (p. 27) **A. 1.** d **2.** f **3.** e **4.** b **5.** c **6.** a **B. 7.** revival **8.** urban **9.** temperance **10.** reformer **11.** abolition

Review History (p. 60) **A. 1.** T **2.** T **3.** F **4.** T **5.** F **6.** F **B. 7.** b **8.** b **9.** a **10.** c

Build Your Skills (p. 93) Answers in students' charts may vary, but should reflect understanding of text and inferences.

Chapter Test (pp. 141–142) **A. 1.** i **2.** c **3.** d **4.** b **5.** j **6.** f **7.** e **8.** k **9.** g **10.** a **11.** l **12.** h **B. 13. a.** C **b.** E **14. a.** E **b.** C **15. a.** C **b.** E

Answer Key

16. a. C **b.** E **17. a.** E **b.** C **18. a.** C **b.** E **19. a.** E **b.** C **C. 20. a. Possible answer:** The goal of the abolition movement was to end slavery. To fight for change, some people supported runaway slaves, founded abolitionist newspapers, and spoke publicly against slavery. **b. Possible answer:** The goal of the women's rights movement was to obtain equal rights for women, including the right to own property and the right to vote. People fought for these goals by hosting the Seneca Falls Convention and lecturing around the country.

Chapter 15 Westward Expansion

Terms to Know (p. 28) **A. 1.** b **2.** b **3.** d **4.** c **B. 5.** joint occupation **6.** Manifest Destiny **7.** forty-niner **8.** mountain man **9.** empresario

Review History (p. 61) **A. 1.** F **2.** T **3.** F **4.** F **5.** T **6.** F **7.** T **8.** F **9.** T **B. 10.** 4 **11.** 2 **12.** 3 **13.** 5 **14.** 1

Build Your Skills (p. 94) **Facts:** "The Anglo-Saxon foot is already at its borders" and "marking its trail with schools, colleges, courts, and representative halls, mills, and meetinghouses" **Opinions:** "over which it will be idle for Mexico to dream of dominion," and "And they will have a right to independence"

Chapter Test (pp. 143–144) **A. 1.** a **2.** c **3.** b **4.** d **5.** b **6.** d **7.** c **B. 8.** c **9.** a **10.** i **11.** f **12.** b **13.** g **14.** e **15.** h **16.** d **C. 17. a. Possible answer:** Yes, because the settlers felt the Mexican government was taking away many of their rights; No, because the settlers were residents of another country and should have abided by its rules and laws. **b. Possible answer:** They were most likely opposed to it because they felt that much of North America belonged to them, not the citizens of the United States.

UNIT 6 A HOUSE DIVIDED

Chapter 16 The Road to War

Terms to Know (p. 29) **Across: 1.** civil war **4.** popular sovereignty **5.** secede **9.** insurrection **Down: 2.** line item veto **3.** Confederacy **6.** emancipate **7.** extremist **8.** provisional **10.** fugitive

Review History (p. 62) **A. 1.** T **2.** F **3.** F **4.** T **5.** T **6.** F **7.** T **8.** T **B. 9.** John Breckinridge, Abraham Lincoln, John Bell, and Stephen Douglas **10.** settlers fought over whether the area should be slaveholding or free **11.** South Carolina **12.** property and could be taken anywhere by their owners

Build Your Skills (p. 95) **A. Northern Views:** Saw Brown as a martyr; someone who died for a holy cause **Southern Views:** Saw Brown and abolitionists as terrorists who encourage slave revolts **B. Northern Views:** Some believed Lincoln would keep slavery from spreading into territories **Southern Views:** Believed Lincoln would try to abolish slavery throughout the United States **C. Northern Views:** South cannot be permitted to leave the Union **Southern Views:** States have the right to withdraw from the Union if they feel their interests are ignored **D. Northern Views:** U.S. interests must be protected; war begins **Southern Views:** The Confederacy asserts its independence

Chapter Test (pp. 145–146) **A. 1.** c **2.** g **3.** a **4.** f **5.** i **6.** b **7.** h **8.** e **9.** d **10.** j **B. 11.** F **12.** O **13.** O **14.** F **15.** F **16.** O **17.** O **18.** F **19.** F **C. 20. a. Possible answer:** The Democratic Party could not agree on one candidate for the presidency. Northern Democrats nominated Douglas. Southern Democrats nominated Breckinridge. A third party, the Constitutional-Union, nominated Bell. When Lincoln won the election, South Carolina seceded from the Union. **b. Possible answer:** Congress maintained a balance through the Missouri Compromise and the Compromise of 1850. Both compromises maintained an equal number of free and slaveholding states.

Chapter 17 The Civil War

Terms to Know (p. 30) **A. 1.** F **2.** T **3.** F **4.** T **B. 5.** b **6.** c **7.** a **8.** d **9.** a

Review History (p. 63) **A. 1.** 2 **2.** 5 **3.** 4 **4.** 1 **5.** 3 **B. 6.** Emancipation Proclamation **7.** Appomattox Court House **B. 8.** British shipyards **9.** African American **10.** drafted **11.** blockade **12.** Petersburg, Virginia

Build Your Skills (p. 96) **Possible answers: Fact:** The South had better leadership during the early years of the war. **Fact:** The Confederacy gains more ships from British shipyards and troops from both countries. **Fact:** General Lee wins the battle and advances further into Union territory. **Consequence:** The Confederacy is not divided in two; troops and supplies can move from east to west.

Chapter Test (pp. 147–148) **A. 1.** i **2.** a **3.** b **4.** j **5.** h **6.** g **7.** c **8.** d **9.** f **10.** e **B. 11.** c **12.** b **13.** a **14.** c **15.** c **16.** b **C. 17. a. Possible answer:** Lincoln could point to the important role his leadership played in winning the war and several Union victories as reasons for supporting him. He could also point to his Emancipation Proclamation, which promised an end to slavery. **b. Possible answer:** The Union had a larger population and better industry and transportation. It also had President Lincoln, who was a strong leader. To win, the Confederacy did not have to conquer the Union, but only had to survive until the Union tired of war.

Chapter 18 Reunion and Reconstruction

Terms to Know (p. 31) **A. 1.** e **2.** a **3.** c **4.** d **5.** b **6.** f **B. 7.** sharecropping **8.** Freedmen's Bureau **9.** scalawag **10.** segregation **11.** Reconstruction

Review History (p. 64) **A. 1.** F **2.** O **3.** O **4.** O **5.** F **6.** F **B. 7.** F **8.** T **9.** F **10.** T **11.** T **12.** T **13.** T

Build Your Skills (p. 97) **Before Reconstruction:** were slaves, had no civil rights **During Reconstruction:** held public office, formed churches, married legally, farmed under the sharecropping system, owned property **Both Time Periods:** were discriminated against, were threatened and terrorized by some white Southerners, many could not vote

Chapter Test (pp. 149–150) **A. 1.** f **2.** e **3.** a **4.** h **5.** b **6.** d **7.** i **8.** c **9.** j **10.** k **11.** g **B. 12.** Congress removed federal soldiers from southern states as a condition of the compromise to elect Hayes. Without soldiers, Reconstruction laws were no longer enforced. **13.** One requirement of the plan was that 10 percent of a state's voters had to promise their loyalty to the Union before the state would be readmitted. **14.** Lincoln was assassinated. Republicans in Congress wanted a plan that would punish the Confederate states and guarantee civil rights for African Americans. **15.** They wanted to make sure that the Civil Rights Act of 1866 could not be ruled unconstitutional by the Supreme Court. **16.** They used violence and fear to try to prevent African Americans from voting and scare carpetbaggers into moving back to the North. **C. 17. a. Possible answer:** He introduced the idea that the federal government should protect citizens' civil rights, especially if the states did not protect those rights; enlarged the army, which was supposed to be the job of Congress; and took away the civil rights of citizens who opposed the war. **b. Possible answer:** They formed secret societies that used violence to frighten African Americans and carpetbaggers; passed laws known as black codes that limited the rights of recently freed slaves in the early years of Reconstruction; and passed Jim Crow laws, which enforced segregation, as soon as Reconstruction ended.

Midterm Exam (pp. 179–186) **A. 1.** c **2.** b **3.** b **4.** a **5.** c **6.** a **7.** d **8.** b **9.** a **10.** d **11.** c **12.** b **13.** b **14.** c **15.** d **16.** d **17.** a **18.** d **19.** a **20.** b **21.** c **22.** c **23.** b **24.** b **25.** a **26.** a **27.** c **28.** a **29.** b **30.** b **31.** c **32.** a **33.** d **34.** d **35.** d **36.** b **37.** d **38.** c **39.** d **40.** b **41.** b **42.** a **43.** c **44.** c **45.** a **46.** d **B. 47. Possible answer:** Life for white plantation owners usually was easier because they typically did not have to do as much physical labor as enslaved Africans. **C. 48.** Essays should discuss the secret societies formed by some white people, such as the Ku Klux Klan. This discussion should include examples of actions these groups took against African Americans. Essays should also discuss how white Southerners worked to deny African Americans the right to vote and developed Jim Crow laws to create a segregated society. Finally, essays should describe how African Americans suffered from terror and violence and were not allowed to vote or spend time in many public places.

Answer Key

Teacher's Resources

UNIT 7 GROWTH AT HOME AND ABROAD

Chapter 19 Life in the West

Terms to Know (p. 32) **A. 1.** homesteader **2.** cooperative **3.** assimilate **4.** transcontinental **5.** platform **B. 6.** c **7.** e **8.** a **9.** b **10.** d

Review History (p. 65) **A. 1. a.** C **b.** E **2. a.** C **b.** E **3. a.** E **b.** C **4. a.** E **b.** C **5. a.** C **b.** E **6. a.** C **b.** E **B. 7.** F **8.** T **9.** F **10.** T **11.** F

Build Your Skills (p. 98) **1.** It shows the battles of the Civil War from 1861 to 1863. **2.** September 1862 **3.** Washington, D.C., Richmond, VA **4.** Seven Days, Chancellorsville, and Bull Run

Chapter Test (pp. 151–152) **A. 1.** The buffalo populations they depended on were hunted almost to extinction. They were forced to move to reservations and were not able to continue their traditional ways. **2.** The railroads charged higher prices for transporting harvested grain to market. **3.** The three industries were farming, ranching, and mining. **4.** Good fences meant the cattle no longer roamed wild, so cowhands were no longer needed to round them up. **5.** They thought it was an empty desert and not a good place to live. **6.** The law gave public land to railroad builders and provided a way for the government to help pay for railroad construction. **7.** Railroad companies sold land not needed for railroad tracks to farmers. They advertised the availability of land to people on the East Coast and in Europe. **B. 8.** a **9.** d **10.** b **11.** b **12.** a **C. 13. a. Possible answer:** Cowhands rode horses around the range in search of wild cattle to round up. They then drove the cattle hundreds of miles north to towns on the railroad lines. They used hot irons to brand cattle for identification. They worked from dawn to dusk, and also took turns standing guard over the cattle for two hours each night. Their work began in the spring, and the cattle drive usually lasted two or three months. **b. Possible answer:** Sitting Bull was one of the Native American chiefs who refused to sign the Fort Laramie Treaty in 1868. His Sioux warriors protested when the government allowed thousands of gold miners into the Black Hills of South Dakota. They defeated General Custer at the Battle of Little Bighorn in 1875. Sitting Bull escaped to Canada, but returned to live on a reservation in 1881. After the Ghost Dance ceremony, many Native Americans talked of leaving the reservations. In response, the government ordered the arrest of Sitting Bull. He was killed by the government troops who tried to arrest him.

Chapter 20 The Rise of Industry

Terms to Know (p. 33) **A. 1.** d **2.** a **3.** e **4.** b **5.** c **6.** f **B. 7.** c **8.** b **9.** a

Review History (p. 66) **A. 1.** false: Most new immigrants lived in cities because most farmland was already owned, and they could not afford to buy the land that was not owned. **2.** false: Andrew Carnegie's factories had poor working conditions and low salaries, and he believed that both poverty and wealth are natural. **3.** true **4.** false: The Chinese Exclusion Act banned most Chinese immigrants from entering the United States. **5.** true **6.** false: Most Asian immigrants entered the United States at Angel Island, near San Francisco. **7.** false: In ethnic communities, people from one culture or nationality live in close contact with one another. **B. Possible answer:** The Bessemer process made refining steel much easier and less expensive. It also produced stronger steel. This method became very popular in the United States, and most steel industries used it. The railroad industry used steel to make railroad tracks. The railroad companies' demand for steel increased because the Bessemer process made steel easier and cheaper to produce. The railroad industry could lay more tracks for less money. The increased number of tracks helped the railroad industry grow.

Build Your Skills (p. 99) Answers will vary.

Chapter Test (pp. 153–154) **A. 1.** Steel production increases. **2.** Persecution, hunger, and war take place in many countries. **3.** Manufacturing, transportation, and communications are improved. **4.** Isaac Singer invents the sewing machine. **5.** Bottles are invented that seal out air. **6.** Workers are often killed on the job. **7.** Railway workers' wages are cut by 10 percent. **8.** Anti-Chinese riots break out in California. **B. 9.** T **10.** T **11.** F **12.** T **13.** F **14.** T **15.** T **16.** F **17.** F **18.** T **19.** T **C. 20. a. Possible answers:**

Both eastern European and Asian immigrants: worked jobs that involved physical labor; were discriminated against because of their customs or because they were willing to work for low pay; lived in ethnic communities. **Experiences of eastern European and Asian immigrants differed:** Asian immigrants lived mainly in California and eastern Europeans lived mainly in East Coast cities; Congress passed a law banning the immigration of Asian immigrants, not eastern European immigrants; Asian immigrants entered the United States at Angel Island; eastern European immigrants entered at Ellis Island. **b. Possible answers:** Workers joined or formed unions to better working conditions and increase pay. They sometimes used collective bargaining, or talks between unions and business owners. Other times they went on strike.

Chapter 21 The Progressive Era

Terms to Know (p. 34) **A. 1.** T **2.** T **3.** F **4.** F **5.** F **6.** T **B. 7.** b **8.** c **9.** a **10.** c

Review History (p. 67) **A. 1.** b **2.** d **3.** b **4.** a **B. 5.** Chinese Exclusion Act **6.** vote **7.** banking system **8.** child labor **9.** Department of Commerce and Labor

Build Your Skills (p. 100) **Facts: Possible answers:** Jane Addams opened Hull House to provide services for the poor people of the neighborhood; Muckrakers helped people see society's problems; W. E. B. Du Bois fought for equality; Ida B. Wells set up clubs to fight lynching; The National American Women's Suffrage Association fought for women's right to vote.
Generalization: Possible answer: Reformers worked to fix social problems.

Chapter Test (pp. 155–156) **A. 1.** i **2.** f **3.** a **4.** h **5.** b **6.** e **7.** g **8.** c **9.** j **10.** d **B. 11.** T **12.** F **13.** F **14.** T **15.** T **16.** F **17.** F **18.** F **19.** T **C. 20. a. Possible answer:** Jim Crow laws kept African Americans from voting and segregated public places. African Americans had separate seating on trains and buses. They went to separate schools and were barred from restaurants that served white customers. **b. Possible answer:** Muckrakers reported on child labor, tenements, conditions in factories, and corruption in government.

Chapter 22 Expansion Overseas

Terms to Know (p. 35) **A. 1.** a **2.** c **3.** b **4.** d **B. 5.** sphere of influence **6.** yellow journalism **7.** imperialism **8.** diplomacy

Review History (p. 68) **A.** checks should be next to 1, 3, 5, and 6 **B. 7.** c **8.** b **9.** b **10.** a **11.** a **12.** c

Build Your Skills (p. 101) Answers will vary.

Chapter Test (pp. 157–158) **A. 1.** d **2.** g **3.** a **4.** i **5.** b **6.** j **7.** c **8.** e **9.** f **10.** h **B. 11.** F **12.** T **13.** T **14.** F **15.** T **16.** T **17.** F **18.** F **19.** T **C. 20. a. Possible answer:** Roosevelt used a "Big Stick" diplomacy; Taft's policy focused on the use of economic power; Wilson's policy focused on the rights of nations. **b. Possible answer:** In engaging in imperialism, the United States was denying other countries freedom and self-determination, the very principles on which the United States was founded.

UNIT 8 A TROUBLED NATION

Chapter 23 World War I

Terms to Know (p. 36) **1.** d **2.** a **3.** e **4.** b **5.** c **B. 6.** mobilize **7.** armistice **8.** victory garden **9.** self-determination **10.** pacifist

Review History (p. 69) **A. 1.** F **2.** F **3.** T **4.** T **5.** T **6.** F **B. 7.** Committee on Public Information **8.** aces **9.** the American Expeditionary Force **10.** League of Nations **11.** war bonds

Build Your Skills (p. 102) Answers will vary.

Chapter Test (pp. 159–160) **A. 1.** c **2.** g **3.** i **4.** j **5.** d **6.** a **7.** e **8.** b **9.** f **10.** h **B. 11. a.** 2 **b.** 1 **c.** 3 **d.** 4 **12. a.** 4 **b.** 2 **c.** 5 **d.** 1 **e.** 3 **C. 13. a. Possible answer:** Many Americans were angered by Germany's harsh treatment of the Belgians. German forces began sinking American ships sailing to England or France. **b. Possible answer:** Opposing forces dug long trenches strung with barbed wire in front of their forces for defense. Germany began using U-boats, or submarines, armed with torpedoes to sink enemy ships. On land, armored tanks, machine guns, and hand grenades killed many soldiers.

Answer Key

Teacher's Resources

Chapter 24 Life in the 1920s

Terms to Know (p. 37) **A. 1.** installment plan **2.** Harlem Renaissance **3.** bootlegger **4.** quota **B. 5.** b **6.** c **7.** a **8.** d

Review History (p. 70) **A. 1.** Teapot Dome **2.** advertisers **3.** Nineteenth Amendment **4.** alcoholic beverages **5.** baseball heroes **B. 6.** F **7.** T **8.** F **9.** F **10.** T **11.** T

Build Your Skills (p. 103) **1.** a radio **2.** it might be something new that they have never seen before **3.** curiosity **4.** New technologies were being developed that had an impact on family life.

Chapter Test (pp. 161–162) **A. 1.** h **2.** c **3.** e **4.** f **5.** b **6.** d **7.** j **8.** i **9.** a **10.** g **B. 11.** b **12.** c **13.** b **14.** d **15.** a **16.** b **C. 17. a. Possible answer:** Ford's mass-produced Model T allowed more people to own a car. New appliances gave people more free time for activities such as reading and watching movies. **b. Possible answer:** African Americans competed with white Americans for jobs and faced unequal conditions, leading to race riots. Ku Klux Klan members took action against African Americans, Catholics, and Jews, sometimes kidnapping, lynching, and beating people.

Chapter 25 The Great Depression and the New Deal

Terms to Know (p. 38) **A. 1.** relief **2.** profit **3.** tenant farmer **4.** conservative **5.** pension **B. 6.** b **7.** d **8.** a **9.** e **10.** c

Review History (p. 71) **A. 1.** c **2.** e **3.** d **4.** a **5.** b **6.** g **B. 7.** "Hoovervilles" **8.** Tennessee Valley Authority **9.** workers **10.** fireside chats

Build Your Skills (p. 104) **1.** The graph shows how much stocks were worth from 1920 to 1932. **2.** $100 **3.** 1929 **4.** $300 **5.** how prices fell after 1929

Chapter Test (pp. 163–164) **A. 1. a.** C **b.** E **2. a.** C **b.** E **3. a.** E **b.** C **4. a.** E **b.** C **5. a.** C **b.** E **6. a.** C **b.** E **7. a.** E **b.** C **8. a.** C **b.** E **9. a.** E **b.** C **B. 10.** F **11.** T **12.** F **13.** F **14.** T **15.** T **16.** F **17.** F **18.** F **19.** F
C. 20. a. Possible answer: President Hoover did not provide assistance to the poor and unemployed. Roosevelt gave people hope—he seemed confident and had a plan for a "New Deal." **20. b. Possible answer:** African Americans lost jobs to white employees and faced discrimination. Many Mexicans who had come across the border to fill jobs during World War I were replaced by white employees. Under the New Deal, many minorities worked through New Deal programs.

UNIT 9 AMERICA BECOMES A WORLD LEADER

Chapter 26 World War II

Terms to Know (p. 39) **A. 1.** F **2.** T **3.** T **4.** T **5.** T **B. 6.** g **7.** e **8.** a **9.** b **10.** d **11.** f **12.** c

Review History (p. 72) **A. 1.** T **2.** F **3.** T **4.** F **B. 5.** g **6.** h **7.** e **8.** c **9.** f **10.** b **11.** a **12.** d

Build Your Skills (p. 105) **1.** Answers will vary. Students should demonstrate an understanding of the woman's strength, independence, and patriotism. **2.** Answers will vary. **3.** Answers will vary. Students should include that the government is encouraging women to be strong. **4.** Answers will vary. Students may suggest that the poster inspired many women to join the workforce, to work harder, and to be strong.

Chapter Test (pp. 165–166) **A. 1. a.** 3 **b.** 1 **c.** 2 **d.** 4 **2. a.** 1 **b.** 3 **c.** 2 **d.** 4 **B. 3.** a **4.** d **5.** b **6.** c **7.** b **8.** d **9.** a **10.** c **C. 11. a. Possible answer:** Students should demonstrate how the United States gained military power through the atomic bomb; how the U.S. economy greatly improved after supplying Allies with war materials; and how not fighting on U.S. soil gave the country an advantage over war-torn nations. **b. Possible answer:** Students should include how Jewish people were treated before the war. They should write about how Jewish homes were taken; how Jewish people were forced to wear a yellow star; how those who were not killed were forced to live in concentration camps; and how they endured horrific conditions in concentration camps.

Chapter 27 The Cold War

Terms to Know (p. 40) **A. 1.** f **2.** b **3.** d **4.** h **5.** g **6.** a **7.** e **8.** c **B. 9.** T **10.** T **11.** F **12.** T **13.** T **14.** F

Review History (p. 73) **A. 1.** 4 **2.** 2 **3.** 5 **4.** 6 **5.** 1 **6.** 3 **B. 7.** Berlin airlift **8.** Truman Doctrine **9.** sports **10.** Warsaw Pact **11.** Red Scare **12.** space technology

Build Your Skills (p. 106) **1.** 8 A.M. in Los Angeles **2.** Cairo, Moscow, Beijing, Toyko, Anadyr **3.** 9 A.M. **4.** Cairo

Chapter Test (pp. 167–168) **A. 1.** d **2.** f **3.** g **4.** h **5.** e **6.** a **7.** c **8.** j **9.** i **10.** b **B. 11.** b **12.** c **13.** a **14.** b **15.** a **16.** a **17.** a **C. 18. a.** Some students will agree and argue that violence only leads to more violence and that true change will come only from convincing people with persuasive, reasonable arguments; other students might disagree and claim that many people and institutions respond only to violence. **b. Possible answer:** Many Americans saw communism as a threat to their way of life, because it went against the ideas of liberty, freedom, and self-government, which were the principles on which the United States was founded.

Chapter 28 The Kennedy Years

Terms to Know (p. 41) **A. 1.** sit-in **2.** guerrilla war **3.** New Frontier **4.** integrate **B. 5.** c **6.** b **7.** d **8.** a

Review History (p. 74) **A. 1.** Freedom Ride **2.** Martin Luther King Jr. **3.** national television **4.** nuclear war **5.** Fidel Castro **B. 6.** T **7.** T **8.** T **9.** F **10.** T **11.** F **12.** F

Build Your Skills (p. 107) **1.** increase **2.** decrease **3.** between 1958 and 1961 **4.** between 1978 and 1983

Chapter Test (pp. 169–170) **A. 1.** h **2.** g **3.** a **4.** d **5.** j **6.** i **7.** l **8.** f **9.** k **10.** b **11.** c **12.** e **13. a.** E **b.** C **14. a.** C **b.** E **15. a.** C **b.** E **16. a.** C **b.** E **17. a.** E **b.** C **18. a. Possible answer:** People watched the brutal way that the police treated the protesters on television. People were angry about what they saw. The federal government pressured the Birmingham city government to end segregation. **b. Possible answer:** The Limited Nuclear Test Ban Treaty was signed by the United States, the Soviet Union, and Great Britain in 1963. The United States and the Soviet Union set up the hotline, an emergency telephone system that would keep the leaders of the two countries in direct contact.

Chapter 29 The Johnson Years

Terms to Know (p. 42) **1.** i **2.** k **3.** c **4.** f **5.** e **6.** a **7.** j **8.** g **9.** d **10.** h **11.** b

Review History (p. 75) **A. 1.** Gulf of Tonkin Resolution **2.** Higher Education Act **3.** Indians of All Tribes **4.** Voting Rights Act **5.** Viet Cong **6.** Tet Offensive **B. 7.** T **8.** T **9.** F

Build Your Skills (p. 108) **Possible answers: Women's Rights:** The National Organization for Women is formed to fight for equal rights in the workplace, education, and politics. Congress passes the Equal Pay Act, which requires that women are paid the same amount as men for the same work. **Mexican American Rights:** Mexican American leaders create the Mexican American Political Association. César Chávez leads an effort to gain better working conditions for Mexican farmworkers. **Native American Rights:** The American Indian Movement (AIM) forms to improve conditions for Native Americans and to change Native American government policies. Congress passes the Indian Civil Rights Act, which protects the constitutional rights of Native Americans and allows them greater freedom to govern their reservations.

Chapter Test (pp. 171–172) **A. 1.** The purpose of Medicare was to provide low-cost health insurance for people over 65. **2.** The goal is to improve run-down areas of American cities. **3.** Police were required to tell suspects about their rights. **4.** They took control of the abandoned penitentiary on Alcatraz Island. **5.** They felt that other countries would also fall to communism. **6.** It convinced them that the war would not be ending soon. **7.** They did not think the bill was necessary. **B. 8.** b **9.** b **10.** d **11.** a **12.** a **C. 13. a. Possible answer:** Television showed the brutal scenes of combat as well as the student protests and announced daily body counts. **b.** Answers will vary.

Answer Key

Teacher's Resources

UNIT 10 MODERN AMERICA

Chapter 30 Turbulent Times

Terms to Know (p. 43) **A. 1.** c **2.** d **3.** a **4.** b **B. 5.** c **6.** b **7.** a **8.** a

Review History (p. 76) **A. 1.** b **2.** c **3.** d **4.** a **B. 5.** Hubert Humphrey **6.** impeachment **7.** the shah to be returned to Iran **8.** *Apollo 11* landed on the moon **9.** balanced budget

Build Your Skills (p. 109) **1. Possible answers:** "You can be sure"; serious face on Ford **2. Possible answers:** "for a Better Future"; picture of Carter with young children **3.** Answers will vary.

Chapter Test (pp. 173–174) **A. 1.** O **2.** O **3.** F **4.** O **5.** F **6.** O **B. 7.** b **8.** b **9.** d **10.** d **11.** a **12.** c **13.** d **14.** b **C. 15. a. Possible answer:** Students might mention that it showed Americans that individuals acting in the name of government sometimes make poor decisions over which the general population has little or no control.
b. Possible answer: The first men walked on the moon in 1969, during the Nixon administration. Nixon approved $5.5 billion in funding for the first six years of the space shuttle program.

Chapter 31 New Challenges for the Nation

Terms to Know (p. 44) **A. 1.** c **2.** d **3.** b **4.** e **5.** a **6.** f **B. 7.** a **8.** c **9.** c

Review History (p. 77) **A. 1. a.** 2 **b.** 1 **c.** 4 **d.** 3 **2. a.** 1 **b.** 3 **c.** 4 **d.** 2 **B. 3.** F **4.** F **5.** T **6.** T **7.** T **8.** F

Build Your Skills (p. 110) **1.** Compare **2.** Discuss **3.** Evaluate **4.** Define **5.** Contrast

Chapter Test (pp. 175–176) **A. 1.** b **2.** f **3.** a **4.** k **5.** g **6.** c **7.** e **8.** d **9.** i **10.** j **11.** h **B. 12.** T **13.** T **14.** T **15.** T **16.** F **17.** T **18.** F **19.** T **C. 20. a. Possible answer:** Bush went against his conservative supporters when he supported the Americans With Disabilities Act and the Clean Air Act. Both acts would place expensive restrictions on businesses. **b. Possible answer:** Clinton's foreign policy led to the loss of eighteen Army Rangers in Somalia and failed to capture the Somali warlord.

Chapter 32 Looking to the Future

Terms to Know (p. 45) **A. 1.** a **2.** c **3.** d **B. 4.** d **5.** b **6.** a **7.** c **8.** e

Review History (p. 78) **A. 1.** tax cuts **2.** fossil fuels **3.** World Wide Web **4.** health insurance **5.** NAFTA **6.** healthcare **B. Possible answers: 7.** laser surgery **8.** Hubble Space Telescope **9.** genetic engineering **10.** energy supplies **11.** nonrenewable resources **12.** diseases

Build Your Skills (p. 111) **Possible answers: 1.** photograph of a crowded expressway **2.** to indicate a cause of global warming **3.** chart showing increases in the earth's temperature **4.** to show the steady rise in the earth's temperature **5.** film footage of droughts, hurricanes, or other natural disasters **6.** to indicate the results of rising temperatures **7.** newspaper or Web site article about the Kyoto Protocol **8.** to show a measure being taken to curb global warming

Chapter Test (pp. 177–178) **A. 1.** b **2.** c **3.** a **4.** c **5.** d **6.** c **7.** a **8.** c **B. 9.** e **10.** a **11.** b **12.** c **13.** f **14.** d **C. 15. a. Possible answer:** It helps by providing more markets for the United States to sell its goods, but it can hurt by prompting U.S. factories—and jobs—to move to countries where labor is less expensive. **b.** Answers will vary; accept reasonable responses.

Final Exam (pp. 187–194) **A. 1.** b **2.** d **3.** b **4.** c **5.** b **6.** a **7.** b **8.** b **9.** b **10.** d **11.** a **12.** c **13.** d **14.** a **15.** d **16.** c **17.** b **18.** a **19.** c **20.** a **21.** c **22.** a **23.** c **24.** c **25.** c **26.** b **27.** a **28.** d **29.** c **30.** b **31.** b **32.** c **33.** a **34.** d **35.** b **36.** b **37.** d **38.** d **39.** a **40.** a **41.** c **42.** d **43.** a **44.** c **45.** a **B. 46. Possible answer:** They were forced off their farms during a drought and migrated west in search of work. **C. 47.** Essays may discuss Kennedy's New Frontier program, his goals for the space program, and his attempts to help developing countries of the world. Students may mention the establishment of the Peace Corps as well as Kennedy's handling of the Cuban Missile Crisis as successes of his presidency. The failed Bay of Pigs invasion as well as the continuation of the Vietnam situation may be considered failures.

CONCEPT BUILDERS

Chapter 1 **A. Olmec:** Mexico's Gulf Coast; 1200–400 or 300 B.C.; one or more of the following: influenced many future cultures, built cities with huge pyramids, invented calendars and writing systems **Maya:** Central America; 1500 B.C.–A.D. 900; one or more of the following: created an empire, developed cities with temples and palaces, recorded their writing on paper made from fig trees, were expert farmers and scientists **Toltec:** from the Gulf Coast of Mexico to Central America; A.D. 900–1200; one or more of the following: created a vast empire based on warfare, created fine buildings and metalwork **Inca:** Andes Mountains in South America; A.D. 1200; one or more of the following: built an empire with a system of roads, had skilled artisans craft gold and silver into religious and personal ornaments **Aztec:** central valley of Mexico; A.D. 1200 or 1350–1500; one or more of the following: built a huge empire after conquering other groups, built the city of Tenochtitlán **B.** Answers will vary.

Chapter 2 **A.** Answers will vary. Responses should accurately reflect chapter content. **B.** Answers will vary.

Chapter 3 **A. Possible answers: Who:** Hernándo Cortés; **What:** Conquered Aztecs; **Where:** present-day Mexico; **When:** 1519; **Why:** To take their land and gold; **Who:** Francisco Pizarro; **What:** Set out to conquer Incas; **Where:** present-day Peru; **When:** 1531; **Why:** To take their gold and silver; **Who:** Juan Ponce de León; **What:** Explored Florida; **Where:** present-day Florida; **When:** 1521; **Why:** To capture land for Spain; **Who:** Francisco Coronado; **What:** Claimed present-day southwestern America for Spain; **Where:** southwestern America; **When:** 1539; **Why:** To find gold; **Who:** Samuel de Champlain; **What:** Established first French settlement; **Where:** present-day eastern Canada; **When:** 1603; **Why:** To start a fur trade for France; **Who:** Henry Hudson; **What:** Explored Hudson River; **Where:** present-day New York; **When:** 1609; **Why:** To find the Northwest Passage to Asia; **Who:** Hernándo De Soto; **What:** Looking for fabled cities; **Where:** Present-day southern states; **When:** 1539; **Why:** To find gold; **Who:** Robert de La Salle; **What:** Explored entire present-day Mississippi River valley; **Where:** Louisiana; **When:** 1682; **Why:** To claim land for France **B.** Answers will vary.

Chapter 4 **A.** Answers will vary, but should include a description of one illustration and its caption from each section of the chapter. Main ideas should be based on a topic dealt with in the illustration and caption. **B.** Answers will vary.

Chapter 5 **A. Middle colonies: system of farming:** larger and more productive farms; **land:** level and pre-cleared of trees; **soil:** extremely rich; **climate:** milder; **crops:** grains; **natural resources:** fur and iron; **industry:** fur trade and iron manufacturing **Southern colonies: system of farming:** both small family farms and large plantations; **land:** broad coastal plain; **soil:** fertile; **climate:** mild; **crops:** tobacco, rice, and indigo; **natural resources:** pine trees; **industry:** tar (from pine trees) **B.** Answers will vary.

Chapter 6 **A. Monarch: made up of:** king or queen; **powers:** approved all actions of colonial governments; **Governor: made up of:** individual selected by monarch; in some cases, selected by proprietor or voting colonists with monarch's approval; **powers:** enforced the laws of the colony and England with the aid of a council; **Assembly: made up of:** group elected by voters in each colony; **powers:** made laws for the colony; **Council: made up of:** wealthy men selected by the governor; **powers:** helped governor approve laws and served as the high court **B.** Answers will vary.

Chapter 7 **A. Cause:** British government wants colonists to pay share of war debt **Effect:** Colonists argue that Parliament does not have the right to tax them; **Cause: Possible answers:** Protests against British troops in Boston; the Townshend Acts **Effect:** Repeal of Townshend Acts; Samuel Adams forms the Committee of Correspondence; **Cause:** Tea Act **Effect:** Intolerable Acts; **Cause: Possible answers:** Battle of Bunker Hill; King George III's refusal to put an end to the Intolerable Acts **Effect: Possible answers:** George Washington named commander in chief of colonial army; Olive Branch Petition sent to King George III; Declaration of Independence **B.** Answers will vary.

Answer Key

Teacher's Resources

Chapter 8 A. **1.** British victory at Brooklyn Heights, New York **2.** American victory over Hessian troops at Trenton, New Jersey **3.** British victory at Philadelphia, Pennsylvania **4.** American victory at Saratoga, New York **5.** British victory at Charleston, South Carolina **6.** American victory over the British navy **7.** American victory at Yorktown, VA **B.** Answers will vary.

Chapter 9 A. **1.** The Articles of Confederation **2.** 13 states **3.** November 1777 **4.** to create a new government to unite the states **5.** Northwest Ordinance **6.** land north of the Ohio River and east of the Mississippi River **7.** 1787 **8.** to create the Northwest Territory **9.** Annapolis Convention **10.** Annapolis, Maryland **11.** 1786 **12.** to discuss problems with the Articles of Confederation **B.** Answers will vary.

Chapter 10 A. **1.** created a Cabinet **2.** passed Judiciary Act of 1789 **3.** approved Hamilton's economic plan **4.** put down the Whiskey Rebellion **5.** subdued Native Americans in the northwest **6.** resolved conflicts with Great Britain **B.** Answers will vary.

Chapter 11 A. **1.** The power of judicial review is used in the *Marbury* v. *Madison* case. **2.** France sells the Louisiana Territory to the United States. **3.** Lewis and Clark set out on their expedition. **4.** James Madison is elected President. **5.** War begins between the United States and Britain. **6.** The British are defeated at Fort McHenry. **B.** Answers will vary.

Chapter 12 **A. Bank of the United States:** opposed the bank; vetoed a measure to renew the bank's charter and then put the bank out of business by taking out all federal deposits **Nullification Crisis:** did not agree with the idea of states' rights and wanted Congress to pass the Force Bill, which would give the President the right to use troops to enforce federal law **Native Americans:** supported their removal to land west of the Mississippi River; ignored Supreme Court ruling giving land rights to the Cherokee and sent in soldiers to force the Cherokee to leave **B.** Answers will vary.

Chapter 13 **A. Samuel Slater:** invention, cotton spinning machine; effect, helped to create textile factories, which brought the Industrial Revolution to the United States **Eli Whitney:** inventions, interchangeable parts/cotton gin; effect, interchangeable parts made mass production possible; cotton gin made cotton South's most profitable cash crop and led to an increase in slavery **Cyrus McCormick:** invention, mechanical reaper; effect, sped up harvesting **John Deere:** invention, lightweight steel plow; effect, helped farmers plow hard soil of the Great Plains **Samuel Morse:** invention, telegraph; effect, allowed people to communicate instantly **B.** Answers will vary.

Chapter 14 **A. Possible answers: 1.** to come to a new country **2.** writings that have excellent form and universal ideas **3.** correction of an abuse or a wrong **4.** the treatment of two groups differently based on something other than merit **B. Possible answers: City life:** Lots of people, big buildings, busy streets, lots of activities, noisier. **Country life:** Fewer people, more nature and open spaces, quieter. **Both:** have roads, people, rules and laws that must be followed, important jobs.

Chapter 15 **A. Possible answers: 1836:** Texas declares its independence from Mexico; Texas wins its independence in the Texas Revolution. **1845:** Texas becomes the twenty-eighth state of the Union. **1846:** The war between the United States and Mexico begins; The United States and Great Britain agree to share the Oregon Territory. **1848:** The Treaty of Guadalupe Hidalgo gives the United States a large territory that includes present-day California, Arizona, New Mexico, Colorado, Utah, and Nevada; Mormons settle Salt Lake City; The discovery of gold in California leads to the California gold rush. **1853:** The Gadsden Purchase marks the completion of the North American boundaries of the United States. **B.** Answers will vary.

Chapter 16 A. **1.** The Fugitive Slave Law turns many Northerners against slavery. **2.** Bleeding Kansas shows that the slavery issue can turn violent. **3.** John Brown's raid on Harpers Ferry angers Northerners and Southerners. **4.** Abraham Lincoln is elected President. **5.** Southern states begin to leave the Union. **6.** Southern states form the Confederate States of America. **7.** Confederate forces attack Fort Sumter. **B.** Answers will vary.

Chapter 17 **A. North:** better transportation; factories; larger population; banks to make loans;

technical schools **South:** slavery; cotton; plantations; spirituals, rebellions **B.** Answers will vary.

Chapter 18 **A. 1.** Congress passes the Thirteenth Amendment to the Constitution. **2.** Abraham Lincoln is assassinated. **3.** Congress passes the Civil Rights Act of 1866. **4.** Congress passes the Reconstruction Act. **5.** The Fifteenth Amendment to the Constitution is adopted. **6.** Rutherford B. Hayes becomes President. **7.** Reconstruction ends. **B.** Answers will vary.

Chapter 19 **A. Possible answers: 1.** wheat **2.** Farmers faced scarce rainfall, lack of trees to build homes and make heat, very hot summers, natural disasters, and loneliness. **3.** buffalo **4.** Cowhands herded them together and drove them to the railroads for transport to the cities. **5.** Cowhands worked long hours, were not paid well, and endured relentless heat, stampedes, storms, and swift river crossings. **6.** gold and silver **B.** Answers will vary. Students should include major points from the chapter.

Chapter 20 **A. Possible answers: Andrew Carnegie:** owned most of the steel industry in the United States; founded Carnegie Hall and the Carnegie Foundation for the Advancement of Teaching; controlled the steel industry by owning most of the businesses needed to make steel **John D. Rockefeller:** owned most of the oil industry; founded the University of Chicago and the Rockefeller Institute for Medical Research; controlled oil industry by buying other oil companies **Characteristics they share:** owned monopolies; gave money to worthy causes; paid workers low wages; had unsafe factories with dangerous working conditions; extremely wealthy **B.** Answers will vary.

Chapter 21 **A. Possible answers: Section I: 1. Problem:** Corrupt politicians gave jobs to people who would help them even if they were not qualified for the job. **Solution:** Pendleton Civil Service Act **2. Problem:** Many people lived in dirty tenements. **Solution:** Hull House, settlement houses **Section II: 3. Problem:** Alcohol hurt the lives of many. **Solution:** Eighteenth Amendment **4. Problem:** Corrupt local government made it hard to solve problems. **Solution:** City commissioners were hired. **Section III: 5. Problem:** Big business stopped competition. **Solution:** Sherman Anti-Trust Act **6. Problem:** Women were not allowed to vote. **Solution:** Nineteenth Amendment **B.** Answers will vary but should reflect students' knowledge of chapter content and understanding of cause and effect.

Chapter 22 **A. Causes:** competition with European nations; desire to spread American culture; establish foreign markets for U.S. goods; increase power and prestige on world stage **Effects:** purchase of Alaska; annexation of Hawaii; control of Cuba, Puerto Rico, the Philippines, and Guam; construction of the Panama Canal; Roosevelt Corollary; Big Stick diplomacy **B.** Answers will vary.

Chapter 23 **A. Possible answers: Cause:** Archduke Ferdinand is assassinated. **Effect:** War breaks out in Europe **Cause:** U-boats sink American ships. **Effect:** Anti-German feelings increase. **Cause:** United States enters war **Effect:** The Allies win the war. **B.** Answers will vary.

Chapter 24 **A.** Facts will vary. **B.** Answers will vary.

Chapter 25 **A.** Answers will vary depending on the headings chosen. **B.** Answers will vary.

Chapter 26 **A. 1. Effect:** Britain and France allowed Hitler to keep the land with the promise that he would not seize any more land. **2. Cause:** Japan runs out of natural resources and wants to build its military. **3. Effect:** The United States enters the war. **4. Cause:** The United States joins the Allies to stage D-day against the German forces. **5. Effect:** Japan surrenders and the war ends. **6. Cause:** Hitler declares his "final solution" policy. **B.** Answers will vary.

Chapter 27 **A. Possible answers: Political:** emergence of Cold War between the United States and Soviet Union; President Truman issues Truman Doctrine; the United States institutes Marshall Plan; the United States enacts Berlin airlift; China becomes Communist; the United States tries to settle various crises in the Middle East;

Truman wins surprise re-election; the United States and allies fight in the Korean War; Red Scare engulfs America; rise and fall of McCarthyism; Eisenhower wins the presidency; the United States and Soviets engage in nuclear arms race; U-2 spy plane incident; formation of the Central Intelligence Agency **Social:** *Brown* v. *Board of Education of Topeka* ends policy of separate but equal; Little Rock school desegregation crisis; emergence of Martin Luther King Jr. as leader of the civil rights movement; growth of the suburbs; more women enter the workforce; influence of television grows; growth of rock and roll; emergence of beat culture **B.** Answers will vary; responses should be supported by appropriate facts and details.

Chapter 28 **A. Possible answers: Civil Rights:** In the 1950s, civil rights issues became increasingly important; the National Association for the Advancement of Colored People (NAACP) worked to end segregation in schools; *Brown* v. *Board of Education of Topeka* ended school segregation; Montgomery bus boycott lasted for 331 days beginning in 1955 and ended with a desegregated bus system; Martin Luther King Jr. emerged as a leader and promoted nonviolent methods. **Cold War:** After World War II, tension increased between democratic and Communist nations; the Soviet Union was worried about an invasion from the west, and the western countries were worried about the spread of communism; the Soviet Union set up Communist governments in surrounding Eastern European countries; countries formed the United Nations; the United States worked to stop the spread of communism; Germany was split into two countries, one democratic and one Communist; the United States sent aid to Turkey and Greece to prevent them from becoming Communist; the Truman Doctrine included measures to help any country that was threatened by a Communist takeover; the Marshall Plan provided funding to rebuild war-torn European countries and prevent the spread of communism; China became a Communist nation. **B.** Answers will vary; answers should include ideas from the chart.

Chapter 29 **A.** Answers will vary. **B.** Answers will vary; paragraphs should include information from the chart.

Chapter 30 **A. 1.** Robert Kennedy is assassinated during his presidential campaign. **2.** Antiwar protesters disrupt the Democratic National Convention. **3.** The Environmental Protection Agency is created. **4.** President Nixon visits China and the Soviet Union. **5.** North Vietnam and the United States agree to a truce. **6.** Congress passes the War Powers Act. **7.** OPEC stops the sale of oil to countries that support Israel. **8.** Nixon resigns as a result of the Watergate scandal. **B.** Answers will vary. Students' answers should include a description of the event and any applicable causes and effects.

Chapter 31 **A. 1.** Sandra Day O'Connor is appointed justice to the Supreme Court. **2.** Money earned from the arms sale to Iran is used to fund Contras in Nicaragua. **3.** Amendments to the Clean Air Act of 1970 are signed. **4.** The Berlin Wall separating East and West Berlin is opened. **5.** U.S. troops launch air raids on the Serbs to end ethnic cleansing in Bosnia. **6.** The first truly democratic election is held in South Africa. **B.** Answers will vary.

Chapter 32 **A.** Answers will vary. **B.** Answers will vary.

THEY MADE HISTORY

Chapter 1 Montezuma **1.** He was the ruler of the Aztec Empire of Mexico from 1502–1520. **2.** The emperor made them pay for buildings he constructed. **3.** He may have believed that Cortés was Quetzalcóatl, a legendary god-king. **4. Possible answer:** Cortés led Montezuma to believe he was a god-king; he then held Montezuma prisoner and tried to control his empire.

Chapter 5 Jonathan Edwards **1.** Edwards held his first revival. **2.** Yale College **3.** He became pastor of his grandfather's church. **4. Possible**

answers: his work as a minister; helping his grandfather in the church

Chapter 8 Margaret Cochran Corbin **1.** She is known as a woman soldier in the Revolutionary War and the first woman in U.S. history to receive a soldier's pension. **2.** She was at the battle because she accompanied her husband. **3.** She was not captured because she was wounded. **4. Possible answers:** Most women supported the troops by cooking and washing; she went beyond that and helped her husband fire a cannon.

Chapter 10 John Jay **1.** John Jay was the first Chief Justice of the United States Supreme Court, a diplomat, Secretary of Foreign Affairs, and governor of New York. **2.** He traveled to Spain to get Spain's support for American independence. **3.** John Jay believed that the Articles of Confederation were too weak and that a Constitution was necessary to improve the nation. **4.** Answers will vary.

Chapter 12 John C. Calhoun **1.** Calhoun resigned to become a senator for South Carolina in order to protect the state's rights during the Nullification Crisis. **2.** Calhoun successfully helped to end the Nullification Crises. **3.** Calhoun was a lawyer. **4. Possible answers:** experience in politics; strong leadership skills; good communication skills

Chapter 16 Henry Clay **1.** Clay is called the Great Compromiser because he proposed compromises three times that kept the country from splitting apart. **2.** Clay was a Senator, a diplomat, and Secretary of State. **3.** He proposed a compromise to avoid civil war. **4.** Answers will vary.

Chapter 17 Sally Louisa Tompkins **1.** She turned it into a hospital. **2.** They wanted to come because it was one of the best in the Confederacy. **3.** It helped her to get more supplies. **4. Possible answer:** She helped others by saving the lives of hundreds of soldiers during the Civil War.

Chapter 20 Nikola Tesla **1.** Tesla is known for establishing AC electricity, making discoveries about wireless communication, and inventing numerous electrical devices; or for his work as an electrical engineer. **2.** He immigrated to the United States because his ideas were unappreciated in Europe; or to try to get Thomas Edison to support his work. **3.** The Niagara Falls Project was the world's first hydroelectric power plant. **4.** Answers will vary.

Chapter 22 William Randolph Hearst
1. He was expelled for excessive pranks and rules violations. **2.** He added huge headlines, sensational stories, and comics. **3.** He lost in his bids to become President, mayor of New York City, and governor of New York State. **4.** Answers will vary.

Chapter 23 James Reese Europe **1.** He became the first African American to lead troops into battle **2.** a union for African American musicians **3.** French Croix de Guerre with Silver Star **4. Possible answers:** He was the first African American to lead troops into battle; he started a music union for African Americans; his band was the first African American band to play in Carnegie Hall; he won the French Croix de Guerre with Silver Star for bravery.

Chapter 26 Elie Wiesel **1.** Wiesel is known for his human rights work; he is also known as a human rights writer, speaker, and educator. **2.** His career was shaped by what he went through. **3.** *Night* is about the things that he went through during and how he felt about World War II. **4.** Answers will vary.

Chapter 28 James H. Meredith **1.** He and his brother were forced to move into a car specifically for black people on a train in the South. **2.** He joined the Air Force. **3.** He helped to end segregation in colleges and universities by becoming the first African American student to attend and graduate from the University of Mississippi. **4.** Answers will vary.

Chapter 31 Laura Welch Bush **1.** She hoped to become a teacher. **2.** She worked as a teacher and as a librarian. **3.** She helped people cope with tragedy. **4.** Answers will vary.

Answer Key

Teacher's Resources

DOCUMENT-BASED QUESTIONS

Analyze a Legend **1.** She believed that without the tree there could be no life. **2.** They brought soil up and placed it on turtle's back. **3.** New pieces of the great tree fell and took root beside her. **B.** Answers will vary.

Magna Carta **1.** d **2.** c **3. Possible answers:** No one must pay for the rights granted in the Magna Carta; no one should be put in jail without legal process. **4. Possible answer:** No one should be put in jail without legal process.

Declaration of Independence **A. 1.** b **2.** d **3.** a **4.** b **5.** c **B. 1.** Answer given **2. Summary:** This section describes the type of government the colonists want. **3. Summary:** This section explains why King George's behavior is not acceptable to the colonists. **4. Summary:** This section explains the things King George and Parliament have done that the colonists see as acts of war. **5. Summary:** In this section, the colonists state their intention to form an independent nation. **6. Summary:** In this section, the colonists proclaim their independence. **C.** Answers will vary. **D.** Answers will vary.

Analyze a Poster **1.** the third day of August **2.** prime and healthy **3.** It shows their strong and hard-working characteristics. **B.** Answers will vary.

Analyze a Letter **1.** It has a mood of concern and disappointment. **2.** The people in the hospital who might not recover. **3.** They die of diseases caught in the hospital. **4.** The hospitals don't have what they need to care for that many people. **B.** Answers will vary.

U.S. Constitution **A. 1.** a **2.** b **3.** b **4.** d **5.** c **B.** Answers will vary. **C.** Answers will vary. **D.** Answers will vary.

Analyze a Personal Account **1.** The Indians started yelling and charging the camp. **2.** The camp that the soldiers had set up. **3.** to make the fire larger **4.** Indians broke into their area. **B.** Answers will vary.

Analyze a Letter **1.** more money to pay for supplies **2.** a plan to use guerrilla warfare **3. Possible answers:** without power, forceful, lacking **4.** Cortés **B.** Answers will vary.

Analyze a Poster **1.** It was looking for men to join in fighting the Civil War. **2.** excited and determined **3.** 43 Liberty Street, N.Y. (opposite the post office) **B.** Answers will vary.

Emancipation Proclamation **1.** c **2.** a **3.** a **4.** those regions that were considered in rebellion against the United States **5.** It urges people who were enslaved to demand extra wages for their labor.

Gettysburg Address **1.** a **2.** c **3.** He meant the nation should have freedom now and forever. **4. Possible answers:** freedom; government by the people and for the people; all men are created equal

Analyze a Diary **1. Possible answers:** surprised, hopeless, fearful **2.** to fight for freedom to govern the country **3.** interference from foreign countries **4.** The war finally turned to favor the North. **B.** Answers will vary.

Chief Joseph's Speech **1.** c **2.** a **3.** c **4.** They have run to the hills and have no blankets or food. **5.** He is tired and his heart is sick and sad. **B.** Answers will vary.

Analyze a Photograph **1.** child labor in the United States **2.** in school **3.** The child in the front is not wearing any shoes and neither child has safety equipment. **4.** to make money for their families **B.** Answers will vary.

Fourteen Points **1.** c **2.** a **3.** d **4.** His Fourteen Points stated ideas to maintain world peace. **5.** He thought the world should be safe for all to live in.

Analyze a Poem **1.** stairs **2.** life has been difficult, even when she tried hard **3. Possible answers:** to let her son know the truth; to hope that her son might have a better life than she; to give her son advice **B.** Answers will vary.

Analyze an Advertisement **1.** The ad says it is a very good quality car. **2.** that the car does not require much maintenance and handles very well **3.** The automobile industry was booming and people wanted new automobiles. **B.** Answers will vary.

"I Have a Dream" **1.** d **2.** b **3.** a **4. Possible answers:** to express hopes for the future of the nation; to express hopes of freedom for all people **5.** He wanted to show his hopes that someday all people would be free.

Analyzing a Personal Essay **1.** so he would learn English **2.** when he heard his parents speaking Spanish. **3.** He did not realize they were speaking Spanish. **4.** He felt very upset. **B.** Answers will vary.

READING, WRITING, AND TEST TAKING

Key Words for a Writing Assignment
1. discuss **2.** explain **3.** illustrate **4.** review

Key Words to Answer Essay Questions
A. 1. Describe **2.** Explain **3.** Evaluate **4.** Discuss **B.** Answers will vary.

Writing an Effective Sentence **A.** Students should have placed a check next to sentence 2. Sentence rewrites will vary. **B.** Answers will vary, but should reflect students' ability to recognize and discuss effective sentences.

Writing an Effective Paragraph **Topic Sentence:** Clara Barton's work as a nurse during the Civil War did not end with the last battle in 1865. **Sentences that should be crossed out:** She was such a good nurse that she was often referred to as the "Angel of the Battlefield." Clara Barton was also a teacher, one of the first women clerks in the U.S. Patent Office, and the founder of the American Red Cross.

Writing an Effective Conclusion **A.** Students should check paragraph 1. Students should rewrite conclusion 2. **B.** Answers will vary.

Writing to Describe **A.** Students should check paragraph 1. Students should circle damp and swampy. Students should draw boxes around bitterly, cold, and winter. Students should underline plant, red, and wild. **B.** Answers will vary.

Writing to Persuade **A. Take a stand:** We should ratify the Constitution. **My audience:** fellow neighbors **Facts to support my position: Possible answers:** A President is needed to enforce laws; a court system is needed to interpret the laws; without the power of taxation, the federal government cannot pay off debts from the Revolution. **Conclusion:** We should support the Constitution. **B.** Answers will vary. Students' paragraphs should include details from their charts.

Writing a Summary **A.** Summaries will vary. **B.** Answers will vary.

Comparing and Contrasting **A. Possible answers: 1.** Both served more than one term. **2.** Both tried to break up business trusts and monopolies. **3.** Both worked to make positive changes in people's lives. **4.** Roosevelt was a Republican; Wilson was a Democrat. **5.** Roosevelt served less than two full terms; Wilson served two complete terms. **B.** Answers will vary.

Fact and Opinion **A. 1.** This is a fact because the information in the statement can be proven. **2.** This is an opinion because the statement cannot be proven. It is a personal feeling. **B. 3.** F: This statement can be proven. **4.** O: This cannot be proven; this is an opinion or belief.

Organizing Information in Chronological Order
A. 1. started, first, after, eventually **2.** World War I started. **B.** Answers will vary.

Organizing Information by Cause and Effect
A. 1. The United States banned British warships from American waters. **2.** as a result **B.** Answers will vary.

Ruling Out Incorrect Answer Choices
A. a. The paragraph does not mention military spending. Reaganomics was designed to increase spending to boost economic growth. **b.** Reaganomics cut taxes for the wealthy and corporations. **c.** Reaganomics is a term for President Reagan's tax-cut plan.

Answering Completion Questions **A. 1.** an opponent of the Union **2.** first southern state to secede from the Union **B. 3.** Abraham Lincoln **Key words:** President; against slavery **4.** Missouri Compromise **Key words:** balance between free and slave-holding states; named after a state

5. Confederacy **Key words:** Southern states; seceded from the Union **6.** slaves **Key words:** Southern plantation owners relied on; treated unfairly

Writing and Editing Checklist Answers will vary.

STUDENT WORKBOOK

Geography Handbook

The Five Themes of Geography **1.** movement **2.** human interaction **3.** location **4.** place **5.** movement **6.** place **7.** region **8.** human interaction **B.** Answers will vary.

Reading a Map **1.** a star **2.** Lincoln **3.** Nebraska and South Dakota **4.** east

Reading a Map **1.** Hartford **2.** Maine, New Hampshire, Vermont, Massachusetts, Connecticut, Rhode Island **3.** 100 miles **4.** south

Reading a Map **1.** a black dot **2.** Los Angeles, San Diego, Dallas, Phoenix, Houston, Philadelphia, New York City, Chicago, San Antonio **3.** west **4.** Spokane and Seattle

Using Latitude **1.** degrees **2.** 0° **3.** South America **4.** South America **5.** South America

Using Longitude **1.** degrees **2.** 0° **3.** Europe and Africa **4.** North America and South America **5.** Europe, Africa, and Asia

Using Latitude and Longitude **1.** San Diego and Seattle **2.** 45°N/95°W **3.** Austin and New Orleans **4.** 35°N/80°W

Map Projections **1.** A flat map allows you to see all the Earth's surface at the same time. **2.** Robinson Projection **3.** Mercator Projection **4.** Mercator Projection

UNIT 1 EARLY AMERICA

Chapter 1 The First Americans

Section I **Possible answers: A. 1.** Hunters followed herds of animals. **2.** A land bridge across the Bering Sea allowed these hunters to cross from Asia into North America. **B. 3.** Native Americans living along the Pacific Coast ate fish and hunted sea animals, such as whales and seals. **4.** Native Americans in the Southwest desert hunted birds, rabbits, and lizards and also gathered seeds, nuts, and roots. **C. 5.** Men usually hunted and fished. **6.** Women gathered plants and cared for children. **Critical Thinking** Answers will vary. Students should note that past history can affect events later on.

Section II **1.** Aztecs **2.** Mississippian **3.** Anasazi **4.** Toltec **5.** Adena-Hopewell **6.** Olmecs **7.** Maya **Critical Thinking** Answers will vary. Journal entries should reflect an understanding of the Inca empire and its people.

Section III **1.** true **2.** false: After cutting and burning trees, the Algonquins planted crops in the cleared land. **3.** true **4.** false: Native Americans of the Great Plains were nomads who followed buffalo herds. **5.** true **6.** false: The Iroquois referred to corn, beans, and squash as the "sacred three sisters." **7.** true **Critical Thinking** Answers will vary. Students should recognize that to survive, groups needed to learn how to hunt, build shelters, plant crops, make boats, and so on.

Using a Map **1.** Mexico (Valley of Mexico) **2.** South America **3.** Aztec and Maya **4.** Cuzco, Tikal, Tenochtitlán, and Machu Picchu

Chapter 2 Early Exploration

Section I **1.** true **2.** false: Before 1400, Africans considered gold and salt to have equal value. **3.** false: Most West Africans living outside of trading centers depended on farming for food. **4.** true **5.** false: African societies considered slavery an acceptable punishment for prisoners of war and criminals. **6.** false: The trading kingdoms of Ghana, Mali, and Songhai were all located on the southern edge of the Sahara. **7.** true **8.** true **Critical Thinking** Answers will vary. Students should recognize that items produced in West Africa were transported by caravans along the Trans-Sahara route to Muslim kingdoms. From there, goods were carried to Europe by Muslim merchants.

Section II **1.** Madeira Islands **2.** Europe **3.** Mediterranean Sea **4.** Holy Land **5.** Portugal **6.** Silk Road **7.** Africa **Critical Thinking** Answers will vary. Students should recognize that trade with Asia made available such items as spices, silk, and gunpowder.

Section III **1.** e **2.** d **3.** a **4.** b **5.** c **6.** f **7.** i **8.** h **9.** g **10.** j **Critical Thinking** Answers will vary. Students should mention such qualities as fear, surprise, and curiosity.

Using a Chart **1.** Vasco da Gama **2.** Bartolomeu Dias and Vasco da Gama **3.** Christopher Columbus **4.** Christopher Columbus and Vasco da Gama **5.** to find gold

Chapter 3 New Settlements in the Americas

Section I **1.** a **2.** d **3.** b **4.** a **B. 5.** The exchange of products between the Americas and Europe. **6.** A fountain that was rumored to give all who drank from it eternal youth. **7.** The system in which Native Americans were forced to work for Spanish landowners. **Critical Thinking** Answers will vary.

Section II **1.** k **2.** l **3.** e **4.** j **5.** f **6.** a **7.** h **8.** b **9.** g **10.** c **11.** d **12.** i **Critical Thinking** Answers will vary. Students may describe poor living conditions in the swampy area of Jamestown. They may write about a lack of food. They may write about negotiating with the Native Americans for food and later fighting with the Native Americans.

Section III **1.** Villages began to raid one another and take captives to sell as slaves to the Portuguese. **2.** They were usually chained, sometimes branded, and packed onto slave ships. **3.** The enslaved Africans traveled in the dark storage areas without much space and were given very little food or water. **4.** Spanish conquistadors began importing African slaves after so many Caribbean natives died that there were no longer enough people to work the plantations. **5.** Spain, Portugal, France, England, and the Netherlands all set up sugar colonies in the Caribbean and imported African slaves. **6.** Portuguese traders first took slaves from Africa as early as the 1430s. **7.** Indentured servants provided labor on the early English sugar plantations. **Critical Thinking** **Possible answer:** In the English colonies, the slave trade increased as fewer indentured servants came to work in America. Slaves became an important part of the economy as the tobacco industry grew.

Using a Chart **1.** the Dutch colonies **2.** the Spanish colonies **3.** 2,501,400 **4.** the English colonies **5.** 1,600,200

UNIT 2 THE AMERICAN COLONIES

Chapter 4 Founding Colonial America

Section I **1.** Martin Luther protests the policies of the Catholic Church. **2.** Pilgrims sail from England to North America on the *Mayflower*. **3.** English merchants receive charter to start a fishing and lumbering colony. **4.** Roger Williams founds the town of Providence. **5.** Thomas Hooker and followers leave Boston. **6.** Colonists attack Pequot settlements along the Connecticut River. **7.** Colonists defeat the Wampanoags in King Philip's War. **Critical Thinking** **Possible answers:** Many settlers did not survive the first winter in the Plymouth Colony. They died of disease, cold, and poor nutrition. Life became easier after Native Americans taught the colonists how to plant corn and trap beavers.

Section II **1.** i **2.** e **3.** l **4.** c **5.** f **6.** k **7.** a **8.** g **9.** d **10.** h **11.** j **12.** b **Critical Thinking** Answers will vary, but should include reference to William Penn buying land from Native Americans and the Duke of York conquering land inhabited by the Dutch.

Section III **Possible answers:** **1.** began with the English settlement of Jamestown **2.** had a lawmaking body known as the House of Burgesses **3.** founded by Lord Baltimore **4.** was a religious refuge for Roman Catholics **5.** raised rice, indigo, and tobacco **6.** split into North Carolina and South Carolina in 1729 **7.** founded by George Oglethorpe **8.** banned slavery until the 1750s **Critical Thinking** Timelines will vary.

Using a Map **1.** Georgia **2.** Maryland and Delaware **3.** five **4.** Massachusetts, Rhode Island, New York

Chapter 5 The Thirteen Colonies

Section I **1.** The English economy was based on the mercantile system. **2.** Manufacturing in colonial towns took place in homes. **3.** Farms in New England were small because of hilly land, rocky soil, and long and cold winters. **4.** In the Southern colonies, tobacco, rice, and indigo were grown. **5.** Some merchants traded illegally with other countries. **6.** The natural resources in New England included fish from the North Atlantic and trees from the forests. **7.** People in the Middle colonies were involved in the fur trade and iron manufacturing. **8.** Enslaved Africans made up the labor force on Southern plantations. **Critical Thinking Possible answers:** The Navigation Acts created tension between England and the colonies because colonies had to pay higher prices for European goods.

Section II **1.** c **2.** b **3.** b **4.** d **5.** c **6.** a **7.** d **8.** d **Critical Thinking Possible answers:** A meetinghouse, a school, a church, and a general store. Explanations will vary.

Section III **1.** false: Most enslaved people lived in the Southern colonies. **2.** true **3.** false: Enslaved Africans were not allowed to gather in public. **4.** true **5.** false: Under the slave codes, children of enslaved Africans were themselves considered enslaved. **6.** false: As a result of the Stono Rebellion, enslaved people in South Carolina were given less freedom. **7.** false: Between 1700 and 1750, the number of enslaved Africans living in the colonies increased. **Critical Thinking** Answers will vary; accept reasonable answers.

Using a Map **1.** rum, cloth, iron goods **2.** north **3.** Atlantic Ocean **4.** enslaved Africans, molasses, and sugar

Chapter 6 Roots of Rebellion

Section I **1.** d **2.** b **3.** d **4.** a **5.** b **6.** a **7.** c **8.** a **Critical Thinking** Answers will vary. Students might suggest that landowners have invested more in the colonies, because they have the expense of buying and/or managing land. Therefore, they should have more of a say in actions that involve their investments. Or students might suggest that landowners thought of themselves as more successful and, therefore, better informed and better able to make key decisions than nonlandowners.

Section II **1.** forts **2.** New France **3.** New England **4.** balance of power **5.** Catholics **6.** King George's War **7.** King William's War **Critical Thinking Possible answer:** Both the English colonists and the French trapped furs on Iroquois lands; therefore, the two groups were competitors in the fur trade.

Section III **A. 1.** King George grants 200,000 acres of the region to Virginia business owners. **2.** The French build Fort Le Boeuf after making friends with rivals of the Iroquois. **B. 3.** William Pitt, the new head of the British government, sends more troops and ships. **4.** Quebec, Montreal, and other French settlements are captured by the British. **C. 5.** In the Treaty of Paris, the French cede northern New France and lands east of the Mississippi River to the British. **6.** The American colonies remain united after banding together for the first time for a common cause. **Critical Thinking** Answers will vary. Students might suggest that the British would have had a difficult time defeating the French without the help of the colonies. The fighting required the coordination of troops from all the colonies. An uncoordinated fighting force might not have been very effective.

Using a Map **1.** Fort Duquesne, Fort Beauséjour **2.** Fort Necessity, Fort Oswego, Fort Le Boeuf **3.** Fort Niagara **4.** Great Britain

UNIT 3 FOUNDING A NATION

Chapter 7 Road to Independence

Section I **A. 1.** f **2.** d **3.** b **4.** g **5.** a **6.** h **7.** c **8.** e **B. 9.** 4 **10.** 2 **11.** 1 **12.** 3 **Critical Thinking** Answers will vary. Students may support the colonists' right to settle the land because they had won access to the Ohio River valley after fighting against the French. Other students may suggest that the colonists' did not have the right to take over lands already occupied by Native Americans.

Section II **1.** resolutions **2.** Boston Massacre **3.** Townshend Acts **4.** Boston Tea Party **5.** Intolerable Acts **6.** Tea Act **7.** Committee of Correspondence **8.** Quebec Act **Critical Thinking** Answers will vary. Students will probably point out that the colonists felt they should have a say in how much of Britain's war debt they should pay, what kinds of taxes were collected to raise the money, and how the taxes were collected.

Section III **1.** true **2.** true **3.** false: Leaders from every colony except Georgia met in Philadelphia for the First Continental Congress. **4.** true **5.** false: The delegates to the First Continental Congress decided to send a petition to King George III explaining their views about taxation and asking for an end to the Intolerable Acts. **6.** false: The purpose of the Declaration of Independence was to explain why the colonies had the right to declare independence from Great Britain. **7.** true **Critical Thinking** Answers will vary. Students might suggest that the king believes the colonies owe so much money to the British government because of the French and Indian War and the protection of settlers that he cannot see why they should refuse to pay. Students may also suggest that the king saw taxing the colonies as an easy way to raise large amounts of money for his use in England and other parts of Great Britain.

Using a Map **1.** Spain **2.** Spain **3.** Great Britain **4.** Atlantic Ocean

Declaration of Independence Handbook

A. 1. Answers will vary. **2.** The new government would draw authority from the people's support. Citizens would follow the laws of the government, but could change laws or governors if their rights were breached. **3.** Answers will vary. **4.** Answers will vary. **B. 5.** Answers will vary. **6.** Answers will vary.

Chapter 8 The Revolutionary War

Section I **Possible answers:** **1.** They were familiar with the land. **2.** The navy controlled the seas. **3.** They felt passionate about the cause. **4.** The troops were well trained and well armed. **5.** Trenton **6.** Princeton **7.** Brooklyn Heights **8.** New York City **Critical Thinking** Answers will vary. Students might say that they do not think the colonies had enough money or experienced leaders to be successful as an independent nation. Students might also suggest that trade would be interrupted, which might have a bad effect on business. Students might also say that, if the Continental army were to lose, the British might make even more trouble for the colonists than they did before the war.

Section II **1.** George Washington retreats to Valley Forge. **2.** Patriots suffer from cold and hunger at Valley Forge. **3.** British troops retreat to Saratoga to wait for reinforcements. **4.** The Patriot victory at Saratoga shows they can win the war. **5.** American troops run out of supplies and surrender at Charleston. **6.** The British army lost many troops in a battle in the Carolinas. **Critical Thinking** **Possible answer:** The British might have won control of New York. If they had done that, they probably would have weakened the Continental army. Britain might have won the war if Howe had stayed with the original plan.

Section III **A. 1.** f **2.** a **3.** b **4.** h **5.** c **6.** g **7.** e **8.** d **B. 9.** 4 **10.** 2 **11.** 1 **12.** 3 **Critical Thinking** **Possible answers:** Why are you going back to Virginia? How did you survive through the winters of 1777 and 1778? How do you feel about Benedict Arnold? How do you think the country can solve its economic problems? What is your favorite memory of the past five years? What do you have to say about the men who served under you?

Using a Map **1.** Oriskany **2.** Saratoga, Bennington, Princeton, and Trenton **3.** Fort Ticonderoga, Brooklyn Heights, Philadelphia, and Brandywine **4.** about 250 miles

Chapter 9 Forming a Government

Section I **1.** false: Thomas Jefferson did not believe the government should tell people what to think and feel. **2.** false: Most Americans did not want to create a monarchy with a king and queen to rule the United States. **3.** false: The Articles of Confederation did not allow for a President or a court system. **4.** true **5.** false: Under the Articles of Confederation, the federal government could not collect money through taxes. **6.** true **7.** true **Critical Thinking** **Possible answer:** The purpose of the Articles of Confederation was to create an alliance between states to defend their freedom. The strengths included equal representation from each state and a weak federal government that would not take power away from states. Weaknesses included that it did not allow for a President to enforce laws, a court system, or the ability for the federal government to tax states.

Answer Key

Student Workbook

Section II **1.** The United States would add to the number of independent states in the country. **2.** Territories would become states when the population was as high as the smallest state. **3.** Land was divided into townships that measured six miles by six miles. **4.** Land could be sold for $640 per section. **5.** Northwest Territory included land north of the Ohio River and east of the Mississippi River. **6.** Ohio, Indiana, Illinois, Michigan, Wisconsin, and part of Minnesota all form the Northwest Territory. **Critical Thinking** Answers may vary. Reasons for joining may include the inability to pay high taxes, the desire for the banks to print more money, and the belief that the United States needs a stronger federal government. Reasons for not joining may include a belief in nonviolence and a small federal government.

Section III **A. 1.** d **2.** c **3.** a **4.** d **5.** b **6.** c **B. 7.** 1 **8.** 3 **9.** 2 **Critical Thinking Possible answer:** The Founding Fathers wrote the Bill of Rights with amendments guaranteeing freedom of speech, religion, and assembly. They did not guarantee freedom for all people. The rights of slaves were not protected.

Using a Map **1.** Ohio, Indiana, Illinois, Michigan, Wisconsin, Minnesota **2.** Mississippi River **3.** Louisiana **4.** Canada

U.S. Constitution Handbook

A. 1. The Preamble states the purpose of the Constitution. **2.** The legislative branch makes laws. The judicial branch interprets the laws. The executive branch enforces the laws. **3.** Answers will vary. **B. 4.** Answers will vary. **5. Possible answer:** Yes. The Thirteenth and Fifteenth Amendments were passed because people decided that African Americans should be free citizens with the right to vote. The Nineteenth Amendment was passed because people decided that women should be allowed to vote.

UNIT 4 BUILDING THE REPUBLIC

Chapter 10 A Government for a New Nation

Section I **1.** Secretary of State, Secretary of Treasury, Secretary of War, Attorney General **2.** Washington, D.C. **3.** the power to tax, coin money, make laws about business, establish post offices, and declare war **4.** John Jay **5.** It would encourage other countries to trade with the United States and thus improve the economy. **6.** Henry Knox **7.** They had already repaid most of their debts. **8.** George Washington **Critical Thinking Possible answer: Benefit:** It allows the Constitution to change with the times and address new issues that arise. **Drawback:** It could lead to an abuse of power by the government.

Section II **1.** state governments **2.** loose interpretation **3.** Federalist Party **4.** whiskey **5.** Democratic-Republican Party **6.** French Revolution **7.** Jay's Treaty **8.** Treaty of Greenville **Critical Thinking** Answers will vary; accept reasonable responses.

Section III **Cause:** French officials demand a bribe from Americans in order to hold diplomatic talks. **Effect:** France and the United States engage in an "almost war," as President Adams suspends trade with France and French and American ships battle each other. **Cause:** Federalists want to stop Democratic-Republican criticism and keep out immigrants, who tended to support the Democratic-Republicans. **Effect:** Several states pass laws nullifying, or canceling, the federal acts. **Critical Thinking Possible answers:** Some students may say that they agree with these beliefs because without states' rights the federal government might grow too strong and powerful; others may say that they do not agree with the supporters' beliefs because they go against federal law and weaken national unity.

Using a Map **1.** 1791 **2.** Lake Ontario and Lake Erie **3.** 1794 **4.** Canada

Chapter 11 An Era of Expansion

Section I **1.** The Federalists wanted New York to take part in their plan to make New England a separate country. They promised to make Burr President of that country if he helped them. **2.** Hamilton had campaigned against Burr when Burr ran for the governor of New York. Hamilton called Burr a dangerous man who had no principles. **3.** During his term as President, laws were passed that many people disagreed with. **4.** Adams thought Jefferson's ideas about government were dangerously extreme. **5.** Alexander Hamilton convinced several members of Congress to change their votes from Burr to Jefferson, and so Jefferson was elected President. **6.** Before the amendment, the candidate with the most electoral votes became President and the runner-up became Vice President. Once the amendment was passed, electors had to vote separately for the two offices. **7.** He wanted a smaller central government. Jefferson believed that citizens would create more wealth and a better society without government interference. **8.** It established the process of judicial review, in which the Supreme Court determines whether or not a law is constitutional. **Critical Thinking Possible answer:** Jefferson believed that giving more independence to state governments would allow citizens who took part in their local and state governments to have more power to create wealth and make the improvements in society that they thought were important.

Section II **1.** 1 **2.** 3 **3.** 4 **4.** 5 **5.** 2 **6.** 2 **B. Possible Answers: Who:** James Madison and Robert Livingston **What:** Buy the Louisiana Territory from France **Where:** The land east of the Rocky Mountains and west of the Mississippi River **Why:** Napoleon needed money for the war **Critical Thinking** Answers will vary. Students should point out that the expedition was organized because Thomas Jefferson wanted information about the new lands the United States had acquired in the Louisiana Purchase. Students may also describe the kinds of information they will gather, the types of supplies they will take, the route they plan to follow, or what they think they might see on the journey.

Section III **1.** e **2.** d **3.** g **4.** a **5.** h **6.** b **7.** f **8.** c **B. 9.** 1 **10.** 4 **11.** 3 **12.** 2 **Critical Thinking** Answers will vary. Students might suggest that too many lives would be lost, that a war would be too expensive for the country, or that buildings, roads, and farms would be destroyed with no guarantee that the United States would gain anything from the conflict.

Using a Map **1.** Arkansas River and Missouri River **2.** New Orleans **3.** Fort Clatsop **4.** Tennessee

Chapter 12 The Nation Grows

Section I **A. 1.** Tariffs should be placed on foreign goods. **2.** The federal government should form a new national bank. **3.** The federal government should improve the nation's transportation systems. **B. 4.** During the period, confidence in the national government grew and political disagreements temporarily disappeared. **5.** Louisiana, Indiana, Mississippi, Illinois, and Alabama joined the union between 1812 and 1819. **6.** It gave the federal government, not state governments, the power to control trade between states. **Critical Thinking** Answers will vary; accept reasonable responses.

Section II **1.** Jackson grew up in the backwoods of South Carolina and educated himself. **2.** Jackson was a spokesperson for democratic causes and ordinary people. **3.** Jackson began the spoils system, the practice of filling positions with political supporters. **4.** Jackson helped develop the convention system, a large meeting of party members to decide important issues. **5.** Jackson vetoed the renewal of the Bank's charter. **6.** Jackson stopped depositing government money in the Bank, which led to its collapse. **Critical Thinking** Answers will vary; accept reasonable responses.

Section III **1.** true **2.** false: In the 1820s and 1830s, the U.S. government adopted a policy of removing Native Americans from land in the East. **3.** false: The Great Plains is the flat central region of the United States. **4.** false: Andrew Jackson supported relocating Native Americans. **5.** true **6.** false: The Supreme Court ruled that the Cherokee could retain control of their land. **7.** false: The long march of the Cherokee to western lands became known as the Trail of Tears. **Critical Thinking Possible answers:** I agree—removal helped Native American groups preserve their way of life. I disagree—removal showed a lack of respect for Native American land claims and changed the way of life of many Native Americans.

Using a Map **1.** United States and Great Britain **2.** the Atlantic Ocean and the Gulf of Mexico **3.** Mexico and the United States **4.** Spain

Answer Key

Student Workbook

UNIT 5 THE NATION EXPANDS

Chapter 13 Life in the North and the South

Section I **1.** muskets that were made with identical parts **2.** the mechanical reaper and the lightweight steel plow **3.** The labor force in Lowell's factory was made up of young unmarried women who lived and worked together. **4.** Most goods were made by hand. **5.** The war kept British imports from entering the United States, while the tariff made foreign goods more expensive. **6.** Parliament passed laws to prevent the export of its industrialized machines. **7.** Factories required a fast and easy way to ship in raw materials and ship out their finished products. **8.** People could send messages instantly. **Critical Thinking** Answers will vary; accept reasonable responses.

Section II **A. 1.** seeds **2.** cash crop **3.** planter **4.** plantation system **5.** textile **6.** Cotton Kingdom **7.** tariffs **8.** cotton gins **Critical Thinking Possible answer:** The North had large cities and the South had large plantations. The northern economy depended largely on manufacturing, while the southern economy depended largely on agriculture. A large population of enslaved Africans was growing in the South but not in the North.

Section III **1.** false: While enslaved people lived in all of the original English colonies, most lived in the South. **2.** false: Slaves enjoyed none of the basic freedoms that other U.S. citizens enjoyed. **3.** true **4.** false: Most enslaved Africans married and developed strong immediate and extended families. **5.** false: Enslaved Africans placed great importance on religion. **6.** false: Some of the Underground Railroad conductors were former enslaved people. **7.** true **Critical Thinking** Answers will vary.

Using a Chart **1.** cotton production in the United States from 1800 to 1860 **2.** 1840 and 1860 **3.** 1840 **4.** 2 million **5.** the production of cotton rising

Chapter 14 The Spirit of Change

Section I **1.** overcrowded **2.** immigrants **3.** public education **4.** enslaved people **5.** diversity **6.** American Party **7.** nativism **8.** government **Critical Thinking** Answers will vary. Students may discuss the job opportunities in America and problems such as overcrowding, disease, and job discrimination.

Section II **1.** c **2.** b **3.** a **4.** d **5.** b **6.** a **7.** c **8.** a **Critical Thinking Possible answers:** America is finally creating its own literature. Some books reflect the American beliefs in transcendentalism and individualism. Others express antislavery attitudes.

Section III **Possible answers: Abolition:** Abolitionists thought slavery should end no matter what the consequences might be. **Communes:** People in communes worked together for the common good. **Temperance:** Alcoholic beverages were outlawed in several states. **Women's Rights:** Women gained more power at home as decision makers. **Critical Thinking Possible answers:** Both movements fought to improve society through freedom. Women's rights groups fought for full equal rights, while abolitionists fought for an end to slavery. Both groups fought for their goals by speaking out. Some abolitionists founded newspapers or helped slaves to escape along the Underground Railroad, while women's rights workers took action by hosting a women's rights convention. Also, women were able to fight for their own rights, while abolitionists or freed slaves advocated for the freedom of others.

Using a Graph **1.** 45,000 **2.** 1840 **3.** 40,000 (between 40,000 and 50,000 acceptable) **4.** 250,000 (between 240,000 and 250,000 acceptable)

Chapter 15 Westward Expansion

Section I **1.** Cheap land and the promise of a new life brought settlers to Texas. **2.** Most settlers resented Mexican customs and laws and had closer trade relations with the United States. **3.** They enacted a law that halted American immigration to Texas and placed a high tax on goods brought in from the United States. **4.** Mexico won the Battle of the Alamo. **5.** The Texas government had no money and feared that Mexico could send in troops to challenge its independence. **6.** Because Texas allowed slavery, its admission as a state would mean that slave states would outnumber free states. **7.** Because it would expand the size of the United States. **8.** He supported the annexation of Texas. **Critical Thinking** Both groups rebelled against and won their independence from a government that they thought was repressive.

Section II A. **1.** c **2.** a **3.** e **4.** d **5.** b **B. 6.** The two countries disagreed over control of Texas. **7.** The two countries disagreed over the boundary of Texas. **8.** Mexico refused to sell New Mexico to the United States. **9.** Mexico refused to sell California to the United States. **Critical Thinking** Journal entries will vary.

Section III **1.** presidio **2.** farming **3.** towns **4.** John Sutter **5.** Father Junipero Serra **6.** companies **7.** slavery **8.** church **Critical Thinking** Answers will vary.

Using a Map **1.** 1845 **2.** the Louisiana Purchase **3.** Mexico **4.** Canada **5.** 1846

UNIT 6 A HOUSE DIVIDED

Chapter 16 The Road to War

Section I **1.** Missouri would join the Union as a slaveholding state. **2.** The rest of the Louisiana Territory would be divided into slave and free by a line. **3.** Maine would join the Union as a free state **4.** California was admitted as a free state. **5.** The slave trade would end in Washington, D.C. **6.** People would decide whether to allow slavery in the rest of the territory from Mexico. **7.** The North wanted a strong federal government. **8.** The South wanted each state to have more power. **Critical Thinking Possible answers:** John Calhoun did not believe the government had the right to interfere with slavery and threatened to secede if the South's demands were not met. Henry Clay worked to create compromises to satisfy both the North and the South. David Wilmot wanted to outlaw slavery in all the new territories.

Section II **1.** true **2.** false: The Fugitive Slave Law required Northerners to help capture escaped slaves and return them to slaveholders in the South. **3.** true **4.** true **5.** false: Senator Stephen Douglas sponsored the Kansas-Nebraska Act. **6.** true **7.** true **Critical Thinking** Answers will vary.

Section III **1.** Free-Soil **2.** emancipate **3.** Charles Sumner **4.** popular sovereignty **5.** Harpers Ferry **6.** slavery **7.** Alabama Platform **8.** secede **Critical Thinking** Answers will vary.

Section IV A. **1. a.** 2 **b.** 3 **c.** 4 **d.** 1 **2. a.** 4 **b.** 1 **c.** 3 **d.** 2 **B. 3.** c **4.** d **5.** a **6.** b **Critical Thinking Possible answers**: They believed that the country was stronger with all the southern states; the two parts of the country depended on each other financially; they thought this would only lead to more fighting over territory.

Using a Map **1.** Lincoln **2.** Breckinridge **3.** New York **4.** Kentucky, Virginia, and Tennessee

Chapter 17 The Civil War

Section I **1.** b **2.** d **3.** a **4.** b **5.** b **6.** c **7.** d **8.** b **Critical Thinking Possible answers**: **Union:** We must fight to end slavery and to preserve the Union. The war will be easily won because of our economic and population advantages. **Confederacy:** The Confederacy has been invaded; we must fight to preserve our way of life and to gain our independence. Other countries will support us because of our cotton crop.

Section II A. **1.** cotton **2.** conscription **3.** trench warfare **4.** blockade **5.** iron plates **6.** Emancipation Proclamation **7.** slavery **8.** women **Critical Thinking Possible answer:** The Confederacy hoped for military and financial support from Great Britain. Britain thought about offering its support because it needed cotton, but this need was not as important after the country began trading for cotton with Egypt and India. Britain was convinced not to support the Confederacy when President Lincoln issued the Emancipation Proclamation, calling for an end to slavery.

Section III **1.** Vicksburg **2.** Gettysburg **3.** Pickett's Charge **4.** habeas corpus **5.** censorship **6.** Wilderness Campaign **7.** Atlanta **Critical Thinking** Answers will vary.

Using a Map **1.** Missouri, Kentucky, Maryland, Delaware, and West Virginia **2.** California and

Answer Key

Student Workbook

Oregon **3.** Richmond **4.** Washington, D.C. **5.** Nebraska, Dakota, Utah, New Mexico, Washington, Colorado

Chapter 18 Reunion and Reconstruction

Section I **1.** i **2.** c **3.** a **4.** g **5.** f **6.** b **7.** e **8.** h **9.** d **10.** j **Critical Thinking Possible answers:** Radical Republicans thought Lincoln's and Johnson's plans made it too easy for southern states to rejoin the Union.

Section II **1.** Tenure of Office Act **2.** wealthy plantation owners **3.** impeachment **4.** Reconstruction Act of 1867 **5.** Fourteenth Amendment to the U.S. Constitution **6.** scalawags **7.** Ulysses Grant **8.** African American men **Critical Thinking** Answers will vary.

Section III **1.** true **2.** false: Many white Southerners reacted to the changes by forming secret societies to oppose the new laws. **3.** false: The Freedmen's Bureau helped find jobs and set up courts to ensure justice for emancipated African Americans. **4.** true **5.** false: The Fifteenth Amendment to the Constitution protected the right of African Americans to vote. **6.** true **Critical Thinking Possible answers:** Most southern states passed laws that indirectly affected African Americans' right to vote. Most African Americans were unable to pay the new poll tax and could not meet the requirement of having a father or grandfather who had the right to vote before 1867.

Using a Map **1.** Colorado, Nebraska, Kansas, Iowa, Illinois, Indiana, Ohio, Pennsylvania, New Jersey **2.** Texas, Mississippi, Georgia, Virginia **3.** Tennessee **4.** Georgia **5.** Missouri, Kentucky, West Virginia, Delaware, Maryland

UNIT 7 GROWTH AT HOME AND ABROAD

Chapter 19 Life in the West

Section I **Possible answers:** **1.** The federal government helped pay for a transcontinental railroad. **2.** Railroads increased conflicts between settlers and Native Americans. **3.** Animals were loaded onto train cars and shipped to markets in cities. **4.** Long cattle drives became annual events. **5.** The last gold rush took place in the Black Hills of South Dakota in 1874. **6.** Where new gold deposits were discovered, towns sprang up almost overnight. **Critical Thinking** Answers will vary.

Section II **1.** For a small registration fee, it offered 160 acres of land to anyone who would agree to live on it and farm it for five years. **2.** There was little rainfall, summers were extremely hot, winters were extremely cold, and there were tornadoes and hailstorms. **3.** They moved back east or to a nearby town, or tried new farming techniques. **4.** They allowed farmers to save money by buying supplies in large quantities and selling products as a large group. **5.** The railroads often charged higher prices to ship grain than they did to ship other products. **6.** They felt taxes should be higher for the rich than for the poor. **7.** to fight some of the problems they were facing **8.** It made sure that railroads charged fair rates. **Critical Thinking** Editorials will vary. Students should discuss the political platform of the Populist Party and explain that the changes it proposed would benefit farmers by reducing railroad charges and taxes, helping pay off debts, and electing representatives and other government officials who wanted to help farmers.

Section III **1.** Dawes Act **2.** Native American wars **3.** reservations **4.** Battle of Little Bighorn **5.** Geronimo **6.** Wounded Knee **Critical Thinking** Answers will vary. Students might suggest that the government troops were justified in trying to keep the conflict in check. They might point out that the Sioux had been threatening to leave the reservation, and the troops were trying to protect settlers who had already made homes in the area. Other students might suggest that the government troops responded too harshly and should not have used machine guns or harmed women and children. They might point out that the Sioux had left the reservation in fear because their chief had just been killed.

Using a Map **1.** Apache, Zuni, and Mojave **2.** Spokane, Blackfeet, Sioux, Chippewa **3.** 1871–1890 **4.** most eastern land shown on the map

Chapter 20 The Rise of Industry

Section I Answers will vary according to the inventions chosen, but should accurately reflect information in the chapter. **Critical Thinking** Answers will vary.

Section II **1.** American Federation of Labor **2.** oil **3.** Gilded Age **4.** strike **5.** steel **6.** investment bankers **7.** Standard Oil Company **Critical Thinking** Speeches will vary.

Section III **Possible answers: 1.** Nativists in the western United States discriminated against Asian immigrants, and were afraid that Asian immigrants would take away their jobs. **2.** Most immigrants got jobs doing physical labor. **3.** Most farmland was already owned when new immigrants arrived in the United States. Most new immigrants could not afford to buy land. **4.** The number of new immigrants that did not blend in with native-born Americans increased in the 1800s. The population of new immigrants increased during the 1800s. **5.** Many Cubans came to the United States to escape the fighting and disorder. **6.** Most immigrants were from rural areas and found it difficult to adapt to life in the city without the support of people from their native countries. Settling into a neighborhood with people of similar background made it easier to survive in a new country. **7.** Many immigrants from northern and western Europe were able to adapt to life in the United States without too much trouble. **Critical Thinking** Essays will vary.

Using a Graph **1.** northern and western Europe **2.** northern and western Europe **3.** The percentage of immigrants from southern and eastern Europe went from being the lowest in 1861–1880 to the highest in 1901–1920. **4.** The percentage of immigrants from northern and western Europe went from being the highest in 1861–1880 to the lowest in 1901–1920.

Chapter 21 The Progressive Era

Section I **1.** widespread poverty and unsafe working conditions **2.** to provide services for the poor people of the neighborhood **3.** William Marcy Tweed was a corrupt New York City politician. **4.** The Pendleton Civil Service Act stopped politicians from giving jobs to friends, family members, or people who could help them financially. **5.** The Jim Crow laws limited the rights of African Americans. The laws prevented them from voting and enforced segregation. **6.** In *Plessy* v. *Ferguson*, the Supreme Court ruled that separate facilities for white Americans and African Americans were legal as long as they were equal in quality. **7.** The Chinese Exclusion Act limited Chinese immigration to the United States in 1882. **8.** The Interstate Commerce Act controlled interstate railroads by requiring them to set "reasonable and just" rates. **Critical Thinking** **Possible answers: Positive:** Businesses expanded quickly, business owners became wealthy. **Negative:** Business owners overcharged the public, railroad owners bribed government officials.

Section II **1.** muckraker **2.** alcohol **3.** city-manager **4.** Progressives **5.** senators **6.** Niagara Movement **7.** direct primary **Critical Thinking** Answers will vary.

Section III **1.** c **2.** a **3.** b **4.** b **5.** a **6.** d **Critical Thinking** Answers will vary.

Using a Map **1.** New Mexico **2.** southeast **3.** New York **4.** 13 **5.** Arizona, Oregon, Kansas

Chapter 22 Expansion Overseas

Section I **1.** Some Americans felt it was best for the United States to stay out of the affairs of other countries and did not think the United States should have an overseas empire. **2.** Some Americans wanted to take American ways of life to other countries. They also felt that the United States had to expand in order to increase its economic strength. **3.** His job was to demand that the Japanese emperor open trade relations. **4.** to buy land to grow sugar cane **5.** The business owners revolted against Queen Liliuokalani's policy. **6.** a policy that would allow any nation to trade in China, even in another country's sphere of influence **7.** The United States, Great Britain, and Germany were given control over parts of the Samoan Islands. **8.** They wanted to rid China of all foreigners. **Critical Thinking** Answers will vary.

Section II **Possible answers: 1.** President McKinley responds to American anger and the

United States goes to war with Spain. **2.** Spain lost most of its empire. **3.** U.S. citizenship was granted to Puerto Ricans. **B. 4.** adopt the Platt Amendment **5.** a U.S. protectorate **Critical Thinking** Answers will vary.

Section III **1.** true **2.** false: Panama was part of Colombia before the rebellion took place in 1903. **3.** true **4.** false: William Gorgas, an army doctor, led the effort to rid the canal zone of the deadly diseases yellow fever and malaria. **5.** false: The Roosevelt Corollary was a follow-up to the Monroe Doctrine and a part of Roosevelt's foreign policy. **6.** true **7.** false: President Wilson sent troops to Mexico to capture the rebel leader Francisco "Pancho" Villa. **Critical Thinking Possible answer:** It enabled U.S. naval ships to travel around the globe more quickly and also made it easier for U.S. merchant ships to transport trade goods throughout the world.

Using a Map **1.** Key West, Tampa, Havana, Daiquiri, San Juan, Hong Kong **2.** east **3.** Daiquiri **4.** South China Sea **5.** San Juan Hill, Manila, Manila Bay, El Caney

UNIT 8 A TROUBLED NATION

Chapter 23 World War I

Section I **1.** 3 **2.** 1 **3.** 2 **4.** 4 **B. Possible answers: 5.** tanks **6.** rolled toward trenches and attacked **7.** zeppelins **8.** carried weapons and used to spy behind enemy lines **9.** submarines **10.** could move underwater and sink enemy ships **Critical Thinking Possible answer:** War could have broken out because the main powers of Europe had already created alliances against each other. Weapons were built up during an arms race and nationalism was very high. The assassination of Archduke Franz Ferdinand was just the trigger that set the war in motion.

Section II **1.** false: In his reelection campaign, President Wilson argued that the United States should remain neutral but prepared. **2.** false: The United States moved closer to war when Germany sank five American ships within one month. **3.** true **4.** false: Communism is a theory in which the economy is controlled by the government, and property is owned by everyone equally. **5.** false: The Selective Services Act required men between the ages of 21 and 30 to register for the draft. **6.** true **7.** true **Critical Thinking** Speeches will vary.

Section III **1.** Château-Thierry was where the first major battle that involved U.S. troops took place. **2.** They often stood in water up their knees, they heard the German guns echoing in their ears, and rats scurried from one trench to another. **3.** The Second Battle of the Marne marked the beginning of Germany's retreat. **4.** They gave troops and supplies of food, weapons, and oil. **5.** It proposed an organization to keep world peace. **6.** It was required to pay $33 billion and give up most of its weapons and some of its territories. **7.** He had not included them in his administration or in the peace conference. **8.** He became ill and suffered a stroke. **Critical Thinking** Proposals will vary.

Using a Map **1.** the Allied nations **2.** Russia **3.** the Allies **4.** Paris and Sarajevo **5.** about 250 miles

Chapter 24 Life in the 1920s

Section I **1.** Warren Harding **2.** assembly line **3.** Teapot Dome **4.** installment plan **5.** electric refrigerator **6.** labor unions **7.** automobiles **8.** advertisers **Critical Thinking Possible answer:** Companies might want people to use installment plans because they allow more people to buy expensive items.

Section II **Musician**: Louis Armstrong, Duke Ellington, Bessie Smith **Writer**: Langston Hughes, F. Scott Fitzgerald, Zora Neale Hurston **Athlete:** Helen Wills, Jack Dempsey, Babe Ruth, Gertrude Ederle **Governor:** Miriam Ferguson, Nellie Tayloe Ross **Critical Thinking** Radio news bulletins will vary.

Section III **1.** e **2.** g **3.** h **4.** b **5.** d **6.** f **7.** a **8.** c **B. 9.** 2 **10.** 4 **11.** 3 **12.** 1 **Critical Thinking** Answers will vary.

Using a Chart **1.** the percentage of people in the United States who lived in urban and rural areas from 1890 to 1920 **2.** 64.9% **3.** rural **4.** 1920 **5.** urban

Chapter 25 The Great Depression and the New Deal

Section I **1.** Investors realized that prices could not rise forever and began selling their stock. **2.** Investors tried to sell as much stock as possible before prices fell even lower. **3.** American industries were making more consumer goods than they could sell. **4.** It loaned money to farm cooperatives and bought surplus crops. **5.** to loan money to banks and insurance companies so they would not go bankrupt **6.** He cut taxes, placed tariffs on foreign goods, and approved more public works. **7.** to place high tariffs on foreign goods and protect U.S. manufacturers **8.** a drought and huge, swirling clouds of dust that forced millions off their farms **Critical Thinking Possible answers:** Students who agree with Hoover's decision might suggest that state and local governments should have developed new ways of taking care of their citizens when other methods did not work. Those who disagree may indicate that the federal government had a duty to take care of state and local governments that had made countless attempts to alleviate their citizens' problems.

Section II **1.** true **2.** false: Mexican immigrants and Mexican Americans living in cities were paid low wages and had poor working conditions. **3.** false: The Bonus Army said they would remain in Washington, D.C. until they received their bonus, which Congress had agreed to pay them. **4.** true **5.** false: Tenant farmers paid landowners for the use of their farmland. **6.** true **Critical Thinking Possible answer:** People were struggling during the Depression. The hard times made people less tolerant of minorities. When unemployment rose, businesses fired minorities and replaced them with white workers.

Section III **1.** to provide a pension to people over age 65 **2.** to protect workers from unfair practices **3.** to protect people's savings in banks **4.** to regulate stocks and give stock information **5.** to build dams to stop flooding and produce electricity **6.** to give loans at low cost to home owners so they could continue making their house payments **7.** to create jobs in public works to stimulate the economy **Critical Thinking Possible answers:** Women played an important role in the New Deal; many groups gained more freedoms; workers were protected and allowed the right of collective bargaining; the government played a larger role in people's lives; the government played a larger role in controlling the economy; Social Security provided people over the age of 65 with a monthly pension; the programs helped people believe that they could end the Depression. **Using a Map** **1.** 6 states **2.** the western part of the country **3.** Florida **4.** about 1,250 miles

UNIT 9 AMERICA BECOMES A WORLD LEADER

Chapter 26 World War II

Section I **Adolf Hitler:** National Socialist Party, or Nazi Party; Germany; The popularity of the Nazi Party grew until he controlled the government. **Benito Mussolini:** Fascist Party; Italy; He forced the king to name him as head of the government. **Joseph Stalin:** Communist Party; Soviet Union; He seized control after Lenin's death. **Critical Thinking Possible answers:** People lost hope in their former government; the depression made people want new leadership; unrest caused by the war allowed dictators to take over by force; people were struggling to survive and did not pay attention to politics.

Section II **1.** a **2.** c **3.** a **4.** b **5.** c **6.** d **Critical Thinking** News reports will vary.

Section III **A. 1.** g **2.** b **3.** e **4.** f **5.** a **6.** c **7.** d **B. 8.** It created jobs and increased demand for war materials. **9.** Midway Island **Critical Thinking** Answers will vary. Students should demonstrate an understanding of the conditions suffered by the people in the concentration camps.

Using a Chart **1.** casualties of World War II **2.** Japan, Germany, USSR, Poland, China **3.** Germany and USSR **4.** Austria

Chapter 27 The Cold War

Section I **1.** false: As part of the Yalta agreement, part of Germany was given to the Soviet Union. **2.** true **3.** false: The alliance known as NATO included the United States, Canada, and ten

European countries. **4.** true **5.** false: After the Communist takeover in China, the Nationalists fled to Taiwan where they formed their own government. **6.** true **7.** false: A crisis began in the Middle East when Egypt took control of the Suez Canal. **Critical Thinking** Answers will vary.

Section II 1. They felt Truman had not done enough to defend the New Deal. **2.** Korea was divided into two parts, North Korea and South Korea. **3.** North Korea invaded South Korea in an attempt to unify the country under a Communist government. **4.** Truman never asked Congress for an official declaration of war. **5.** MacArthur wrote a letter attacking the Truman administration. **6.** a territory in which the military is excluded **7.** They were accused of giving atomic secrets to the Soviet Union. **8.** When he announced that the U.S. Army was filled with Communists, many Americans decided he had gone too far. **Critical Thinking** Answers will vary. Answers should reflect that McCarthy made public charges against people without having any proof to support such charges.

Section III Possible answers: 1. passage of the Federal Aid Highway Act **2.** NASA was created to oversee the nation's space program. **3.** He created the Department of Health, Education, and Welfare. **4.** Little Rock school crisis/Montgomery bus boycott **5.** U.S. takes a tougher stand against the Soviets **6.** Soviets shoot down U.S. U-2 spy plane **7.** creation of the Central Intelligence Agency **8.** military advisors sent to help South Vietnamese fight Communists **Critical Thinking** Answers will vary. Answers should reflect that the United States and the Soviet Union were engaged in a competitive arms race. Thus, neither side wanted to commit to banning the building of nuclear weapons.

Section IV 1. suburbs **2.** baby boom **3.** Levittown **4.** television **5.** rock and roll **6.** generation gap **7.** TV generation **8.** women **9.** Jackie Robinson **Critical Thinking** Answers will vary.

Using a Graph 1. the number of Americans who lived in rural, urban, and suburban areas from 1921 to 1960 **2.** 1921–30 **3.** 1931–40 **4.** suburban areas **5.** the number of people living in the suburbs rising

Chapter 28 The Kennedy Years

Section I Who: CIA-backed Cuban exiles and some Americans **Where:** Bay of Pigs, Cuba **When:** April 17, 1961 **Why:** to overthrow Fidel Castro **Who:** Nikita Khrushchev **Where:** East Berlin, Germany **When:** 1961 **Why:** to keep people from leaving Communist East Germany **Critical Thinking** Answers will vary.

Section II A. *Engel* v. *Vitale* **B.** *Gideon* v. *Wainwright* **C.** *Baker* v. *Carr* **1.** School officials could not force students to say a prayer. **2.** Prayer in schools went against the Constitution's freedom of religion. **3.** Any person accused of serious crimes had the right to a lawyer. **4.** If the person could not afford a lawyer, the government would pay for one. **5.** Election districts must have almost equal populations so that each person's vote would have equal importance. **6.** This case established the idea of one person, one vote. **Critical Thinking** Answers will vary.

Section III Possible answers: 1. The protesters were nonviolent and remained seated. **2.** It took place in February of 1960. **3.** Rides used to break the segregation rules at bus stations across the South. **4.** A group of protesters boarded two buses in Washington, D.C. **5.** Protest for an end to segregation in Birmingham, Alabama.
6. Authorities in Birmingham struck back hard at the thousands of marchers. **7.** Protest was led by Martin Luther King Jr. to celebrate the one-hundredth anniversary of the Emancipation Proclamation. **8.** Martin Luther King Jr. delivered the "I Have a Dream" speech. **Critical Thinking** Newspaper articles will vary.

Using a Graph 1. federal funding for the space program between 1950 and 1965 **2.** increase **3.** about $1 billion **4.** 15 years **5.** federal funding for the space program rising

Chapter 29 The Johnson Years

Section I Project Head Start: Helps prepare children from low-income families for elementary school. **Department of Housing and Urban Development:** Worked to improve run-down areas of cities. **Wilderness Preservation Act:** Preserved 9.1 million acres of land as wilderness, no permanent roads or buildings could be built in these areas. **Elementary and Secondary Education Act:** Gave $1.3 billion to schools to pay for textbooks and special education classes. **Higher Education Act:** Provides student loans and gives money to universities for research. **National Foundation on the Arts and the Humanities:** Encouraged the growth of the arts and the study of the humanities. **Medicare:** provides low-cost health insurance for people age 65 and over and younger people with certain disabilities **Critical Thinking** Answers will vary.

Section II **A. 1.** 4 **2.** 2 **3.** 5 **4.** 3 **5.** 1 **B. 6.** d **7.** b **8.** a **9.** b **Critical Thinking** Answers will vary.

Section III **1.** The Viet Cong were supporters of communism in South Vietnam. **2.** Many people felt he was corrupt and ruled like a dictator. **3.** The Gulf of Tonkin Resolution was set off by North Vietnamese ships attacking U.S. boats off the Vietnamese coast. **4.** Operation Rolling Thunder was a sustained bombing campaign against North Vietnam. **5.** American troops faced unfamiliar territory, dense jungles, booby traps, land mines, and surprise attacks. **6.** Poor whites, African Americans, and other minorities were groups of Americans most affected by the draft. **7.** They fled the country, joined the National Guard or reserve training corps, or burned their draft cards and simply refused to go. **8.** The Tet Offensive made many U.S. leaders feel the war could not be won. **Critical Thinking** Timelines will vary.

Using a Graph **1.** 1960, 1962, and 1964 **2.** 1968 **3.** 3.8 billion dollars **4.** from 1960 to 1962

UNIT 10 MODERN AMERICA

Chapter 30 Turbulent Times

Section I **1.** false: The My Lai massacre was committed by U.S. soldiers against South Vietnamese civilians. **2.** true **3.** false: On April 30, 1975, North Vietnamese troops captured Saigon. **4.** true **5.** true **6.** false: As a result of the 1973 truce, the United States continued bombing in Cambodia. **7.** true **Critical Thinking** **Possible answers:** The truce did not really put an end to the fighting. North Vietnamese troops were allowed to remain in South Vietnam, so attacks on South Vietnam continued. U.S. bombing in Cambodia and Laos continued even after U.S. troops were removed from North Vietnam. The truce resulted in some progress, but fell short of ending the war.

Section II **1.** House Un-American Activities Committee **2.** Supreme Court **3.** Democratic National Committee **4.** Environmental Protection Agency **5.** Communist countries **6.** affirmative action **Critical Thinking** Answers will vary. Students may suggest that Nixon did not want to suffer the embarrassment or humiliation of an impeachment trial. They may suggest that he did not want the American people to learn even more about the actions he took to hide what he knew about the Watergate break-in.

Section III **Event:** WIN program **President:** Ford **Description:** Ford's plan to reduce inflation by cutting spending. **Outcome:** Americans did not take the program seriously. **Event:** Three Mile Island Accident **President:** Carter **Description:** problem at nuclear power plant; threatened spread of radioactive material **Outcome:** thousands were evacuated; fear of nuclear power increased **Event:** Nixon Pardoned **President:** Ford **Description:** Ford pardoned Nixon; freed Nixon from any possible penalties **Outcome:** American people saw pardon as a political favor; did not regain respect for White House **Event:** Camp David Accords **President:** Carter **Description:** agreement between Egypt and Israel **Outcome:** Egypt recognized Israel as a nation; Israel returned Sinai Peninsula to Egypt **Event:** Iran Hostage Crisis **President:** Carter **Description:** more than 60 Americans held hostage in U.S. embassy **Outcome:** Carter's abilities as leader questioned when hostages were held for over a year **Critical Thinking** Answers will vary. Students who agree might point out that Ford was justified in pardoning Nixon because he was attempting to restore the public's confidence in the White House. Those who disagree might suggest that Nixon should not have been treated differently and should have at least gone to trial.

Answer Key

Student Workbook

Ford's decision may have been a factor in his losing the 1976 election, but other issues may have also contributed to his losing the presidency.

Using a Map **1.** five **2.** California **3.** three **4.** Nixon

Chapter 31 New Challenges for the Nation

Section I **1.** c **2.** a **3.** d **4.** d **5.** b **6.** d **Critical Thinking** Answers will vary.

Section II **1.** Americans With Disabilities Act **2.** Clean Air Act **3.** Tiananmen Square **4.** Panama **5.** Operation Desert Storm **6.** Berlin Wall **7.** apartheid

Section III **1.** false: President Clinton's main foreign policy strategy was to support developing governments in foreign countries. **2.** false: Because of the U.S. failure in Somalia, President Clinton did not send troops to Rwanda. **3.** true **4.** true **5.** true **6.** false: Operation Enduring Freedom began when the United States dropped bombs on targets in Afghanistan. **7.** true **Critical Thinking** Timelines will vary.

Using a Map **1.** Baghdad **2.** the Persian Gulf **3.** 400 miles **4.** Jordan and Iraq **5.** the Red Sea

Chapter 32 Looking to the Future

Section I **1.** false: One of the earliest models of a workable computer came in 1946 and was called ENIAC. **2.** true **3.** false: In 1998, the United States began working with other countries to build an International Space Station. **4.** true **5.** false: Genetic engineering is the act of working on genes to change, or copy them. **6.** true **Critical Thinking** Answers will vary.

Section II **1.** to help the economy grow **2.** It cut tariffs among more than 100 trading nations. **3.** The population is aging and medical technology continues to improve. **4.** Many of today's immigrants are from Latin American and Asia, while most of the early twentieth century immigrants were from European countries. **5.** Machines do some of the work that people used to do; many of today's factories tend to need skilled workers with more technical education. **6.** They feel that it promotes better learning. **7.** They offer low or no-cost health insurance to the children of these families. **8.** They provide medical aid, food, and transportation to seniors. **Critical Thinking** Answers will vary. Some students might say healthcare reform because it is important for all Americans to have access to some form of healthcare. Others might say finding ways to keep the United States competitive in the global market so that the country does not continue losing jobs.

Section III **A. 1.** d **2.** c **3.** e **4.** a **5.** b **B. 6.** Kyoto Protocol written to try and slow global warming; governments worldwide banned the use of CFCs. **7.** World Health Organization works to help people achieve a decent level of health; healthcare professionals working to find cures for diseases. **Critical Thinking** Answers will vary.

Using a Graph **1.** the number of people age 65 and older in the United States from 1995–2005 **2.** 34 million **3.** 35 million **4.** 1/2 million **5.** increase